Introduction to AutoCAD® 2009

The Academic Solution

Sina Sepehri

Free tutorials are available at www.vesdesign.com/download.html

Art/Cover Design: Sina Sepehri

ISBN: 978-1-61539-927-7

Special thanks to my former students Chris Conover and Jon Winner for their time and dedication.

Introduction

Since its infancy, just a decade ago, the emerging field of digital design has revolutionized the thought process of designers and allowed teams of talented individuals to collaborate faster and with far more precision than ever before. Using the Internet, seamlessly across the U.S. and the Globe, oceans of new talent are being incorporated into production.

The emerging technology of Computer-Aided-Drafting & Design has offered both two- and three-dimensional modelers new ways of thinking and has clearly challenged the traditional minds requiring them to utilize new and digital tools to bring ideas to reality.

Today with its design-centric mindset, AutoCAD is offering designers, drafters, engineers, architects, interior designers, and students tools that allow for speed, precision, consistency and legibility all in a collaborative environment. With over 4 million users around the world, the leading drafting software has set the tone for CAD standards, giving the well-trained users mobility and flexibility.

Introduction to AutoCAD® 2009: The Academic Solution is a set of step-by-step AutoCAD tutorials designed specifically for academia. Whether they are used as a standalone or in conjunction with other standard AutoCAD textbooks, you will find these tutorials to be well-structured, informative, and easy to follow. In order to maximize your success, it is best to follow the procedure step-by-step and not skip any instructions.

This Text consists of 12 Chapters. Every Chapter corresponds to and is equivalent to a week of instruction and assignments in the CAD course. There are also three practical projects that you will work on throughout the semester.

As you reach the end of the book, you should feel confident in your knowledge of the essentials. Keep in mind that practice is crucial for retaining the knowledge, making you an efficient AutoCAD user.

Table of Contents

iv

Course Snapshot

Terminology Used in This Book

Bold – A word in bold letters signifies that it is an AutoCAD-specific term or that it is a very specific item (i.e., a specific color, object, or name).

Bold Italics – A number that is displayed in both bold and italic signifies that it is to be entered by means of the keyboard.

By doing the following: – A sentence ending with the term "by doing the following:" signifies that you are about to be given step by step bulleted instructions as to how to perform a specific operation for the first time.

Command: _____ – The **Command Prompt** is the location where you instruct AutoCAD to perform a specific task. For example, typing in **"Erase"** at the **Command Prompt** and then pressing the *[Enter]* key, instructs AutoCAD to erase one or a group of Objects. Also note that in AutoCAD, with very few exceptions, the cursor is always automatically positioned at the **Command Prompt**.

Pointer device – Typically is your mouse, however; you may be using a pen tablet, a digitizer, or any other device which may serve the same function.

Click – Refers to picking the "left" Pointer Button of the mouse. If the right pointer button is to be selected, you will be specifically instructed to **Right-click**.

Double Click – Clicking a pointer button on your mouse twice without pausing or hesitating between clicks.

Drag – Refers to pressing down the left pointer button while moving/dragging the mouse to a new location and then releasing the button.

[ENTER] – Refers to pressing the **[Enter]** key on the keyboard. As you will see, any keyboard entry at the **Command Prompt** will require an **[ENTER]**. However in the later Chapters, at times it may be expected of you to press **[ENTER]** after a Command entry without specific instructions.

Note: – A note generally furnishes you with information and explains concepts but does not require you to take any action.

Pick – Refers to left clicking within the Drawing space (i.e., Pick Circle **C1** refers to left clicking on Circle **C1**.) The terms Pick and Select are interchangeable.

Select – Refers to picking a menu item/tool or a pre-existing Object by clicking on it using the mouse (i.e., "Select **Erase**" means that you should select the **Erase** Icon/tool as opposed to typing the Command *Erase*).

Toggle – Refers to a setting that has a switch mode (i.e., **On, Off**). There are different methods of toggling:

1. **Function keys**. The function keys are located along the top row of your keyboard and are identified by the letter *F* and a number. Each function key is assigned to a specific AutoCAD function. For instance, pressing F9 will Toggle your **Snap** settings to **On/Off**.

2. **Control Keys**. Control keys are another way of allowing for shortcuts. Control keys are used by holding the CTRL key, and then pressing another key. For instance, CTRL+2 will toggle the **DesignCenter**.

3. **Toggle switches**. Many AutoCAD settings can also be Toggled from dialog boxes as shown below. As an example, when the **Endpoint** OSnap mode Toggle is selected, a check mark appears and the setting is Toggled to *On* as shown below.

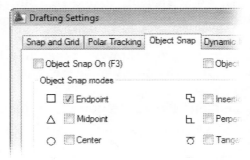

4. **Toggle Buttons**. Buttons located in the **Status Line** are another way of toggling certain settings. There are many buttons located in the **Status Line** that can be Toggled by the mouse. When a button appears depressed, it is set to **On**; otherwise, it is set to **Off**. For instance, in the first image shown below, **Snap** is Toggled to the **Off** position. The second image shows **Snap** Toggled **On**. These buttons will be covered in more detail later.

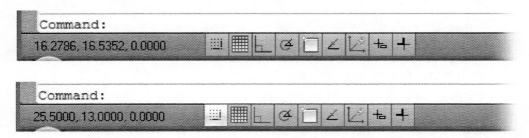

User Specified – This term is used when requesting a non-specific entry where the exact size or location for Drawing an Object (or a group of Objects) is flexible; i.e., "Create a Circle in a User Specified location as shown below" means that you can approximate the size and location similar to a given diagram.

Other Terminology and Information

CAD: A general term meaning Computer-Aided Drafting or sometimes Computer-Aided Design. This term is not specific to AutoCAD.

CADD: A general term meaning Computer-Aided Design and Drafting.

CAD Station: A computer station that has CAD software installed (in this case AutoCAD) and preferably has other peripherals such as a plotter and sometimes a digitizer. The advantages of using a CAD station over manual drafting are basically speed, repeatability, accuracy, and easy editing.

AutoCAD: With over 4 million users, this Autodesk® product is currently the most widely used CAD software in the industry.

Commercial Version: This is the version of the CAD program that is purchased for professional design and drafting and is for commercial use. In other words, you may use the license for profit.

Student Version: This version is available to students who are enrolled in three or more credits at a degree-granting educational institution or those who are enrolled at a nine-month certificate-granting program. The Student Version is also available to registered K-12 students who can confirm current enrollment. Although the educational software has the same functionality as the commercial, it cannot be used for the purpose of profit.

Purchasing Autodesk products: Autodesk software such as AutoCAD, Inventor®, Rivet®, 3ds MAX®, Civil 3D® and many others can be purchased from Autodesk directly or through Authorized Autodesk Resellers around the country. For more information, you can go to the Autodesk estore at **http://estore.autodesk.com** where you can also locate resellers near you. You can also check with your school's bookstore.

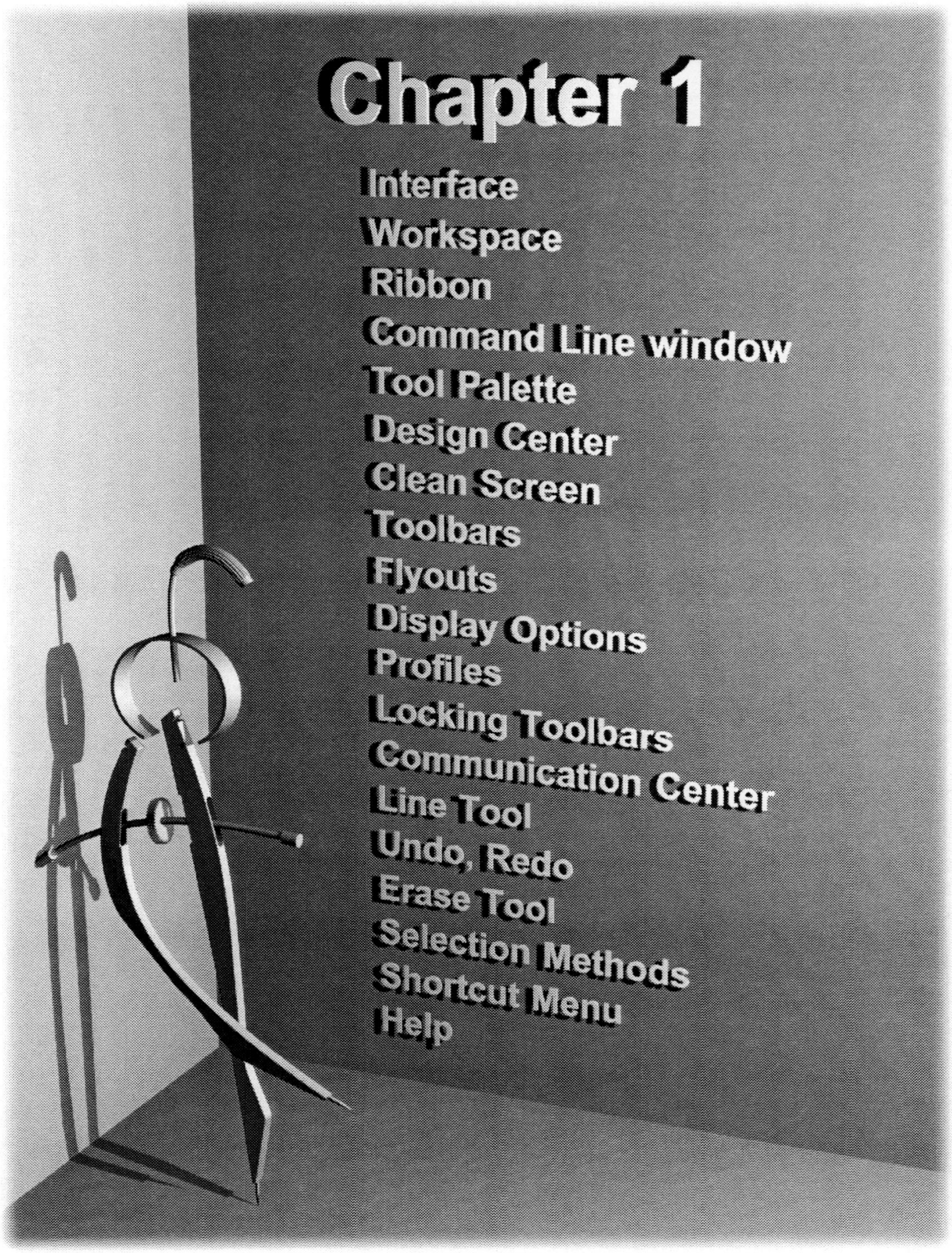

Chapter 1

Interface
Workspace
Ribbon
Command Line window
Tool Palette
Design Center
Clean Screen
Toolbars
Flyouts
Display Options
Profiles
Locking Toolbars
Communication Center
Line Tool
Undo, Redo
Erase Tool
Selection Methods
Shortcut Menu
Help

2

The AutoCAD Interface

1. Launch AutoCAD by doing the following:

    - From the Microsoft® Windows Interface, select the **Start** button as shown below.

    - Select the **AutoCAD 2009** icon as shown below. {AutoCAD is launched}

Note: AutoCAD can also be launched from the Desktop by double clicking on the shortcut.

Note: Your **AutoCAD® 2009** software may be running on the **Microsoft® Windows®** **Vista™** or the **Windows XP®** operating system. Although the above image is captured using **Windows Vista,** the **Windows XP** interface is also similar. Consult with your Instructor.

4

Workspaces

Note: Once you are inside AutoCAD, it is common practice to select the proper **Workspace** that is suitable to your working environment. AutoCAD 2009 allows for three distinct workspaces. A **Workspace** is defined as a set of tools that are grouped and organized so that you can work in a custom and task-oriented environment. Soon you will learn how to only display the set of **Tools** that are specific to your needs. In fact in chapter 8, you will learn to operate AutoCAD without the use of any Toolbars. This mode is often referred to as the **Expert Mode**. In the steps below, you will view the **2D Drafting & Annotation** workspace and finally move forward using the **AutoCAD Classic** workspace.

1. Select a **Workspace** by doing the following:

   - In the upper left corner of the AutoCAD screen, select the **Menu Browser** icon as shown below.

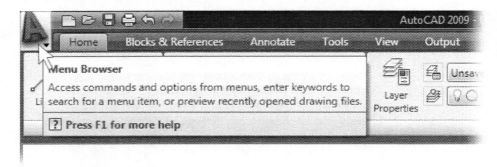

   - As the **Menu** list appears, select **Tools**, and then select **Workspaces**.

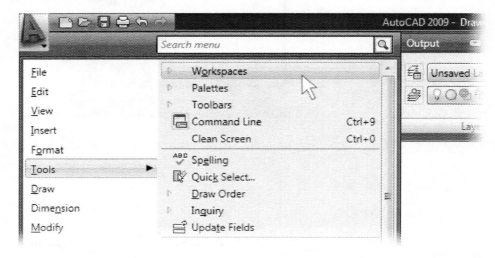

- Regardless of your current **Workspace**, select the **2D Drafting & Annotation** workspace as shown below.

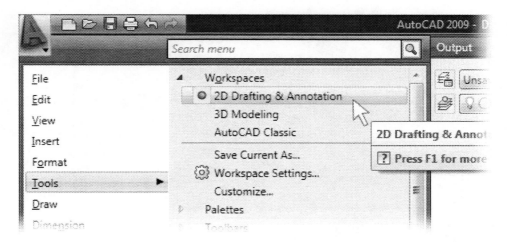

Note: In the **2D Drafting & Annotation** workspace shown below, by default, your buttons (also referred to as **Tools**) are grouped inside several **Panels**. These **Panels** are grouped by **Tabs** and positioned inside a **Ribbon** shown by the diagram below. Keep in mind that as you start AutoCAD, the **Toolbars**, **Menus**, and **Panels** etc. that are displayed on the screen may or may not be those of the default settings, since with little effort they can be loaded and closed. Therefore if your screen looks slightly different than the image shown below, it is ok for now.

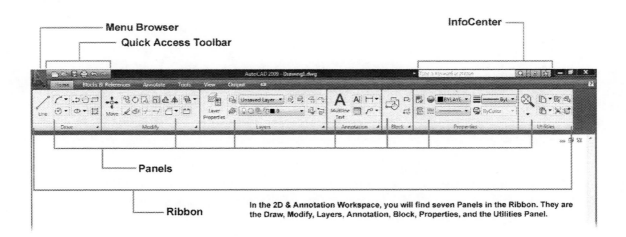

In the 2D & Annotation Workspace, you will find seven Panels in the Ribbon. They are the Draw, Modify, Layers, Annotation, Block, Properties, and the Utilities Panel.

- Select the **Menu Browser** icon, then **Tools** and finally **Workspaces** as shown below.

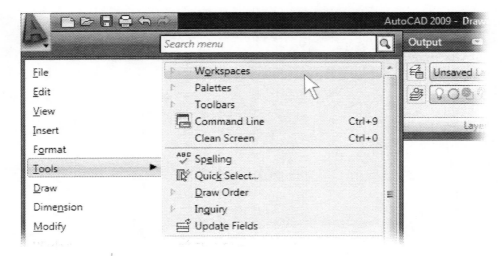

- From the list of **Workspace,** select the **AutoCAD Classic** workspace as shown below. {The **AutoCAD Classic** workspace appears on the screen}

Note: Switching between **Workspaces** is also possible by selecting the **Workspace Switching** button located in the lower portion of the screen as shown below.

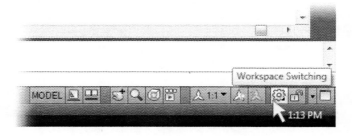

Note: The **AutoCAD Classic** default interface is composed of nine distinct areas as shown below. In the event that the **Menu Bar** (as labeled in the image below) is missing from your screen, specific instructions given on the next page will help place it back onto the screen.

As you begin AutoCAD, the **Toolbars** and **Menus** that are displayed on the screen may or may not be those of the default settings, since with little effort they can be loaded or closed. As you will see in the **Toolbars** exercise, since these are "**Floating**" toolbars, you may **Undock (Float)** or **Dock** them as you please. Later, as you learn about **Profiles**, you will also be able to save your own preferred display settings.

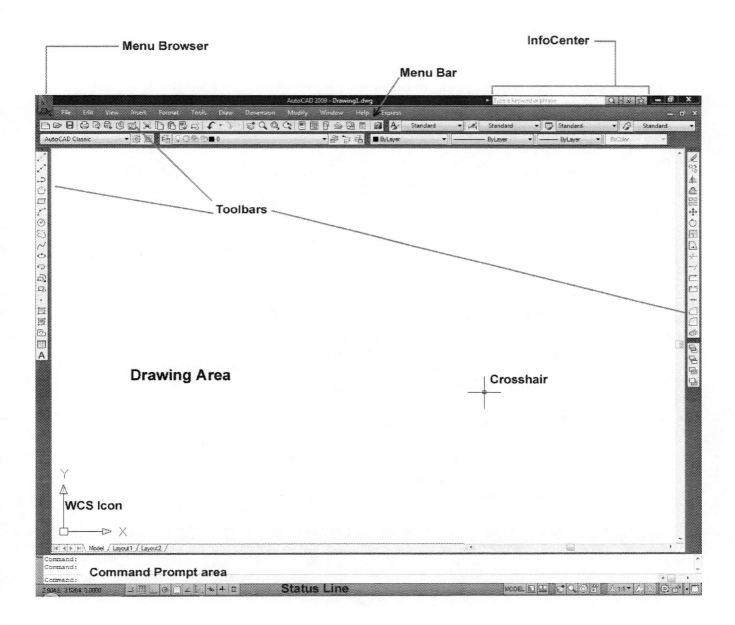

- In the event that you have any other toolbars such as **AutoDesk Impression** or the **Tool Pallets** placed on the screen, you may close them by selecting the **[X]** in the upper right corner of that particular window as shown below.

Note: By default, AutoCAD 2009 interface no longer displays the **Menu Bar** on the screen as shown missing by the image below. In the event that the **Menu Bar** is missing from your screen, it is important to retrieve it as the rest of these tutorials depend on it. Please follow the instructions below so that your screen displays the **Menu Bar** similar to the image displayed at the bottom of this page.

2. Place the **Menu Bar** on to the screen by doing the following:

- Press the **Escape** key on the keyboard to escape any previous command that may be running. {The cursor is placed at the command line and AutoCAD is ready for your instructions}

- Type **menubar** and then press the **Enter** key.

- When you are asked to enter a new value for the MENUBAR <0>, type *1* and then press the **Enter** key. {The **Menu Bar** is placed on the screen as shown below}

Ribbon

The **Ribbon** Palette allows for a central location where you can locate most of the **Tools**. These **Tools** are grouped using several **Panels**.

1. Toggle the **Ribbon** Palette by doing the following:

    - From the Menu Bar, select **Tools, Palettes** and then **Ribbon** as shown below.

As the **Ribbon** Palette is placed on the screen, you can see that by default, it is composed of 6 tabs. They are **Home**, **Blocks & References**, **Annotate**, **Tools**, **View**, and **Output**. Each of these tabs has several **Panels** that could be easily customized. As an example, when the **Home** tab is selected, you can see that by default, it has the **Draw**, **Modify**, **Layers**, **Annotation**, **Block**, **Properties**, and the **Utilities** Panels.

    - In the **Draw** Panel (or any of the Panels), right-click the mouse in the background area as shown below. {Menu appears}

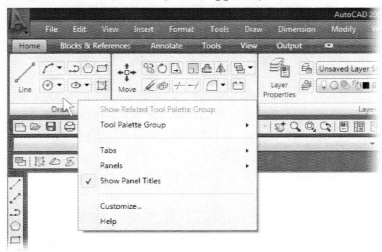

- Make sure that the **Show Panel Titles** is checked as shown below.

- From the drop-down list, select the **Tabs** item and make sure that all 6 tabs (**Home**, **Blocks & References**, **Annotate**, **Tools**, **View** and **Output**) are checked as shown below.

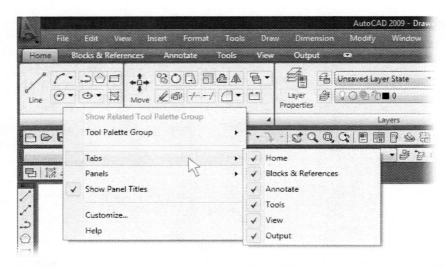

- Select **Panels** from the list and make sure that all 7 Panels (**Draw**, **Modify**, **Layers**, **Annotation**, **Block**, **Properties**, and **Utilities**) are checked as shown below.

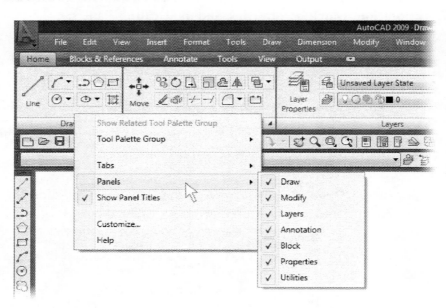

- Select the mouse anywhere within the screen area. {The **Ribbon** menu is closed.}

2. **Minimize/Maximize** the **Ribbon** by doing the following.

- To the right of the **Output** tab, select the **Minimize to Panel Titles** drop-down as shown below.

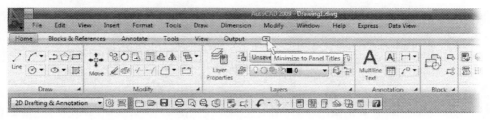

- Notice that only the **Panel Titles** of each Tab within the **Ribbon** are showing as shown below. Moving the mouse onto a **Panel** name (such as the **Draw Panel**) of the **Home** Tab, will momentarily expand the **Panel**. Moving the mouse away from the **Panel** will automatically close it.

- From the **Ribbon**, select the **Minimize to Tabs** drop-down as shown below.

- Notice that only the **Tabs** are showing within the **Ribbon**.

- From the **Ribbon**, select the **Show Full Ribbon** drop-down as shown below.

- The **Full Ribbon** appears on the screen as shown below.

12

- From the Menu Bar, select **Tools, Palettes** and then **Ribbon.**

- The **Ribbon** is removed from the screen and you are back to the default look of the **AutoCAD Classic Workspace** as shown below.

Note: Although this book has introduced the **Ribbon** and its arrangement, to cover AutoCAD functionality, it will move forward using the **AutoCAD Classic Workspace** and will use **Toolbars** (as opposed to the buttons of the **Ribbon, Panels,** and its **Tools**). It is recommended that AutoCAD users fully implement the Ribbon starting with **AutoCAD 2010**.

Command Line

For the purpose of this book, it is critical that the **Command Line** window (also referred to as the **Command Prompt** window shown on page 7) is always present on the screen as it is needed for almost every step of these tutorials. In the event that you accidentally close the **Command Line** window or that you find it to be missing from the screen, you need to bring it back. To Toggle/bring back the **Command Line** window, from the Menu Bar, select **Tools**, then from the drop-down list, select **Command Line** as shown below.

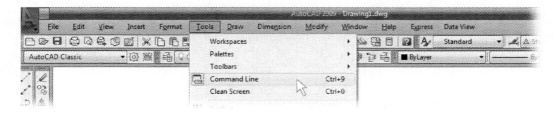

In the event that you accidentally attempt to close the **Command Line** window, AutoCAD will display a warning-like window informing you of your intention. In this case, again it is important to select the **No** option (as shown below) to keep the **Command Line** window present on the screen.

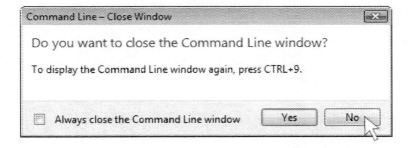

Tool Palettes Window

As you have noticed from the above exercise, the **Tool Palettes Window** as shown below is one of the items that from time to time may appear on the screen. Although the **Tool Palette Window** will be discussed in greater depth later, it is important to know how to Open and Close it. The steps are as follows:

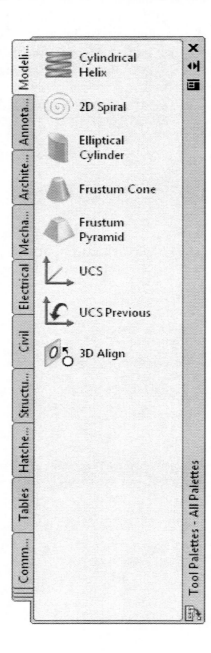

1. Toggle the **Tool Palettes Window** by doing the following:

- From the Menu Bar, select **Tools, Palettes** and then **Tool Palettes** as shown below.

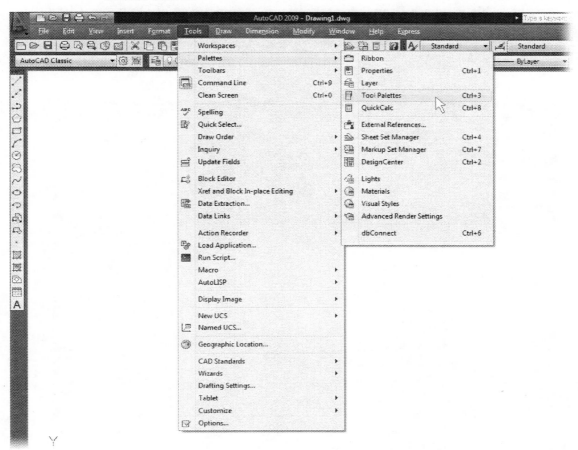

- Repeat as necessary to Toggle *On*. {**Tool Palettes Window** will appear somewhere on screen.}

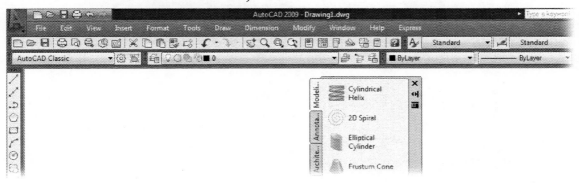

- Repeat the process to Toggle *Off* the **Tool Palettes window**.

DesignCenter

As the name indicates, the **DesignCenter** allows for a design-centric working environment. This is where Drawings and different components of Drawings (discussed later) can be shared from one Drawing to another or even among designers at remote locations. Again since it is too early to take advantage of this tool, you will Toggle it a few times and finally set it to the *Off* position.

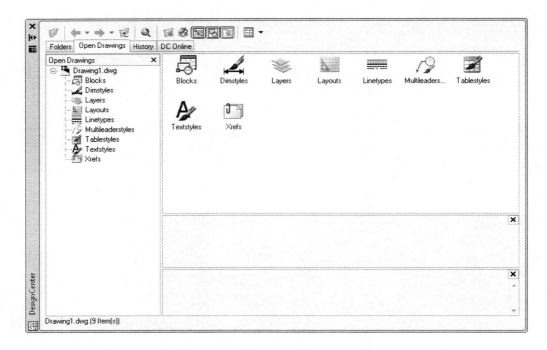

1. Toggle the **DesignCenter** by doing the following:

   - From the Menu Bar, select **Tools, Palettes** and then **DesignCenter**.

   - Toggle the **DesignCenter** *On* and *Off* several times and finally Toggle it *Off*.

Clean Screen

By using the **Clean Screen** option, all of the toolbars are cleared from the screen as shown below. As you surely agree, working with no toolbars on the screen and only typing aliases (short entry for Commands) is the technique of an advanced user. Therefore, this technique is not intended to be used this early in the process but rather for you to be aware of its availability. You will use this option in detail in later chapters.

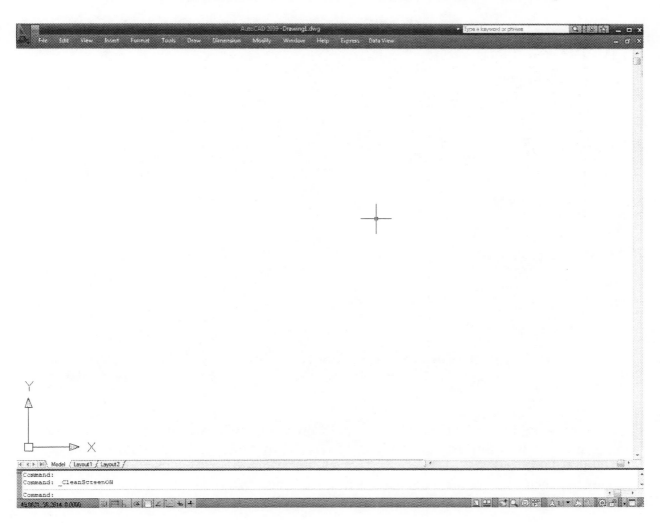

18

1. Toggle the **Clean Screen** option by doing the following:

- From the Menu Bar, select **View** and then **Clean Screen** as shown below.

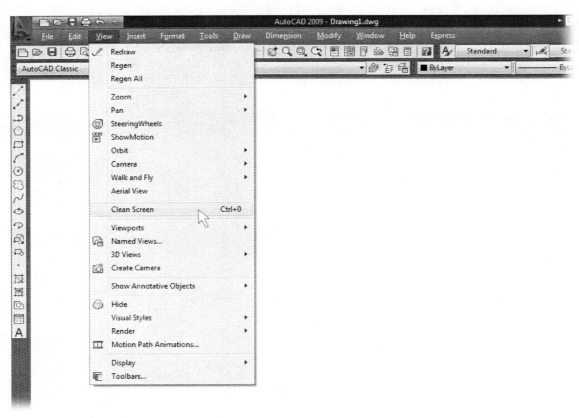

- Toggle the **Clean Screen** option, as you did above, to *On* and *Off* a few times and finally turn this option *Off* so that the toolbars are displayed again.

Note: At the end of each chapter, a short-key representation of each function is given. As an example, **Clean Screen** can be Toggled **On/Off** by pressing the **0** (zero) key while holding **CTRL;** and since there are no Tools on the screen when Clean Screen is in use, a command such as the **Line** Command can be activated by typing in **L** followed by the **[Enter]** key. You will use the **Clean Screen** mode is chapter 8.

Toolbars

1. Load **Toolbars** by doing the following:

    *   Right-click on any existing Tool. (The **Toolbars Shortcut Menu** will appear)

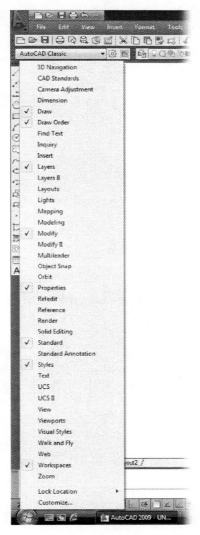

    *   Make sure that the **Draw, Draw Order, Layers, Modify, Properties, Standard, Styles, and Workspaces** Toolbars are Toggled *On* (as shown by the check marks), and that all other toolbars in the list are Toggled *Off*. As AutoCAD is first installed, these 8 toolbars are automatically set to **On** by default.

Note: As a **Toolbar** is Toggled *On* (selected), the shortcut menu displaying the list of toolbars will automatically close and the selected toolbar will appear somewhere on the screen.

2. Close a **Docked** toolbar by doing the following:

*   Use the pointing device to select and hold the **Modify** toolbar on the **Title Bar** as shown below on the left, then drag the toolbar to the center of screen and release as shown below on the right.

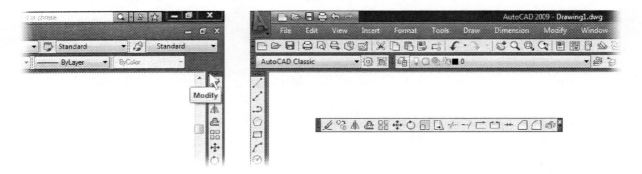

*   Click on the **Close** button **[X]** in the upper right corner of the **Modify** toolbar as shown below. {The **Modify** toolbar will disappear.}

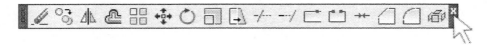

Note: The **Close** button, indicated by [X], is a standard Microsoft® Windows feature and will appear on most every toolbar, window, program, dialog box, etc.

*   Again, right-click on any tool and as the Toolbar Shortcut Menu appears, Toggle the **Modify** toolbar to **On**. {The **Modify** toolbar will appear as a floating toolbar in the middle of the Drawing area.}

3. **Dock** a **Floating** toolbar by doing the following:

- Use the pointing device to select and hold the **Modify** toolbar on the **Title Bar** as shown below on the left. Drag the toolbar towards the left side of the screen and flush against the **Draw** toolbar as shown below on the left. As the toolbar is aligned vertically, release the mouse button. {Toolbar **Docks** vertically as shown below on the right.}

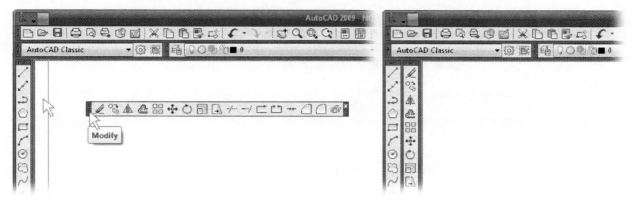

Note: As you can see, it is possible to place a toolbar in any location you choose. From here on out, this book will maintain the **Draw** and **Modify** toolbars on the left-hand side of the screen.

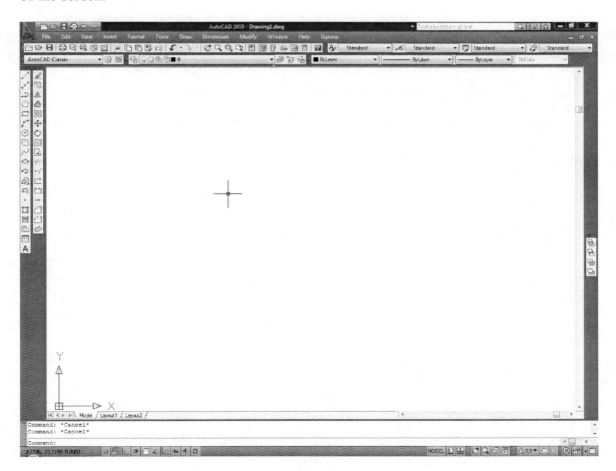

Flyouts

Certain tools have a hidden toolbar associated with them. These tools display a small black wedge in the bottom right corner of the button. As an example, notice in the picture below, there is a small wedge/triangular symbol in the lower right corner of the **Zoom Window** button as shown by the location of the pointer.

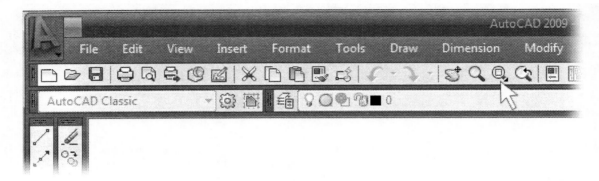

If and when you click and hold the mouse on buttons with **Flyouts**, the **Flyout** will appear as shown below. This can help reduce the number of tools that have to remain on the screen at any given time.

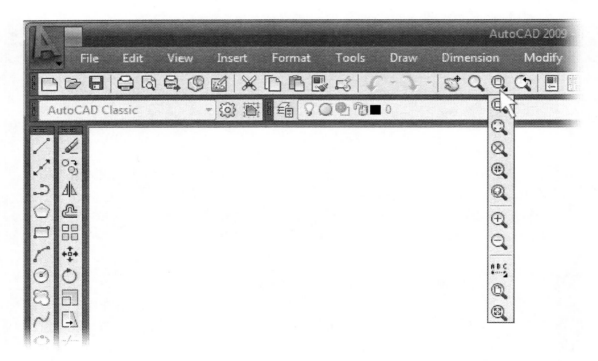

Display Options

1. Change the **Display Colors** of the AutoCAD interface by doing the following:

   - From the Menu Bar, select **Tools** then **Options** as shown below.

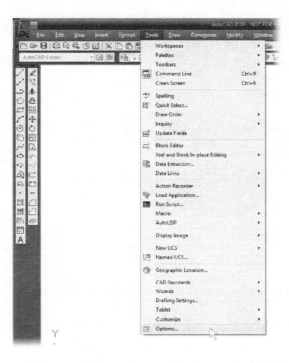

   - As the **Options** dialog box appears, select the **Display** tab as shown below.

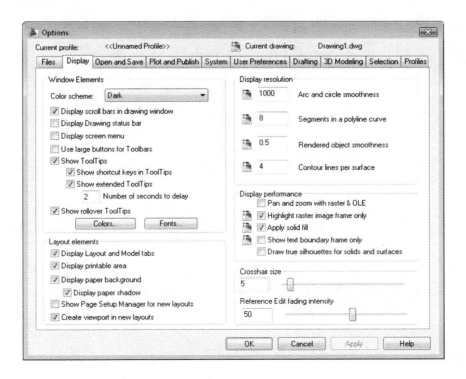

- Select the **Colors** button under **Window Elements**. {The **Drawing Window Colors** dialog box will appear as shown below.}

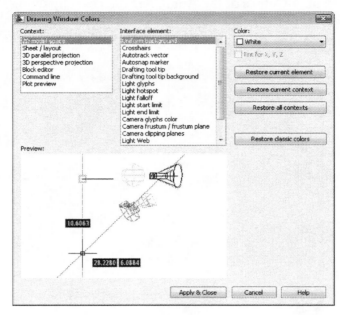

- In the **Context** area, make sure that **2D model space** is selected.

- In the **Interface element** area, make sure that **Uniform background** is selected.

Note: You can select the item that you wish to change the color of by selecting it from the **Interface Element** list. The area you have currently selected is the **Uniform background**.

- Click on the **Color** drop-down menu as shown below.

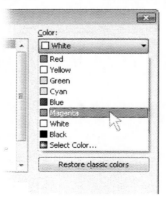

- Click on **Magenta** in the drop-down menu. {The background color in the **Preview** area will change to magenta.}

- In the **Context** area, select **Command line**, and in the **Interface element** area, select **Uniform Background.**

- Use the **Color** drop-down menu again to change the color to **Yellow**.

- Select **Apply & Close**. {The **Drawing Window Colors** dialog box will close and the display colors visible behind the **Options** dialog box will change accordingly.}

- Select the **Colors...** button from the **Window Elements** pane of the **Options** dialog box again.

- Select **Restore all Contexts**. {The warning will appear stating that all of the interface elements in all contexts will be restored.}

- Select **Restore** and then select the **Apply & Close** button.

- Select **OK** in the **Options** dialog box. {The **Options** dialog box is closed.}

Note: The background color of the Drawing area is set to black again. Although this book uses a white background for printing purposes, it is intended for you to stay with default settings throughout the book.

2. Change the **Crosshair Size** by doing the following:

- Select **Tools** and then open the **Options** dialog box again.

- Click on the **Display** tab.

- For the **Crosshair size** type in *20* in the text box.

- Click **OK**. {Notice that the **Crosshair** size is modified.}

- Change the **Crosshair** size in the **Options** dialog box to **100**. {Notice how the crosshairs extend to the boundaries of the Drawing area.}

26

Note: When you are first learning AutoCAD, it is usually best to use a default **Crosshair** size. In certain instances, as illustrated below, a large Crosshair size can help line up Objects that are far apart.

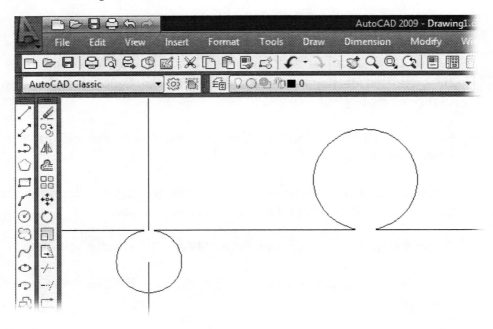

- Change the **Crosshair size** back to **5**.

Profiles

When there are multiple users on the same system, creating your own **Profile** can be very useful. Loading your own **Profile** will set toolbar arrangement, background color, etc., to your personal preference.

1. Use a **Profile** to save your favorite **Display Settings** by doing the following:

   - From the Menu Bar, select **Tools,** and then select the **Options** dialog box.

   - Click on the **Profiles** tab of the **Options** dialog box. {The **Profile** tab appears, possibly with more **Available profiles** than shown below.}

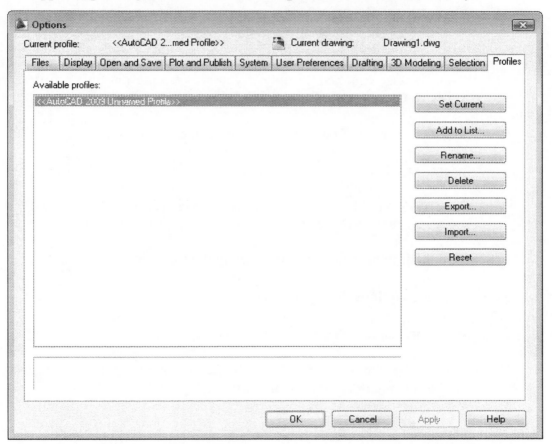

   - Take note of the **Current profile**, most likely **<<Unnamed Profile>>**, **<<Profile1>>** or **<<Vanilla>>**.

- Click **Add to List...** {The **Add Profile** dialog box will appear as shown below.}

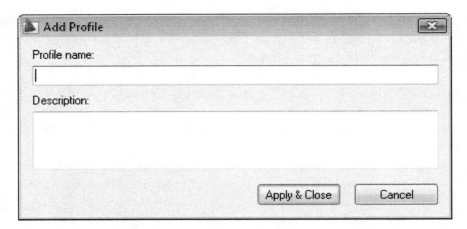

- Type in your name for the **Profile name**, i.e., **Smith John**. Leave Description blank because it is helpful only if you are creating multiple profiles. Select **Apply & Close**. {Your Profile is listed.}

- Select your profile from the list. {Your name is highlighted.}

- Select **Set Current**.

- Click **OK**. {Although your profile is loaded, screen appearance may not change since your profile settings are the same as the original settings.}

2. **Set** the default **Profile** to **Current** by doing the following:

- Open the **Options** dialog box again.

- Make sure that the **Profiles** tab is selected.

- Select <<**Unnamed Profile**>>, <<**Profile1**>> or any profile that is designated by your instructor as your default profile.

- Click **Set Current**.

- Click **OK**.

Note: If you are using these tutorials in a classroom setting, do not use the **Reset** button without consulting with your instructor. Also make sure not to **Delete** the default profiles such as the <<**Unnamed Profile**>>, << **Profile1**>> or <<**Vanilla**>>.

Note: When using a shared system, such as a classroom computer, if and when using your own profile, it is important to set the **Profile** back to the classroom/lab default. Therefore, it is good practice to switch the profile back to the original settings such as **<<Unnamed Profile>>** (or a profile designated by your instructor) before leaving the computer lab.

Many teaching institutions install **Network Security** software in their computer labs. This is to improve system stability, protect against viruses, and avoid unnecessary Internet downloads, etc. In many cases, this type of software does not allow for your AutoCAD Drawing files to reside/stay on certain **Drives** and/or **Folders**. It is for this reason (and more) that you should save your files to a specific **Drive** and **Folder** as designated by your **Instructor**. Furthermore, in the future, you may notice that your **Profile** created in the above exercise is no longer available. This could also be due to the Network Security software. In any event, starting with chapter 2, the book will no longer use **Profiles**. Consult with your instructor regarding this matter.

Again, this book positions the **Draw** and **Modify** toolbars on the left side of the screen; however, for the sake of consistency, your exact toolbar arrangement may be designated by your instructor.

30

Lock/Unlock Toolbars

Note: AutoCAD allows for locking of docked and floating toolbars and palettes. The instructions below demonstrate how to lock/unlock your toolbars and palettes. This book recommends that in general, you leave your toolbars/palettes unlocked because locking them may affect other users. Therefore, when you are using a shared station such as in a computer lab, make sure that your **Profile** is set as the **Current Profile** before proceeding. Consult with your instructor about locking any toolbars permanently.

- Set your **Profile** as the **Current Profile.**

- **Click** on the **Lock** icon located on the right-hand side of the **Status Bar** as shown below. {The Shortcut Menu appears.}

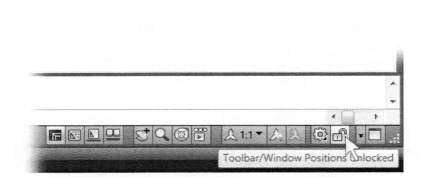

- From the Shortcut Menu, select **Docked Toolbars/Panels** as shown below.

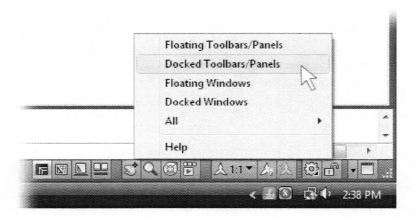

- Notice that the **Lock** icon changes to the locked position as shown below and all Docked Toolbars are locked.

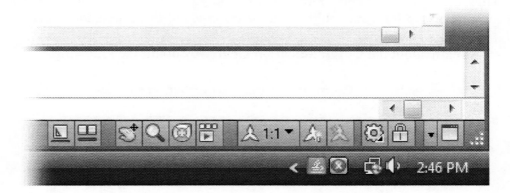

- **Click** on the **Lock** icon.

- From the shortcut menu, select **All** and then **Unlocked**.

- Set the Profile back to the **<<Unnamed profile>>** or any Profile that is designated as your default Profile.

Communication Center

The **Communication Center** helps you stay informed on the latest AutoCAD updates and announcements. Furthermore, you can control the polling frequency by specifying how often you would like to be informed of these announcements.

1. Learn about the **Communication Center** by doing the following:

   - Select the **Communication Center** button as shown below.

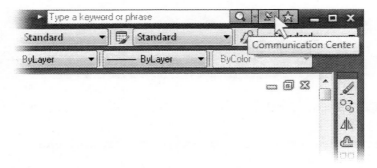

   - Select the **InfoCenter Settings** button as shown below.

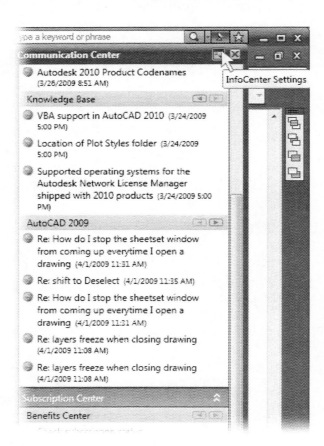

- As the **Info Center Settings** dialog box appears, you can specify your country and polling frequency. However, for the purpose of this book, select the **Cancel** button as shown below.

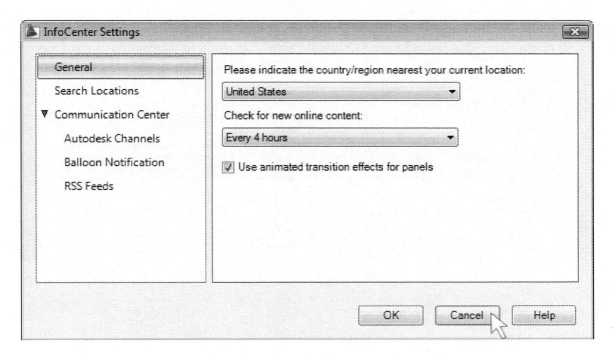

Status Bar

1) In the **Status Bar** located in the lower portion of the screen, move the mouse onto the **Snap Mode** icon as shown below.

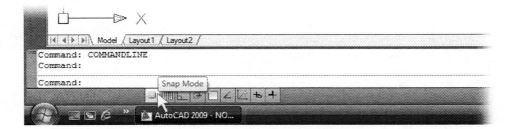

- Right-click on the **Snap Mode** button. {Shortcut Menu appears}

- From the list, make sure that the **Use Icons** item is Toggled to **On** as shown below.

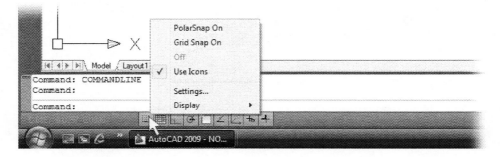

- Again from the shortcut menu list, select **Display**.

- Make sure that **Snap, Grid, Ortho, Polar, OSnap, OTrack, Dynamic UCS, Dynamic Input**, and **Lineweight** Toggle buttons are all set to **On**.

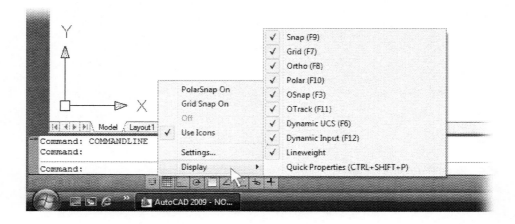

Note: From left to right, the **Status Bar** icons read **Snap Mode, Grid Display, Ortho Mode, Polar Tracking, Object Snap, Object Snap Tracking, Allow/Disallow Dynamic UCS, Dynamic Input, Show/Hide Dynamic UCS.**   You can verify this list by moving the mouse onto each button to see the pop-up balloon. As you progress through this book, most of these terms will be defined and better understood. From this point on, the book will use the short terms **Snap**, **Grid**, **Ortho**, **Polar**, **OSnap**, **Otrack**, **DUCS**, **Dyn**, and **LWT** when referring to these buttons. For the time being, make sure that all buttons are Toggled to *Off* as shown above.

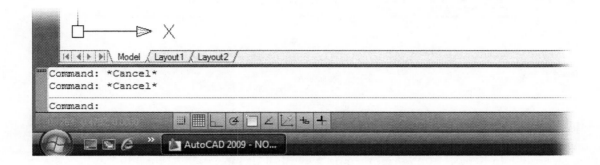

Model Tab

Just above the **Command line window** as shown below, you will find the **Model** tab. Despite the fact that the two **Layout** tabs: **Layout1** and **Layout2** are also listed here and available for use, it is expected of you to remain in the **Model** tab.

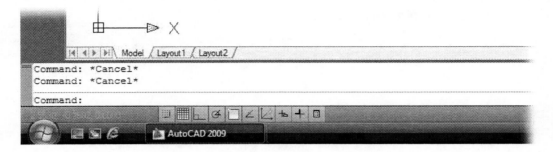

In the event that you accidentally find yourself in **Layout1** or **Layout2** as shown by the image below, you will be placed in **Paper Space** as opposed to the usual **Model Space**. This change is indicated by the right triangle symbol of the image shown below.

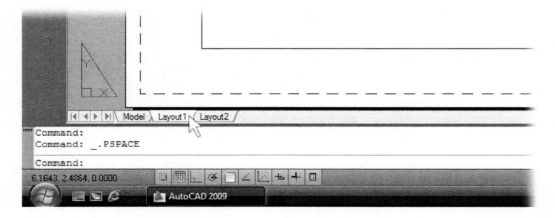

In that case, make sure that you change back to **Model Space** by selecting the **Model** tab as shown below. You will learn about **Model Space**, **Paper Space** and **Layouts** in chapter twelve.

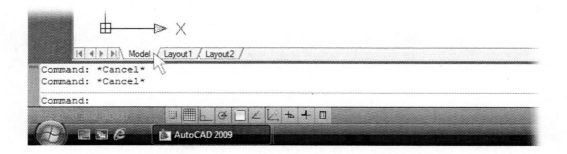

Line

1. Create a **Line** by doing the following:

    - Select the **Line** tool from the **Draw** toolbar.

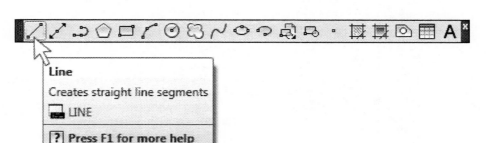

Note: In the beginning stages, keeping track of the **Command Prompt** (located in the bottom left portion of the screen) is essential. This is how AutoCAD communicates with the user, and therefore it is important to keep an eye on the **Command Prompt**.

- The **Command Prompt** now states that you are in the **Line** Command and prompts you to "Specify first point:"

- Move the pointing device into the Drawing area and Pick any User Specified point. {The **Command Prompt** reads: "Specify next point or [Undo]:"}

- Pick a second point in the Drawing area as shown below. {The **Command Prompt** reads: "Specify next point or [Undo]:"}

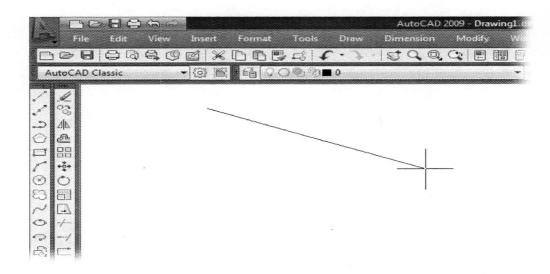

- Pick a third point in the Drawing area as shown below. {The **Command Prompt** reads: "Specify next point or [Close, Undo]:"}

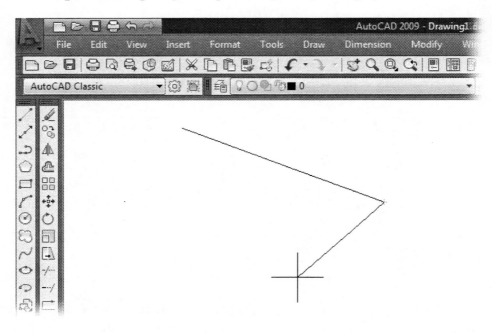

- Pick a fourth point in the Drawing area as shown below.

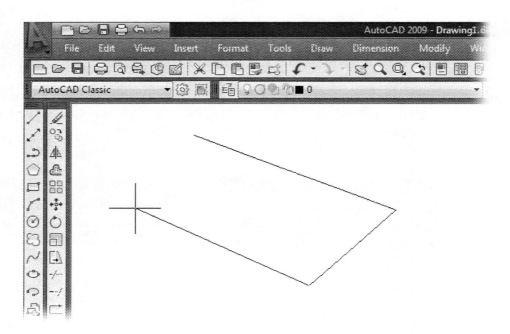

- Type *U* (for **Undo**) then *[ENTER]*. {As you move the mouse, notice that the last drawn line has disappeared.}

Note: At the **Command Prompt**, the words that appear in the brackets [ ] such as **Undo** or **Close** are referred to as **Options**. To choose an **Option**, you can type in the Capital letter portion of an **Option's** name and then *[ENTER]*.

- Use your pointing device to pick a fourth point again. {The **Command Prompt** reads: "Specify next point or [Close, Undo]:"}

- Type *C* (for **Close**) then *[ENTER]*. {Shape closes and you exit the **Line** Command.}

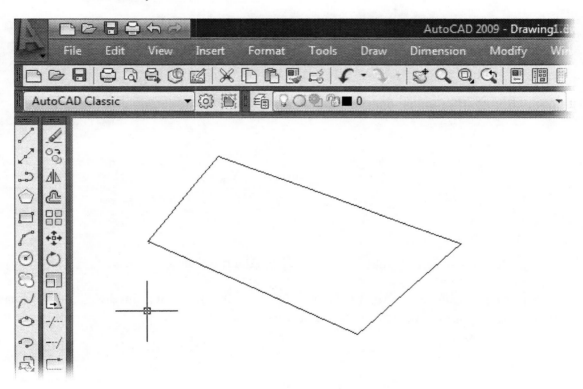

Note: The **Close** option will pick the first point of the sequence again. This will ensure that the shape is "airtight" and that it does not have any gaps between the lines. Unintended gaps can cause complications with more advanced functions.

Undo, Redo

The **Undo** Command is used to reverse the last command performed. You may also click the **Undo** button instead of manually entering the command.

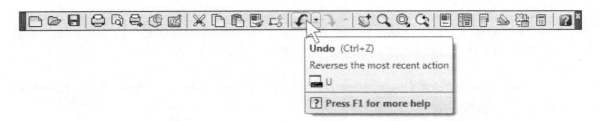

The **Redo** Command is used to reverse an **Undo**. You may also click on the **Redo** button instead of manually entering the Command.

Both of these Commands can be repeated a multiple number of times.

Note: In the Line exercise, **Undo** was used as an option within the **Line** Command. However, as you will observe in the **Erase** exercise, **Undo** can serve as an options as well as a Command.

Erase (Selection Methods)

1. **Erase** Objects by doing the following:

   - Select the **Erase** button from the **Modify** toolbar. {The cursor will turn into a pick box.}

   - Using the pick box, select any edge of the quadrilateral as shown below. {The selected line will turn dotted, meaning that the line is in the **Selection Buffer**.}

Note: At this point, more selections could be made and added to the **Selection Buffer**.

   - Press *[ENTER]*. {The line is erased.}

   - Command: *U* then *[ENTER]*. {The *U* reverses the **Erase** Command and the line reappears.}

2. **Erase** Objects using the **Window** selection method by doing the following:

Note: When using the **Window** selection method, a rectangular **Window** is used to select a group of Objects without having to select each Object individually. This is particularly useful when there are many Objects to be selected.

   - Select the **Erase** button. {The pick box appears.}

42

- Create a **Window** by picking about point **P1**, then **P2** as shown below on the left. {Only the upper left line will be selected as shown below on the right.}

Note: In this example, the **Window** (by default in a transparent blue color) was created from left to right, and therefore only the Objects that fall completely within the **Window** are selected. As long as the selection window is created from left to right, this will occur, even if it is created from bottom left to top right.

- *[ENTER]*. {The selected Line disappears.}

- Command: *U* then *[ENTER]*. {The line will reappear.}

- Select the **Erase tool** again.

- Use the **Crossing** method for your selection by picking about Point **P1**, then **P2** as shown below to the left. {All Objects that cross the edge of the **Crossing** window will be selected as shown below on the right.}

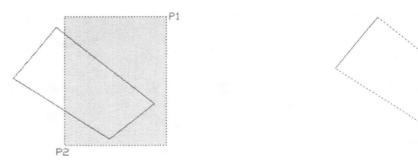

Note: As shown in this example, the **Crossing** selection method is always created from right to left, so any Objects that cross the boundary of the **Crossing,** and those inside (by default in a transparent green color), are put in the **Selection Buffer**. As long as the selection is created from right to left in any manner, **Crossing** will occur.

- *[ENTER]*. {The Objects in the **Selection Buffer** are erased.}

- Command: *U* then *[ENTER]*. {The lines reappear.}

3. **Remove** Objects from the **Selection Buffer** by doing the following:

- Select the **Erase tool**.

- Use **Crossing** to select the entire quadrilateral.

- Type *R* (for **Remove**) then *[ENTER]*.

- Pick the upper right edge as shown below. {The Object is removed from the **Selection Buffer** and therefore is displayed as a solid line again as shown below.}

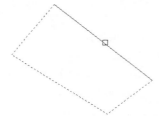

- Press *[ENTER]*. {All Objects except the removed line are erased.}

- Command: *U* then *[ENTER]*. {The lines reappear.}

Note: Instead of typing R (for Remove), you may hold down the **Shift** key while selecting Objects to **Remove** from the selection buffer.

44

4. **Erase** using the **Fence** option by doing the following:

- Select the **Erase tool**.

- Type *F* (for **Fence**) then *[ENTER]*.

- Pick about Point **P1**, then about **P2** as shown below.

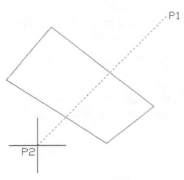

Note: When using the **Fence** option, the order of entry of P1 and P2 is irrelevant.

- *[ENTER]*. {The lines crossed by the **Fencing** will be added to the **Selection Buffer** as shown below.}

- *[ENTER]*. {Objects in the **Selection Buffer** are erased.}

- **Erase** the remaining two **Lines** by using any one of the selection methods.

Shortcut Menu

1. Use the Shortcut menu to **Close** a **Line** by doing the following:

    - Start the **Line** Command and pick four User Specified points as shown below and remain in the **Line** Command.

    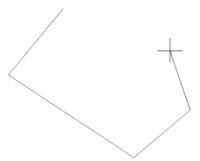

    - Use your pointer device to right-click anywhere in the Drawing area. {The Shortcut menu will appear as shown below.}

    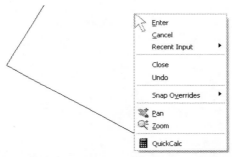

    - Select **Close** from the Shortcut menu.   {Object will **Close** as shown below.}

Note: The Shortcut menu is a convenient tool and easily accessible by right-clicking, thus allowing for quick entry. Also note that the content of the **Shortcut menu** varies depending on the current task.

Note: The selection methods discussed above can be combined in any order within the same operation. Furthermore, these selection methods are not specific to the **Erase** Command and can be used for other Commands that require **Object** selection.

2. From the Menu Bar select **File**, and **Exit**.

- When asked to save changes to the Drawing, Select **No**. {The application closes.}

Note: At the end of every chapter, you will find a summary of covered Command Aliases and Hot Keys. An alias is a shortcut for a Command. As an example, the alias for the Line Command is **L**. So you could activate the line Command by selecting the **Line** tool, by typing the Command name **Line** at the Command prompt (followed by pressing **Enter**) or by typing in the alias L (followed by pressing **Enter**). Some other examples of aliases are **Z** for **Zoom** and **CP** for **Copy**. Hot Keys also perform certain functions that allow for speed. These are used for opening and closing menus by holding one key while pressing another. As an example the PROPERTIES tool palette can be opened/closed by means of CTRL+1. In Chapter 8, you will formally put this concept to use.

Help

1. Launch **AutoCAD 2009**.

2. From the Menu Bar, select **Help** and then select **Help** again as shown below.

Note: The **AutoCAD 2009 Help** window appears as shown below. If you do not see the Help window, it may be minimized at the bottom of the screen.

3. Select the **Index** tab and then in the **Type in the keyword to find:** field, enter **erase.**

4. Use the mouse to select the **Erase** command from the list and then *[ENTER]*.

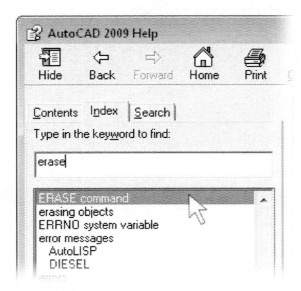

5. In the right side of the **Help** window, make sure that the **Quick Reference** tab is selected.

Note: Here you can also learn the concept and procedure for a command or topic.

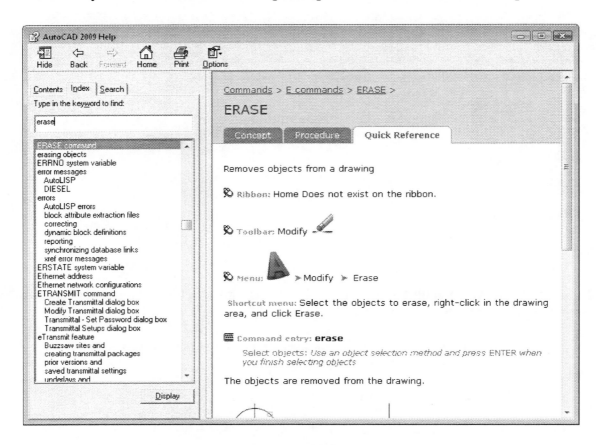

6. Close the **AutoCAD 2009 Help window** by selecting the [X] as shown below.

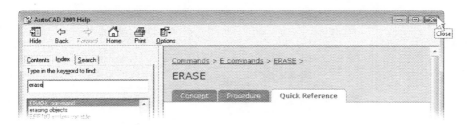

7. From the Menu Bar, select **Help**, and then **New Features Workshop**. {The New Features Workshop window opens as shown below.}

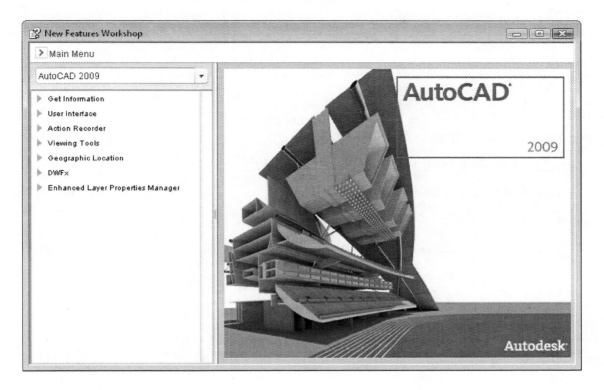

Note: The **New Features Workshop** demonstrates the recent changes and updates that have taken place within the software. This requires a good understanding of the versions preceding the new **Features Tutorial** as it serves more as an upgrade tutorial as opposed to a ground-up explanation.

8. **Close** the **New Features Workshop** window.

9. **Exit** AutoCAD.

Aliases and Hot Keys

CROSSHAIR SIZE.. CURSORSIZE

ERASE .... E

LINE L

UNDO .... U

TOGGLES CLEAN SCREEN MODE.. CTRL+0

TOGGLES DESIGN CENTER WINDOW.. CTRL+2

TOGGLES PROPERTIES WINDOW .... CTRL+1

TOGGLES TOOL PALETTES WINDOW.. CTRL+3

TOGGLES COMMAND-LINE WINDOW .... CTRL+9

Assignment 1

Objectives:

1. To practice setting your **Profile** as the current **Profile.**
2. To practice loading the **<<Unnamed Profile>>** or any other **Profile** as designated by your instructor.

Instructions:

1. Launch AutoCAD.

Note: Your **Profile** should already be available from the previous tutorial.

2. From the **Options...** dialog box, set your **Profile** as the **Current** profile by highlighting your name and then selecting **Set Current.** {Current Profile reads "Your name"}

3. While in the **Options** dialog box, select the **Display** tab and then select the **Color** button to:

   - Select a **2D model space, Uniform background** color of your choice.
   - Select a **Command Line, Uniform background** color of your choice

4. Adjust the **Crosshair size** to a suitable size of your choice.

5. **Exit** the **Options** Dialog box by selecting **Apply & Close** and then **OK**.

6. Make sure to have these eight toolbars Toggled to *On* so that they appear on the screen.
   - **Draw**
   - **Draw Order**
   - **Layers**
   - **Modify**
   - **Properties**
   - **Standard**
   - **Styles**
   - **Workspaces**

7. Your assignment is completed by setting the default profile (**<<Unnamed profile>>**) as the **Current** profile. This should reset your screen color, crosshair size, etc. back to the original settings.

8. **Exit** AutoCAD without saving any changes as your **Profile** is saved already.

Chapter 2

File Management

Rectangular Coordinate System

Polar Coordinate System

Create and Save a Drawing

File Safety Precautions

File Security Precautions

Setting Up a Drawing

File Recovery

Working with Multiple Files

Plotting Basics

54

File Management

In this section, you will learn to create folders. A folder is the location where files, in your case Drawing files, are saved. Many teaching institutions use the common practice of automatically creating student folders using their names and/or ID numbers. These student folders are often placed on a network drive such as F:, T:, or H: or a portable **USB Flash Drive**. An example of a folder and its associated path may be **K:\Engineering Technologies\Smith_David_02,** where a common folder such as David Smith 02 is created on the K: Drive under the Engineering Technologies folder as shown below.

You are about to go through the process of creating your folder. While going through this process, your screen may look slightly different as the steps displayed below are for Microsoft® Windows Vista™. However, considering that you may be running AutoCAD 2009 on Windows XP®, your interface may differ slightly. Consult with your Instructor.

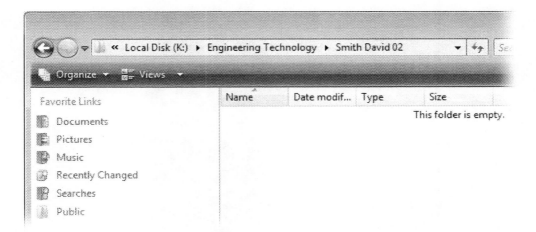

In the event that you have a folder assigned to you, skip the remaining portion of this section and move on to the Rectangular Coordinate Systems section located on page 58.

The instructions below will help you in creating and renaming your folder by first creating a folder with the generic name **"My CAD Stuff"** and then **Renaming** it using your **"NAME."** This exercise will create your folder on the **Local Disk (C:).** However, if you have access to an external drive such as a **USB Flash Drive**, you may use it instead.

1. Create your folder by doing the following:

    - From the Microsoft Windows® Interface, select the **Start** button located in the lower left corner of the screen, and then select **Documents** as shown below.

    - As the **Documents** Folder appears, **Right Click** inside the window as shown below. Also note that in your case, this Folder may contain other file and/or folders.

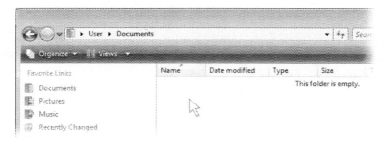

- From the shortcut Menu, select **New**, and then **Folder** as shown below. {A **New Folder** appears. It is highlighted, and cursor is located to the right of the name. Since the name is already highlighted, you don't need to back space.}

- Type in the new name: *My CAD Stuff* and then *[ENTER]*.

- Double click on the folder **My CAD Stuff**. {You are inside the folder. The name appears at the **Address field**, and it is obviously empty.}

- Select the **Back** button as shown below. {It will take you "back" out of the folder and to the **Documents** folder}

- Right-click on the **My CAD Stuff** folder and select **Rename**. {Name is highlighted.}

- Type in your last name followed by your first name, i.e., **Smith David**

- *[ENTER]*. {Folder is Renamed to your name.}

- Click on the **Close** button in the upper right corner of the window.

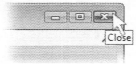

Note: From this point on, for the sake of consistency, the book will refer to your folder as your **My CAD Folder.**

Rectangular Coordinate System

A coordinate system allows you to keep track of the position of points. In the first part of this discussion, you will be exposed to the **Rectangular Coordinate System** independent of AutoCAD. For the time being, this is a general discussion about coordinate systems and does not pertain to AutoCAD directly. Later in this chapter, you will be instructed to apply your knowledge to AutoCAD.

The **Rectangular Coordinate System** is composed of two number lines known as the **X** and **Y** axes positioned in the horizontal and vertical direction respectively. The point where the two axes cross is known as the **Origin**. The position of any point such as point P below, can be shown using a pair of numbers. The two numbers are known as the X and Y coordinates and are measured along the two axes.

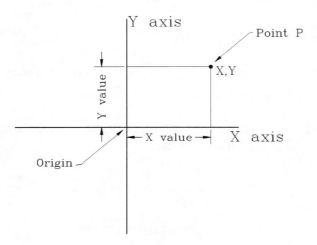

As an example, you can get to point **P1** located at 4,3 by walking from the **Origin** 4.0 units to the right (+) along the X axis, and then 3 units up (+) along the Y axis.

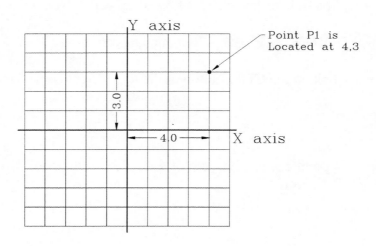

Here are several other examples of points and their coordinates displayed using the **Rectangular Coordinate System**.

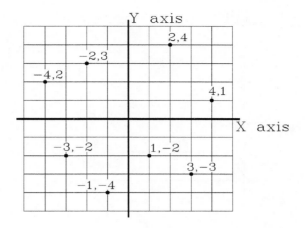

Finally, here are more examples of Points that fall on the X and/or Y axes.

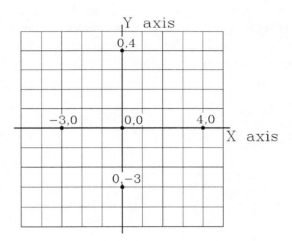

The coordinate system above is more specifically referred to as the **Absolute Rectangular Coordinate System** since the positions of all the points are measured with respect to the **Origin** 0,0 , which is a fixed absolute point.

The example below shows a 3 x 2 rectangle with point **P1** located at 1,1. See if you can find the coordinates of the other three corners, **P2**, **P3**, and **P4**. {Answers are given at the end of the Chapter prior to the assignment.}

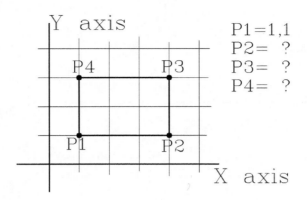

There are times when the location of a point is only known with respect to another point and not necessarily to that of the **Origin**. In the figure below, the designer/draftsperson may not know where **P2** is in relation to the **Origin**, but instead may know where **P2** is with respect to **P1** (point of intersection of the arc and the line). Therefore, at times, it is beneficial to be able to locate points **Relative** (with respect) to other known points rather than measure points with respect to the **Origin**.

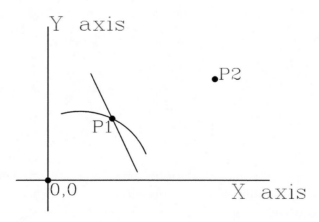

In AutoCAD, the last/previous point entered is interpreted as the relative **Origin**. Therefore when constructing a shape such as the rectangle above, the first point **P1** is best entered in absolute mode, and **P2**, **P3** and **P4** could be entered in either absolute or relative mode.

To enter the coordinates of a point in the relative mode, you must use the **@** symbol. Also note that the two coordinates are separated by a comma. Here is the example of a point entered in the relative mode: **@3,2**.

Next you will go through a discussion of constructing a 3 x 2 rectangle starting at 1,1 in the counter-clockwise order, by determining the coordinates of the points **P2**, **P3** and **P4** relative to the last point entered. In other words, you will be going through a discussion for filling in the blanks of the table below.

With respect to **P1**, **P2** is located at @___ , ___

With respect to **P2**, **P3** is located at @___ , ___

With respect to **P3**, **P4** is located at @___ , ___

With respect to **P4**, **P1** is located at @___ , ___

In order to locate **P2** with respect to **P1**, you must think of the **Origin** of the coordinate system being at **P1** as shown below by the dashed lines. Then **P2** is simply located 3,0 from **P1**, or @3,0.

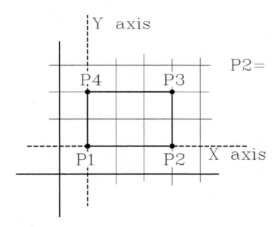

In order to locate **P3** with respect to **P2**, you must think of the **Origin** of the coordinate system being at **P2** as shown below by the dashed lines. Then **P3** is simply located 0,2 from **P2**, or @0,2.

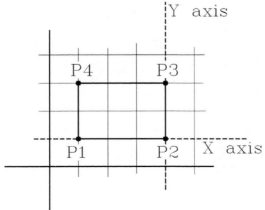

In order to locate **P4** with respect to **P3**, you must think of the **Origin** of the coordinate system being at **P3** as shown below by the dashed lines. Then **P4** is simply located -3,0 from **P3**, or @-3,0.

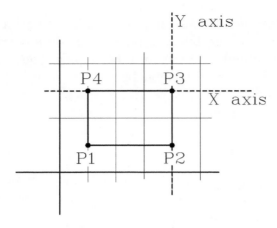

Finally, going back to **P1** is as simple as typing in 1,1, however, for the sake of practice, you will accomplish this by using the **Relative Coordinate System**. In order to locate **P1** with respect to **P4**, you must think of the **Origin** of the coordinate system being at **P4** as shown below by the dashed lines. Then **P1** is simply located at 0,-2 from **P4**, or @0,-2.

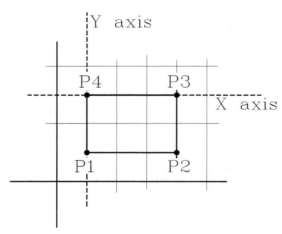

Now that you have a firm understanding of the **Rectangular Coordinate System**, see if you can determine the coordinates of **P2** and specifically **P3** of a Horizontally positioned 3 inch equilateral triangle with **P1** located at 1,1 as shown below.

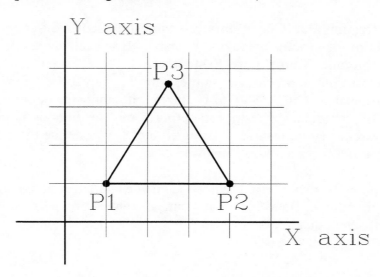

Do not dedicate more than a few minutes to this calculation. The discussion will follow on the next page.

P1 = 1,1

P2 = ___ , ___

P3 = ___ , ___

64

Polar Coordinate System

In the **Rectangular Coordinate System**, you used two variables, X and Y, to define the position of a point on the X-Y plane. However, there are instances where using the **Rectangular Coordinate System** can be less than the ideal choice. For instance, in the case of the previous example, point **P3** (top corner of triangle) is actually located at coordinates 2.50,3.59807621 making it cumbersome for keyboard entry. Another type of coordinate system for defining the position of points is the **Polar Coordinate System**. Here, instead of using X and Y, you define the position of a point by the notation **r** and **theta** as shown below.

r and **theta** are also referred to as **Magnitude** and **Direction**, meaning a length of **r** and angular direction of **theta**. Here are some examples of a point falling on the **Polar Plane** in four different quadrants.

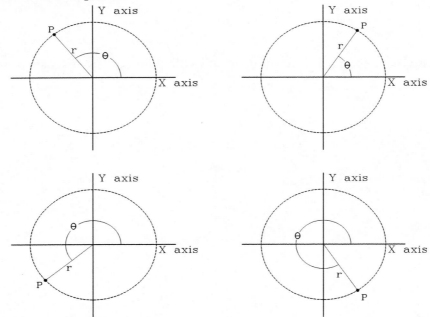

In order to be able to use the **Polar Coordinate System** successfully, it is essential that you fully understand the concept of angles and to be able to measure angles in degrees. Angles are measured from the positive X axis in the counter clock-wise (CCW) direction. CCW is considered positive. For the purpose of this course, the topic of angles is considered to be a prerequisite. Hopefully the diagrams on the following page serve as means of review and not as an introduction.

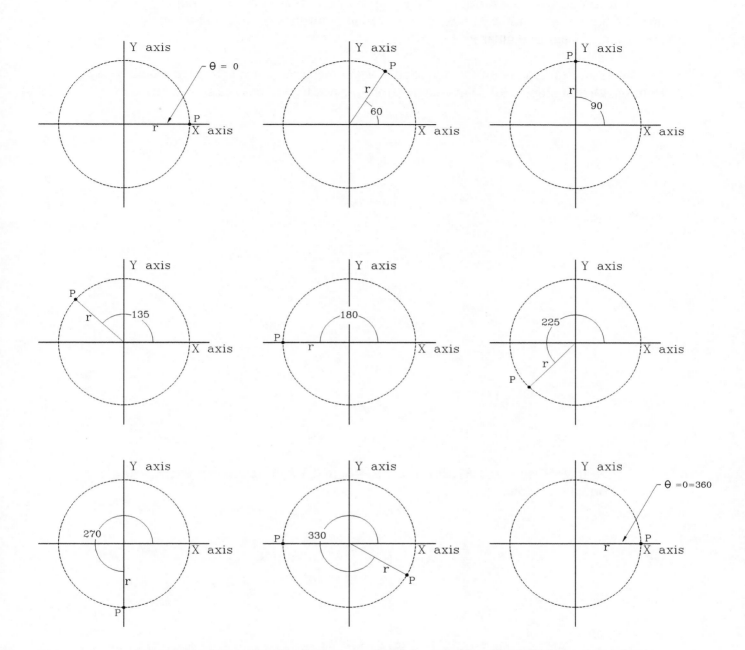

A complete turn of point P along a circle is considered a 360 degree rotation or one revolution. Pay special attention to the value of **theta** in all nine diagrams above.

In order to locate a point on the **Polar Plane**, it would be helpful if you could imagine a polar grid in the mind's eye. Here the polar grid is based on a 1-unit circular grid and a 15-degree angular grid.

As an example, point **P1** is located at **4<30** meaning that it is located 4 units away from the **Origin** along a 30 degree angle (from the positive X axis) as shown below.

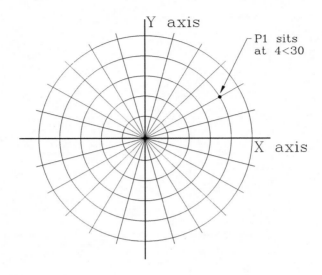

See if you can place **P2, P3, P4, P5, P6,** and **P7** on the **Polar Plane** using the given information below.

P2 = 4<45

P3 = 3<90

P4 = 2<105

P5 = 5<225

P6 = 3<270

P7 = 2<345

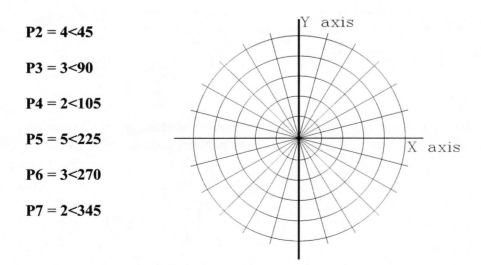

Refer to the end of the Chapter for the solution.

Now lets go back to the problem of Drawing a 3-unit equilateral triangle starting at 1,1.

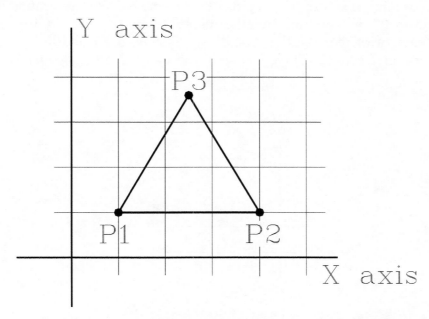

Knowing that the sum of the interior angles of any triangle is 180 degrees, and that this triangle is an equilateral, the 3 interior angles are equal, and therefore each must be 60 degrees as shown below. Note that angle **a** = 180 – 60 = 120 and since alternate interior angles are equal, angle **b**= 60.

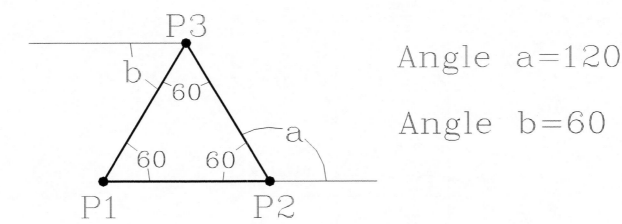

Angle a=120

Angle b=60

Next you will use your knowledge of the **Relative Polar** Coordinate System to construct this triangle. Knowing that **P1** is located at **1,1** and that it is the first point in a sequence, it is best to use the **Absolute Rectangular** Coordinate System for locating this point. In order to get to **P2**, in using the **Relative Polar** Coordinate System, it would help to imagine the **Origin** of the **Relative** Coordinate System at **P1** and thinking of navigating strictly east from **P1** to **P2**. Therefore, with respect to **P1, P2** is **@3<0** .

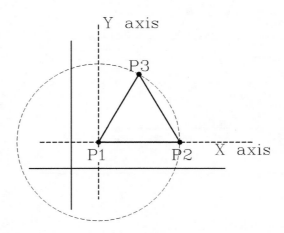

In going from **P2** to **P3** of the figure below, you already know that each interior angle is **60** degrees, however since you always measure the traveling angle with respect to the positive X axis, the angle of interest is **a,** below, and so **P3** is determined as **@3<120**.

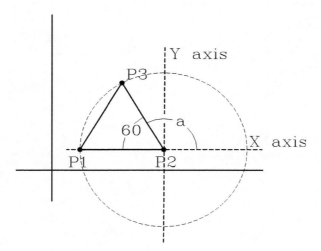

Going from **P3** to **P1** is as easy as 1,1 in **Absolute Rectangular** mode. However, again, let's give ourselves a challenge and practice the **Relative Polar** instead of the **Absolute Rectangular** Coordinate System.

Knowing that the **Origin** of your **Relative** Coordinate System is set at point **P3** (last point of entry) and that you always measure the navigation angle from the positive X axis, you need to calculate angle **c**. Angle **c** = 180 + **b**, and **b** = 60 from above. Therefore **c = 180 + 60 = 240**.

And so going from **P3** to **P1** requires an input of *@3<240*.

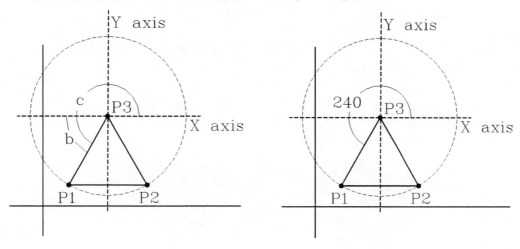

Later in this chapter, you will Launch AutoCAD and use your knowledge of coordinate systems to create geometry, but first you will learn about File Management so that you will have a location to save your work.

Create and Save a Drawing

1. Create a **Drawing** by doing the following:

   - Launch AutoCAD and make sure that you are using the **AutoCAD Classic** workspace. {You will be placed in a blank Drawing.}

   - **Close** any unnecessary Palettes or Toolbars. Refer to the image below.

   - Command: **Zoom** and then *[ENTER]*.

   - Type *all* and then *[ENTER]*. (The **Zoom** Command will be covered thoroughly in later Chapters.)

   - Use the **Line Command** and the pointing device to draw a triangle at a User Specified location as shown. Make sure to use the **Close** option to keep the shape "airtight".

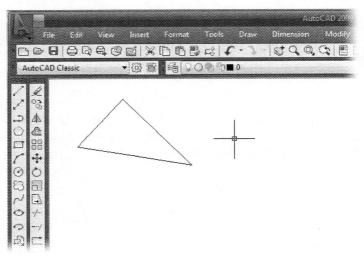

2. Create **Text** by doing the following:

   - **Toggle Caps Lock key** to *Off*. {The **Caps Lock** Toggle indicator located on the keyboard is set to the off position.}

   - Command: *Text* then *[ENTER]*. (Do not abbreviate the Command *Text*)

   - Pick start point of **Text** below the triangular shape as shown below.

   - **Specify Height <0.2000>** press *[ENTER]*.

Note: The **Height** shown in brackets is the default **Text Height**. Pressing the Enter key will enter the default value.

- The **Rotation Angle** default is **<0>** therefore *[ENTER]*.

- Type the text ***triangle*** then *[ENTER]*. {Cursor moves to the next line.}

- Press the *[ENTER]* *key* again to exit the **Text** Command.

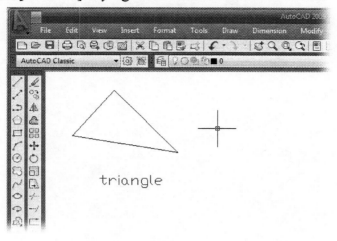

3. **Save** a Drawing file to your Folder by doing the following:

- From the Menu Bar, select **File**, then select **Save As**. {**Save Drawing As** dialog box appears.}

- Click in the **Save in** drop-down text box as shown by the pointer.

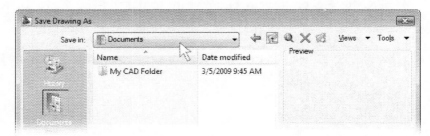

- Move the pointer onto the Network drive E,T,H,K etc. where your assigned folder is located as specified by your *Instructor* and select. In the diagram below, the **Local Disk (K:)** is being shown as an example. {**Save in** text box changes to that specific drive.}

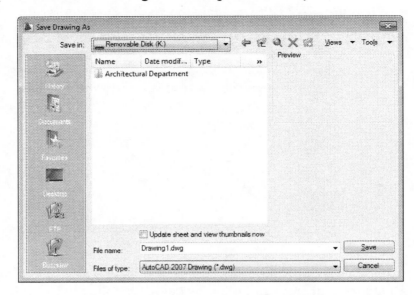

- In the **Save Drawing As** dialog box, Select the **Views** drop-down menu and then Select **List** as shown below. If **List** is grayed out, it is already selected. {Folders are displayed in a Listed format.}

- If necessary, scroll to find your **My CAD Folder**, *i.e., Smith, David.* [To locate your specific folder, you may need to select a subfolder.}

- Select your folder. {Folder name is highlighted.}

- Press the **Enter** key to enter your folder. {The **Save in** text box now reads: **My CAD Folder(your name).**}

- In the **File Name** text box, select the default name **Drawing1.dwg**. {The file name will highlight automatically when selected.} Type in the new name: ***Shapes***

Note: When entering a new file name, the file type (**.dwg**) does not need to be typed in because AutoCAD will automatically assign this extension.

- In the **Files of type** text box, check file type to be **AutoCAD 2007 Drawing (*.dwg)**

- Now that you have your **Save in** Location, **File name** and **Files of type** set as shown below, select the **Save** button.

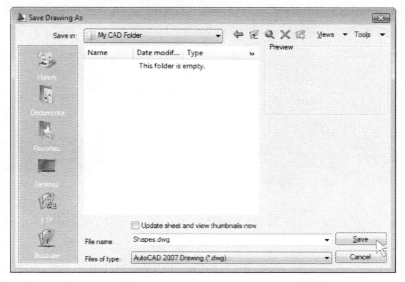

4. **Save** your progress by doing the following:

- Draw the quadrilateral at a User Specified location as shown below the triangle, and use the **Text** Command to label the shape as shown. Remember that you must *[ENTER]* twice to exit the **Text** Command.

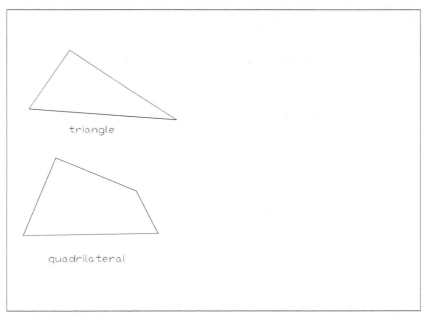

- From the Menu Bar, select **File** and then **Save**.

Note: When you save a Drawing for the first time, you must use the **Save As** option. This way, your **Save in** folder and **file type** are assigned properly. From this point on, to save your progress, you can use the **Save** Command (also known as *Qsave*). This is because the system is already aware of the **Save in folder**, **File name** and the **file type** that you have selected.

- Draw and label the five sided figure at a User Specified location as shown below.

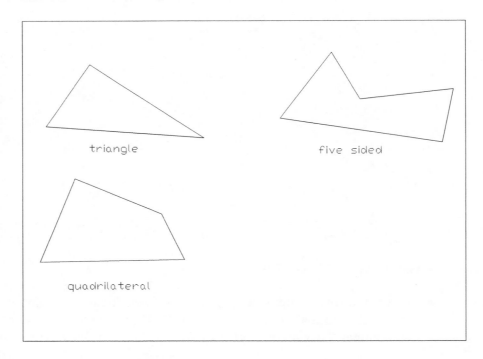

5. **Edit Text** by doing the following:

- Double click on any character of your text string that reads "five sided". {The **Edit Text** field will appear.}

- Use the **Edit Text** field to change the Text to read *irregular pentagon* and then **[Enter]** twice.

6. In the **Standard Toolbar**, select the **Save** button as shown below.

7. Verify the **Open and Save** options by doing the following:

- From the Menu Bar, select **Tools** and then select **Options...** as shown below.

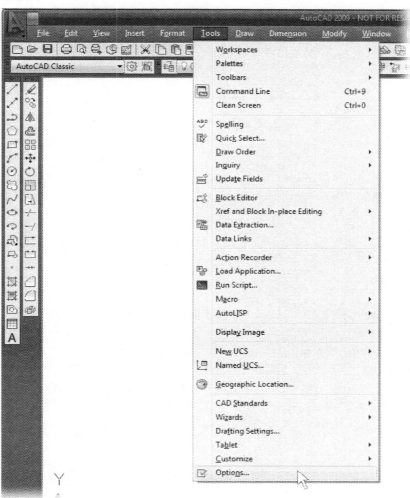

- When the **Options** dialog box appears, click on the **Open and Save** tab, as shown on the next page.

- Verify that in the **File Save** area, the **AutoCAD 2007 Drawing (*.dwg)** is the default selection as shown below.

- In the **File Safety Precautions** area of the **Open and Save** tab, verify that the **Create backup copy with each save** option is Toggled to *On* as shown below.

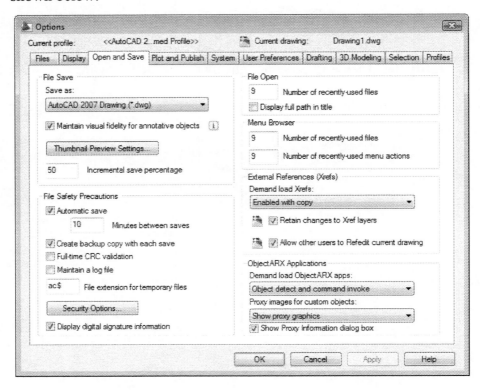

8. Select **OK**.

9. Select **File** then **Exit** AutoCAD and select **Yes** to save changes to the Drawing.

Note: As you may have noticed from the above diagram, AutoCAD has the option to save your Drawing file to an older version. This allows you to work with clients who may be working with an older release. You can also translate AutoCAD files to be read by other drafting and design software packages. However, this form of translation is discussed in the next Volume and is out of the scope of this book.

File Safety Precautions

1. View your folder content by doing the following:

    *   At the Microsoft Windows® interface, select **Start,** then **Computer**.

    *   Locate your Drive as assigned by your **instructor** (or the alternate drive that you chose earlier in this chapter).

    *   Double Click on your **Folder**.

    *   From the Menu Bar select **View** then **List**. {Your files are displayed}

Note: Despite the fact that you have saved your **Shapes** Drawing file a total of three times, as you can see, there are only two files stored in your **My CAD Folder**; one is the **Shapes.dwg** and the other is **Shapes.bak**. As an example, if you save your daily progress at about ten minute intervals, at the end of the day, you may have selected the **Save** button a total of 48 times. Therefore the system keeps record of your 48th **Save** as a **Drawing** file, and the 47th as your **Backup** file, and all other previous files are overwritten. In the event that a **Drawing** file is erased, corrupted or unintentionally altered, you can rely on the **Backup** file by renaming it to a **dwg** file type.

    *   Close the **My CAD Folder** window.

2. **Preview** and **Open** your pre-existing file by doing the following:

    *   Launch AutoCAD. {You will be placed in a new blank Drawing.}

    *   From the Menu Bar select **File**, then **Open** as shown below.

78

- From the **Select File** dialog box, select **Shapes** Drawing. {Drawing Preview displays on the right as shown below.}

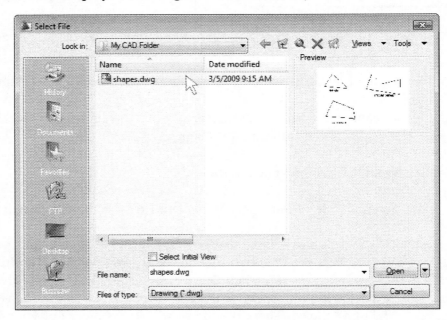

Note: If **Shapes** Drawing is not listed, use the **Look in** pull-down menu to locate it.

- Click **Open**.

- Draw and label the star shape at a User Specified location as shown below.

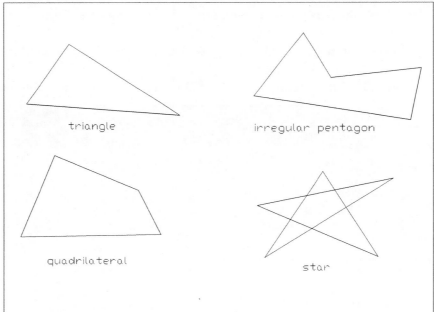

- Remain in the Drawing and move to the next section.

File Security Precautions

1. Enable **Password Security Option** by doing the following:

    *   From the Menu Bar, select **Tools** and then **Options...** {The **Options** dialog box will appear.}

    *   Click on the **Open and Save** tab of the **Options** dialog box.

    *   Click on the **Security Options...** button in the **File Safety Precautions** area as shown below.

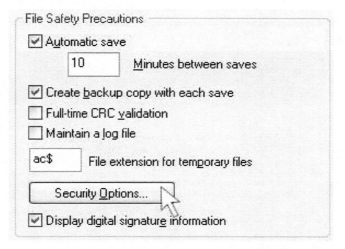

{The **Security Options** dialog box will appear as shown below.}

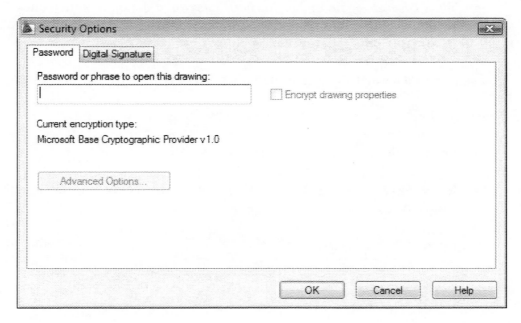

- Enter *Discrete* as the **Password or phrase to open this Drawing**. {The **Password** will appear as bars for security purposes.}

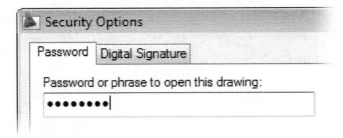

- Click **OK**. {A dialog box will appear asking you to **Confirm Password** as shown below.}

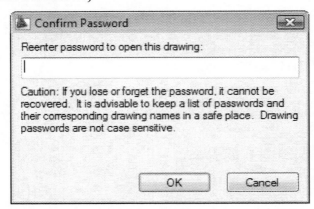

- Type *Discrete* again in the **Confirm Password** dialog box then click **OK**.

- Click **OK** in the **Options** dialog box.

Note: You can also **Password Protect** at the time of saving.

2. **Password Protect** when **Saving** a Drawing by doing the following:

- From the Menu Bar select **File** then **Save As**.

- In the **Save Drawing As** dialog box, select the **Tools** pull-down menu as shown below.

- Select **Security Options** from the **Tools** pull-down menu as shown below. {The **Security Options** dialog box will appear the same as it did through the **Options** dialog box asking you for a password.}

- Change the Password to *Protected*.

Note: Once a Password has been assigned to a Drawing, it is not necessary to reenter it every time you save.

- **Save** the Drawing. {**Save Drawing As** dialog box asks if you want to replace file.}

- Select **Yes**.

- From the Menu Bar, select **File** and then **Close**.

3. **Open** a **Password Protected** Drawing File by doing the following:

- From the Menu Bar, select **File** and then **Open** if necessary.

- Locate your **Shapes** Drawing file and click **Open**. {A dialog box will appear asking for your **Password** as shown below.}

- Type in your Password *Protected* in the text field and click **OK**. {File is open}

Note: In the event that you decide to **Password Protect** a file, <u>it is essential that you remember your password. If you forget or lose your password, your file is lost</u>; therefore, at the beginning stages, it is recommended that you keep a copy of your file without a password in a remote location such as on a flash drive. Consult with your instructor as to whether your assignments should be **Password Protected**.

4. **Exit** AutoCAD by doing the following:

  - From the Menu Bar select **File** and select **Exit**.

Note: If and when necessary, you can use the **Security Options** dialog box to remove a password from a password-protected file. This can be done by selecting and deleting the password, as shown by the dots below, of the **Security Options** window and then select **OK**.

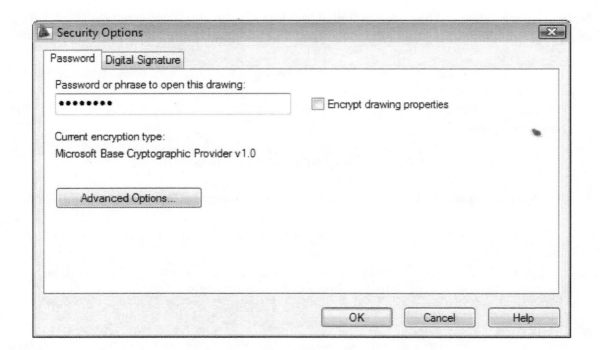

<u>Setting Up a Drawing</u>

1. Launch AutoCAD. {You will be placed in a new blank Drawing.}

2. Select **Units** and set **Precision** by doing the following:

   - From the Menu Bar select **Format** and then **Units**. {The **Drawing Units** dialog box will appear.}

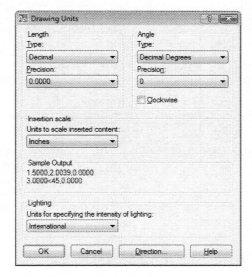

Note: As you begin a new Drawing, it is essential that a proper **Drawing Unit** type is chosen.   AutoCAD supports **Architectural**, **Decimal**, **Engineering**, **Fractional** and **Scientific** units. For this exercise, you are keeping the **Units** as **Decimal.** This book will use the **Architectural** and **Decimal** units only.

   - In the **Drawing Units** dialog box under **Length**, drop-down and change the **Precision** to two decimal places (0.00).

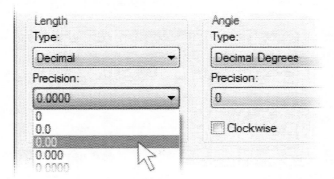

   - In the **Angle** area of the **Drawing Units** dialog box, change **Decimal Degrees Precision** to one decimal place (0.0).

84

Note: While a maximum of 8 decimal places can be displayed, the actual **Precision** of the AutoCAD environment is 14-16 decimal places. The remaining decimal places are for internal use and computational purposes only.

- Click on **OK**.

Note: Once your Units are assigned, you need to define the boundaries of your Drawing (working space). Since the amount of **Electronic Paper** (or space to draw in) is practically unlimited, your geometry (a set of Objects) is always modeled in actual size and dimensions. The **Limits** Command sets the amount of **Electronic Paper** needed for each given Drawing. Although AutoCAD uses a default value of 12 x 9 for the **Limits**, here you will be using a Drawing area of 9 x 6.

3. Set **Limits** by doing the following:

   - From the Menu Bar click on **Format**, then **Drawing Limits**.

   - The **Command Prompt** asks for the coordinates of the lower left corner. To keep the default settings <0.00,0.00> press *[ENTER]*.

   - The **Command Prompt** then asks for the upper right corner. Type *9,6* then *[ENTER]*.

   - Command: *Zoom* then *[ENTER]*.

   - From the list of options, type *All* then *[ENTER]*.

Note: Zoom All adjusts your view so that you see the entire **Limits** of the Drawing area. You should always use the **Zoom** Command and then the **All** option after setting new **Limits**. The **Zoom** tool will be discussed in depth in chapter 6. Chapters 1-5 do not require any Zooming and Panning, etc. For now, in the event that you accidentally **Zoom** in/out of the Drawing, (such as in the case of accidentally turning the mouse wheel), simply press the **Esc** key and then **Zoom All** to move forward with your lesson.

4. From the **Status Line** make sure that **Snap**, **Grid**, **Ortho**, **Polar**, **OSnap**, **OTrack**, **Ducs** and **Dyn** are set to *Off* as shown below.

5. Construct geometry using the **Absolute Rectangular** Coordinate System by doing the following:

   - Select the **Line** tool.

- Specify first point: *1,1* then *[ENTER]*.

- Specify next point or [Undo]: *4,1* then *[ENTER]*.

- Specify next point or [Undo]: *4,3* then *[ENTER]*.

- Specify next point or [Close/Undo]: *1,3* then *[ENTER]*.

- Specify next point or [Close/Undo]: *1,1* then *[ENTER]*.

- Specify next point or [Close/Undo]: *[ENTER]*. {Cancels the **Line** Command.}

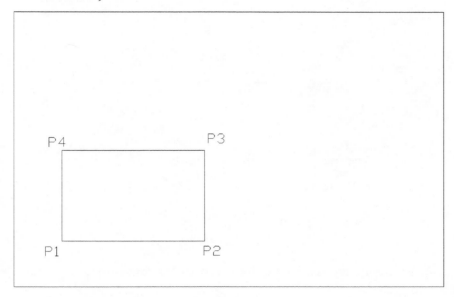

- Command: *Erase* then *[ENTER]*.

- Type *ALL* then *[ENTER]*.

- *[ENTER]*. {Finishes the Command and the Rectangle will be erased.}

6. Construct geometry using the **Relative Rectangular** Coordinate System by doing the following:

Note: The @ symbol is entered by holding down the **Shift** key while pressing **2** near the top row of the keyboard. If you mistype, prior to pressing the return key, you may use the **Backspace** key to correct the entry; otherwise you will need to **Undo** the last entry.

- Command: *Line* then *[ENTER]*.

- Specify first point: *1,1* then *[ENTER]*. {Starting sequence in absolute mode.}

86

- Specify next point or [Undo]: *@3,0* then *[ENTER]*.

- Specify next point or [Undo]: *@0,2* then *[ENTER]*.

- Specify next point or [Close/Undo]: *@-3,0* then *[ENTER]*.

- Specify next point or [Close/Undo]: *C* (for **Close**) then *[ENTER]*.

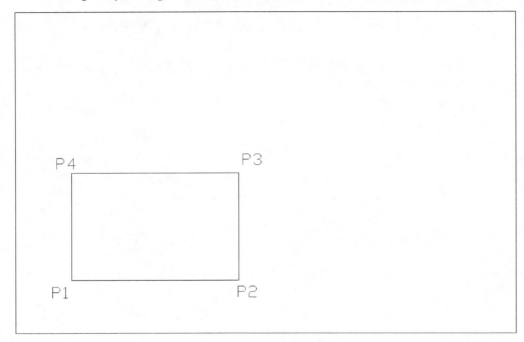

7. Construct geometry using the **Relative Polar** Coordinate System by doing the following:

- Select the **Line** tool.

- For the start point, type *5,1* then *[ENTER]*. {Starting sequence in **Absolute Rectangular** mode.}

- Type *@3<0* then *[ENTER]*.

- Type *@3<120* then *[ENTER]*.

- Type *@3<240* then *[ENTER]*.

- Specify next point or [Close/Undo]: *[ENTER]*. {Cancels the Line Command}

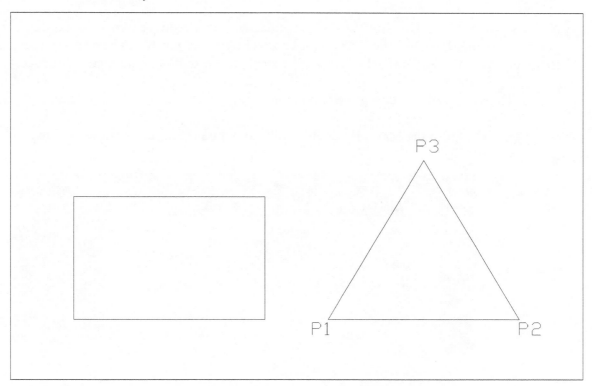

- Use the **Line** tool to create a rectangular border with these coordinates: **0,0 9,0 9,6 0,6** and **Close** shape.

- Use the **Text** Command to add your name in the upper left corner of the Drawing. Exact location is your choice. Use a **Text Height** of *.20*

- **Save As** Drawing to your folder as *Plotting Practice.dwg*.

- **Close** this Drawing and move to the next section.

<u>File Recovery</u>

Note: If and when a Drawing file is corrupted, you can recover part or hopefully all of the data for the damaged file. This can be done by checking for the errors by using the Recovery tool of the AutoCAD Utility. The steps below demonstrate recovery process.

1. **Recover** a file by doing the following:

    • From the Menu Bar, select **File**, and then **Recover** as shown below.

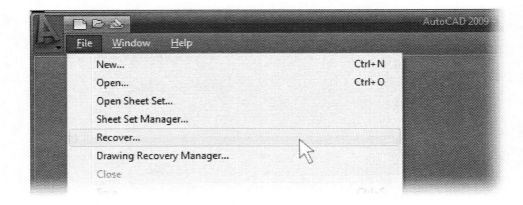

    • From the **Select File** window, select your folder.

    • From your folder, select the **plotting practice.dwg** file and **Open**.

As shown below, you are alerted by a message that the **Audit** has detected no errors. In the prompt line, it is further stated that all Objects were audited and that no errors were found or fixed.

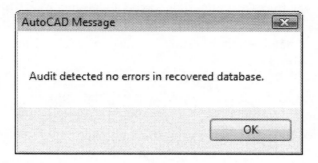

In any instance, where there are actual errors found within the **Audit** process of a file, **Recovery** will give the option to salvage as much of the corrupted data as possible by asking the question:

Fix any errors detected? [Yes/No] <N>:

If you chose not to correct the errors, the output will list the number of errors, but fix none, and if you enter **yes**, the **Audit** log file will be saved as an **(adt)** file.

Please note that **Recovery** is not always a perfect process. Therefore, you should make a habit of frequently saving your progress, so that when corrupt data is detected, you can fall back on to the last saved copy of the file or even the backup file. If you are interested in a better understanding of the **Recovery** and the **Audit** processes, you can refer to the **HELP** option and use the **index tab** to search for **Recovery**.

- Select **OK** to close the **AutoCAD Message** window. {File is opened without any detected errors.}

Working with Multiple Open Files

Now that you have at least two Drawing files saved to your **Your Folder**, it is useful open and work with more than one file at a time. It is also just as important to remember to close files that no longer need to remain open because too many unnecessary open files at a given time can slow down your system.

1. **Open** more than one file at a given time by doing the following:

    - From the Menu Bar select **File**, then **Open**. {The **Select File** dialog box will appear.}

    - If necessary, use the **Look in** pull-down menu to locate your **My CAD Folder**.

    - Click on **Shapes.dwg** and select **Open**. {Password dialog box appears.}

    - Enter the password *Protected* and select **OK**. {You are placed inside **Shapes.dwg** Drawing.}

    - Note that your **Plotting Practice.dwg** file is already **Open** since this file may be open from the **File Recovery** exercise.

2. Work with multiple open files by doing the following:

    - From the Menu Bar select **Window**. {All of the currently opened files (in this case only two) will be listed as shown below}

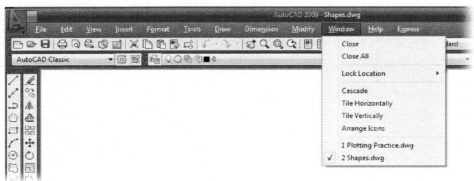

- From the drop-down list, make sure that **Shapes.dwg** is selected. {**Shapes.dwg** will be brought to front to work on}

- Hold down the **Ctrl** key on your keyboard while pressing the **Tab** key several times. {You will cycle through all the open files (in this case 2) one at a time.

- Make sure that **Shapes.dwg** is your currently **Open** file.

3. **Close** files by doing the following:

- From the Menu Bar select **Window**, and then **Close**. {The current file will close and **Plotting Practice.dwg** will remain open.}

- From the Menu Bar select **Window**, then **Close All**.

Note: If you get into a habit of keeping multiple files open unnecessarily, you may find yourself trying to Open an "already open file" which has been sitting/"hiding" in the background. In this case, AutoCAD will alert you that the file you are trying to open is in use by another user and the alert dialog box will give you the option to open the file as read-only.

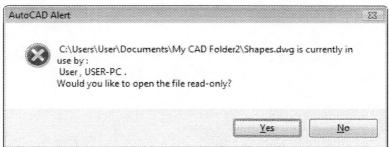

To avoid this situation, make sure to properly **Close** unneeded Drawing files before opening another. Also keep in mind that as you advance through these tutorials, it is intended for you to work on only one assignment at a given time.

- Remain in AutoCAD and move to the next section.

Plotting in AutoCAD

This section assumes that you have access to a plotter or printer and that it is turned on.

1. Plot a Drawing by doing the following:

   - **Open** the **Plotting Practice.dwg** file again.

   - From the Menu Bar, select **File** and then **Plot**.   {The **Plot-Model** dialog box appears.}
   - From the Menu Bar, select **File** and then **Plot**.

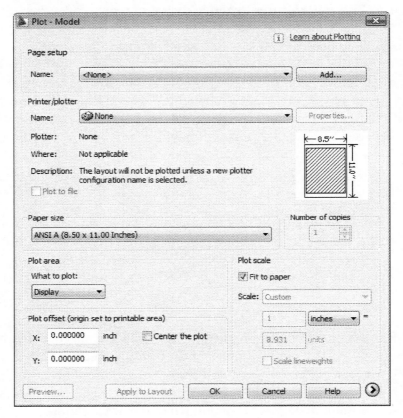

   - If your **Plot-Model** dialog box is not fully expanded as shown below, then click on the **More Options** button in the lower right corner of the dialog box. {**Plot-Model** dialog box expands.}

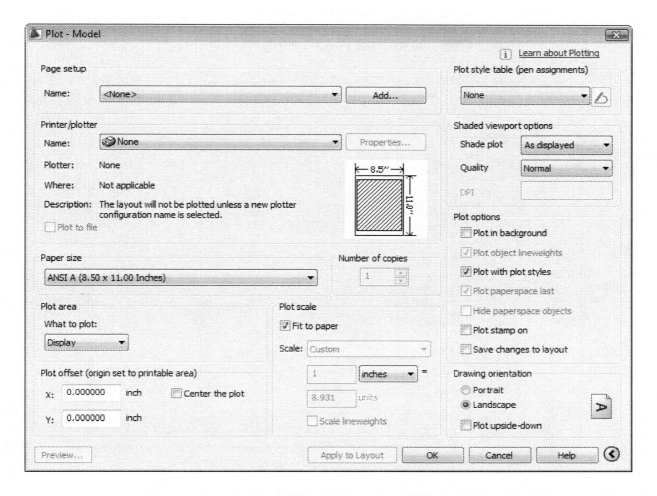

- In the **Printer/plotter** area, next to **Name**, use the drop-down menu to select a plotter. Ask your instructor for your available and configured plotters.

- In the **Paper size** section, make sure that **Letter** (8.50 x 11.00 in.) is selected as your **Paper Size**.

- In the **Plot area,** use the drop-down menu to select **Limits**.

- In the **Plot offset** area, Toggle the **Center the plot** option to *On*. {The X and Y values may vary from what you see above.}

- In the **Plot scale** area, Toggle the **Fit to paper** option to *Off* and then use the **Scale** drop-down menu to set **Scale** to **1:1**.

- In the **Drawing orientation** section, Toggle *On* **Landscape**.

- Once your settings match those above, click the **Preview** button. {A plot preview will appear displaying the Drawing in relation to the selected paper size as shown below.}

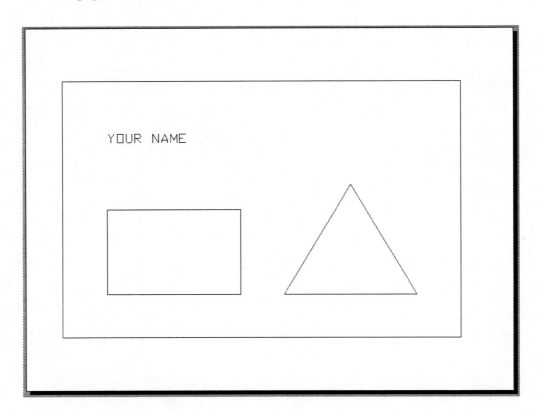

- Click on the **Close Preview Window** button as shown below.

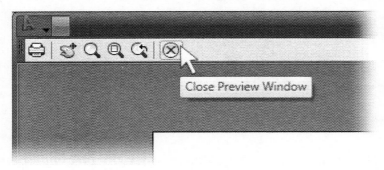

- Double check all the settings one last time and select **OK** to make a plot.

Note: This plot is not an assignment.

- **Exit** AutoCAD without saving changes.

<u>Answers</u>

1. These are the answers to the Rectangular Coordinate question on page 61.

   P2 = 4,1   **P3** = 4,3   **P4** = 1,3

2. Below is the solution to the Polar Coordinate question on page 64.

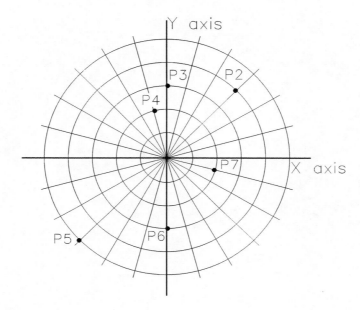

Aliases and Hot Keys

PLOT..PRINT

TEXT .... TEXT

EXIT AUTOCAD .... CTRL+Q

OPEN FILE.. CTRL+O

PLOT...CTRL+P

SAVE ....CTRL+S

SAVE AS .... CTRL+SHIFT+S

<u>Assignment 2</u>

Objective:

1. To practice starting AutoCAD.
2. To practice the **Rectangular** and **Polar Coordinate Systems** entry.
3. To practice pointing device entry.
4. To practice Naming your Drawing file and **Saving** to the designated Folder.
5. To practice **Text** Command basics.

Instructions:

1. Launch AutoCAD. {You will be placed in a blank Drawing.}
2. Keep **Units** as **Decimal** with **Precision** set to 2 decimal places (**0.00**).
3. Set **Limits** to Lower Left Corner *0,0* and Upper Right Corner *9,6*.
4. **Zoom All** to view your entire **Limits**.
5. Make sure that in the **Status Line**, **Snap**, **Grid**, **Ortho**, **Polar**, **Osnap**, **Otrack**, and **Dyn** are set to *Off*.
6. **Save As** the Drawing file to your folder. Name it **"ASSIGN02_ _ _.dwg"** where the 3 blanks are your initials.
7. Use the **Line** Command to create a border at the edge of your Drawing area using the following Absolute coordinates:

   - **P1** is located at 0,0
   - **P2** is located at 9,0
   - **P3** is located at 9,6
   - **P4** is located at 0,6

8. Create a rectangle using the **Line** Command by entering the following Absolute Coordinates:

   - **P1** is located at *0.6, 4.4*
   - **P2** is located at *3.3, 4.4*
   - **P3** is located at *3.3, 5.7*
   - **P4** is located at *0.6, 5.7*

98

9. Create a triangle using the **Line** Command. Start at **P5** (located at Absolute Coordinates *0.5,1.9*) and work counterclockwise and use the given dimensions to determine the Relative Rectangular Coordinate inputs.

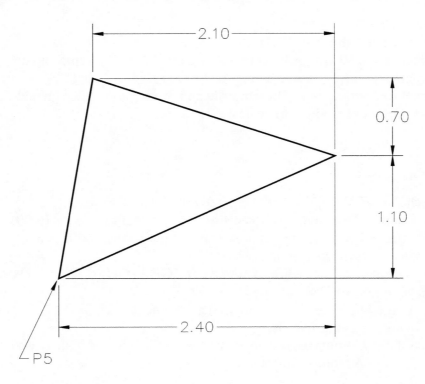

10. Construct the hexagon starting the **Line** at **P6** (located at Absolute Coordinates *6.5,3.8*) and work counterclockwise knowing that the angle of each side (measured from the positive x-axis) increases by **60** degrees: **0, 60, 120, 180** etc. The length of each side is 1 unit. Use the **Relative Polar Coordinate System**.

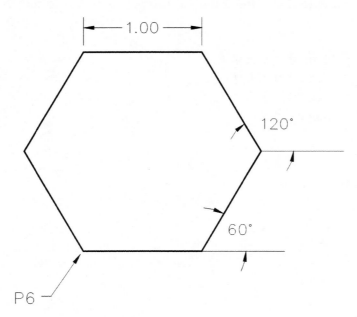

11. Create the diamond shape (rhombus) using the **Line** Command and the **Relative Polar Coordinate System**. Use the dimensions given on the diagram below by starting at point **P7** located at coordinates *8.0,1.7*. If needed you may refer to the hint given below.

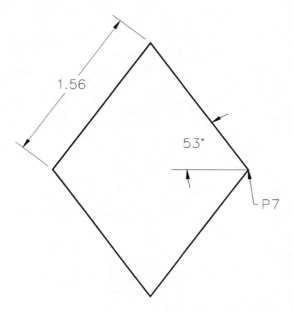

Hint: To construct each side of the Rhombus, you need to calculate the polar angle in question with respect to the local X-axis. For a better understanding refer to the diagram below

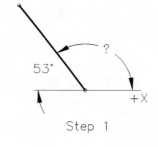

Step 1

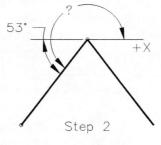

Step 2

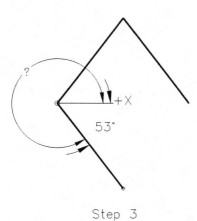

Step 3

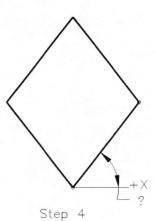

Step 4

12. Use the **Line** Command and your pointing device/mouse to create a five-sided shape at a user-specified location similar to that shown below.

13. Use **Text** with *0.1* **Height** to label each shape and add your information as shown on the following page.
14. Check your work to match that of the next page.
15. **Save** your Drawing again before plotting.
16. Select a **Plotter**.
17. Preview and Plot Drawing using the following settings:

- Paper size: Letter (8.50x11.00 **inches**)
- Plot area: Limits
- Plot offset: Centered
- Plot scale: 1=1

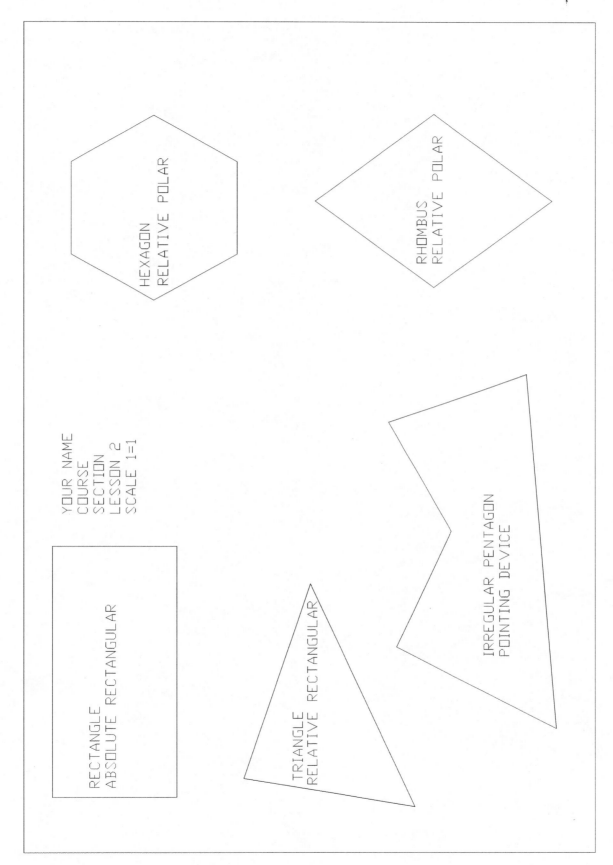

Chapter 3

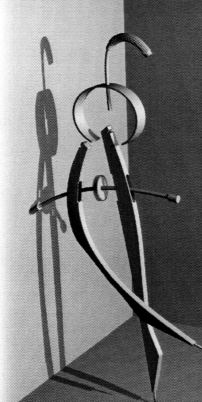

Orthographic Projection
Auxiliary Views
Section Views
Grid
Snap
Coordinate Tracking
Ortho
Dynamic Input
Templates
Circle Basics
Layers

Orthographic Projection

In the diagram below, an Orthographic Projection drawing is obtained by suspending an Object in a transparent box. This creates six planes of projection, and therefore results in six Principle Views. These Planes are Front, Top, Right, Left, Back and Bottom. In the diagram below only three of the six principle planes are used to construct the three Orthographic Views (Front, Top, and Right) with arrows representing the line of sight for each View.

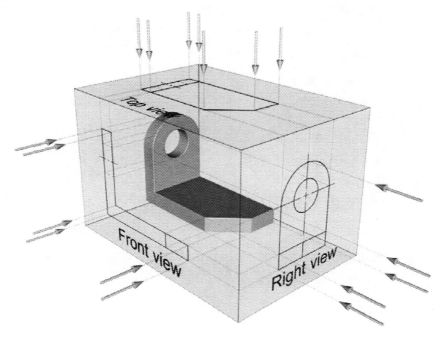

By unfolding this imaginary box in a specific orientation as shown below, a three view orthographic drawing representing the Front, Top, and Right Views is obtained.

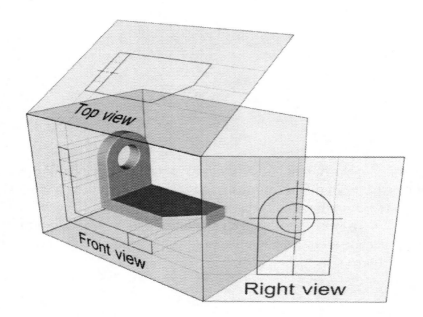

Here are the three sides of the box fully unfolded with the views placed in their final position. This is the standard Orthographic view placement used in industry. Also note that the light-weighted imaginary projection lines demonstrate the alignment of the Views. In particular, note that even the Top and Right Views are aligned through the construction line CL1.

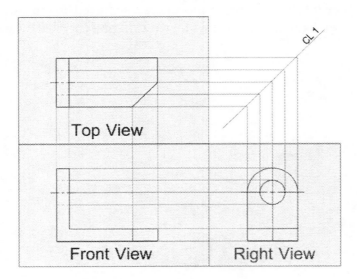

Removing the unfolded imaginary box will result in the actual three view orthographic projection drawing.

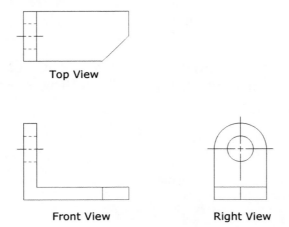

Pay special attention to the different line types used in the Orthographic Projection shown above. In addition to the Solid/**Continuous** line type which represents the visible edges of the Object, there are two other line types: **Hidden** and **Center**. Hidden lines represent the hidden edges not seen from a particular view/line of sight, whereas Center lines are used to indicate the center of circles and arcs, or at times represent the axis of symmetry of Objects such as cylinders.

In the event that an Object has any inclined planes, they will not appear in true length in any of the six Principle Views discussed above. For instance, note that the circle within the Right View of the figure below appears as an ellipse in the Front View.

Circle located on the inclined face of the right view is represented as an ellipse in the front view

Projected length of Radius

True Length of Radius

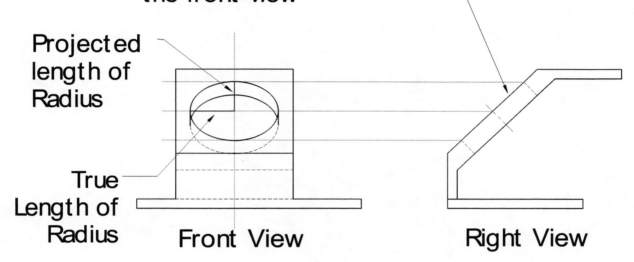

Front View

Right View

Auxiliary Views

In cases such as the Object above, where you have an inclined surface in your geometry, it is customary to define a new line of sight which is perpendicular to the inclined plane as shown below. This projection, known as Auxiliary Projection, will allow for the plane of interest to show in true length. An Auxiliary Projection is not aligned with any of the six principle views, thus allowing for Objects on inclined planes to appear in true size.

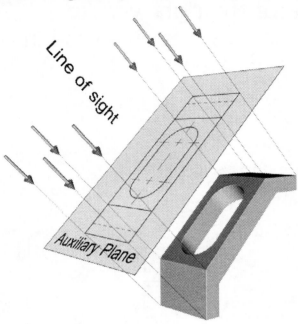

Below, an Auxiliary View drawing is created by projecting lines from the Right View of the given Object.

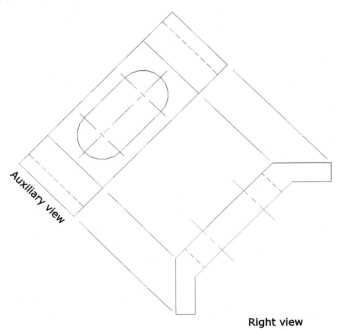

Right view

Section Views

At times, the interior features of a design may be hard to visualize. A Section View allows for clarity of hidden components by slicing an Object using an imaginary cutting plane. As the cutting plane slices the Object, its intersection with the Object is conventionally shown by a Line Hatch pattern. The line of sight for viewing the sectioned Object is perpendicular to the cutting plane as represented by the arrows shown below.

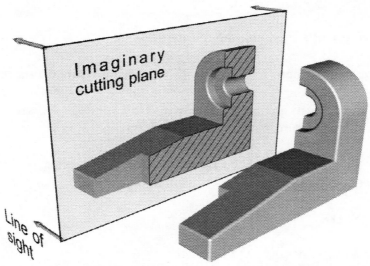

Below, the Front View displays the cutting plane used to create the Section View.

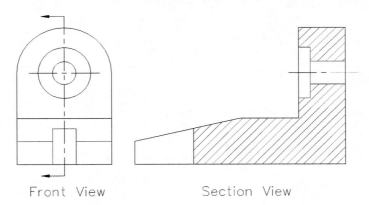

Front View   Section View

Note: The three topics discussed above are meant only to give you a basic understanding of Orthographic Projections, Auxiliary Views, and Section Views. Although this discussion will serve as sufficient for continuing through these tutorials, for a more in-depth understanding of these topics, you can refer to any books on engineering drawing concepts.

Setting Up a Drawing (review and continuation)

1. Launch AutoCAD. {You will be placed in a blank Drawing.}

2. From the Status Bar, make sure that **Snap**, **Grid**, **Ortho**, **Polar**, **Osnap**, **Otrack**, **Ducs**, **Dyn**, and **Lwt** are set to *Off* as shown below.

3. Set **Drawing Units** by doing the following:

    - Type *Units* then *[ENTER]*. {The **Drawing Units** dialog box will appear.}

    - In the **Length** area of the **Drawing Units** dialog box, set **Type** to **Decimal** and **Precision** to 2 decimal places (**0.00**).

    - In the **Angle** area of the **Drawing Units** dialog box set **Type** to **Decimal Degrees** and **Precision** to 1 decimal place (**0.0**).

    - Click **OK**.

4. Set proper **Limits** by doing the following:

    - Type *Limits* then *[ENTER]*.

    - Type *0,0* then *[ENTER]*.

    - Type *9,6* then *[ENTER]*.

    - Command: *Zoom* then *[ENTER]*.

    - Type *All* then *[ENTER]*.

5. Set **Grid** by doing the following:

    - Command: *Grid* then *[ENTER]*.

    - Enter a **Grid Spacing** of *1* then *[ENTER]*.

Note: Grid is simply a visual aid by means of displayed dots. This effect gives you a better sense of the Drawing area and size. As you assign a value to **Grid**, it is automatically Toggled to *On*. You can also Toggle the **Grid On** and *Off* by either pressing **F7**, or by selecting the **GRID** button on the **Status Line**.

6. Set **Snap** by doing the following:

- Move the cursor around the **Drawing Area** and note how it moves freely. {This is because **Snap** is currently set to *Off*.}

- Command: *Snap* then *[ENTER]*.

- Specify a **Snap Spacing** of *0.5* then *[ENTER]*.

- Move the cursor around the **Drawing Area** and note how the cursor snaps to the set interval. As you will see later, this will help you draw with precision.

Note: As you assign a value to **Snap**, it is automatically Toggled to *On*. You can also Toggle **Snap** *On* and *Off* by either pressing **F9**, or by toggling the **SNAP** button on the **Status Line**. As you will see in the next step, **Grid** and **Snap** can also be set from the **Drafting Settings** dialog box. There, you can set the **Grid** behavior to be **Adaptive** so that in the event that you **Zoom** in/out of a Drawing, The **Grid** value will change to a subdivision/multiple of the initial **Grid** value respectively. However, this book will move forward without the use of the **Adaptive Grid**.

7. Set the **Snap** and **Grid** settings by doing the following:

- From the Menu Bar click on **Tools**, then **Drafting Settings**. {The **Drafting Settings** dialog box will appear.}

- Click on the **Snap and Grid** tab and in the **Grid behavior** area, Toggle **Adaptive Grid** to *Off*.

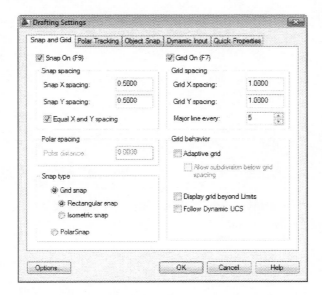

- Make sure that your settings are the same as above and click on **OK**.

8. Use the **Line** tool to draw a border at the extents of your **Limits** by doing the following:

- Command: *Line* then *[ENTER]*.

- Type the coordinates: *0,0* then *[ENTER]*.

- Type *9,0* then *[ENTER]*.

- Type *9,6* then *[ENTER]*.

- Type *0,6* then *[ENTER]*.

- Type *C* (for **Close**) then *[ENTER]*. {The shape will **Close**.}

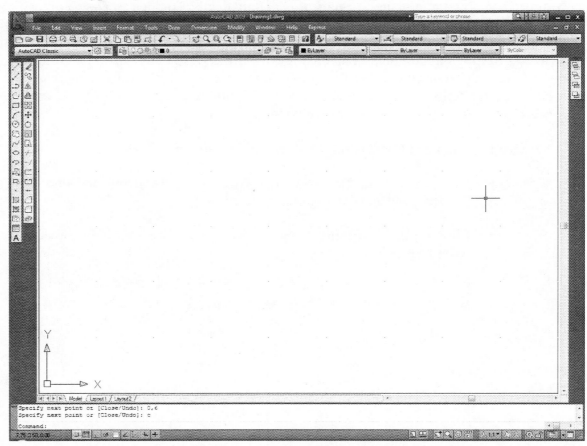

Note: As in the case above, when you enter coordinate values using the keyboard, the crosshair position is irrelevant.

9. Determine suitable **Snap** and **Grid** values by doing the following:

Note: You are about to construct two very similar shapes with slightly different dimensions as shown below.   You will see that some adjusting of the **Grid** and particularly the **Snap** settings will help to accomplish this task.

In the shape on the left, having the dimensions of 1.25, 2.5, 2.75, 0.75, and the fact that P1 is located at 2.25,3.25 signifies that a **Snap** value of 0.25 will best accomplish this task.   However, considering the size and the start point of the shape on the right, the **Snap** value needs to drop-down to 0.1 before construction. As a general rule, it is good practice to set the **Grid** to a multiple of the **Snap** value.

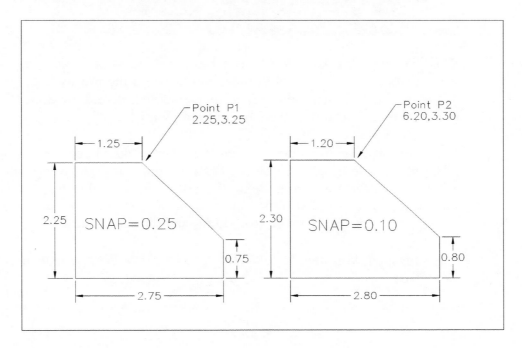

- Set **Grid** to *0.5*.

- Set **Snap** to *0.25*.

- Command: *Line* and then *[ENTER]*.

- Type the coordinates of **P1** as *2.25,3.25*.

114

Note: Once you enter the starting point of a shape, selecting the coordinate tracking display button within the Status Bar as shown below will Toggle the display of **Coordinate Tracking** between **Relative Polar**, **Absolute Rectangular**, and *Off*. {You will see this change taking place in the **Coordinates** display located on the left side of the **Status Line**.}

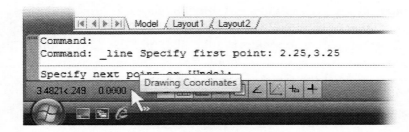

- While in the **Line** Command, use the mouse to select and Toggle the Coordinate display button until the Coordinates of the **Status Line** switch to **Polar** mode. {**Coordinate Tracking** is set to **On**, and the **Status Line** tracks your coordinates of the **Line** in **Polar** form.}

- Continue drawing the shape shown below in a counterclockwise order using the mouse as your input device, and notice how the **Snap** settings and the ability to track your **Polar Coordinates** (your distance traveled), together help accomplish this task. Also, at any time, if you pick the wrong point, use the **U** option (for **Undo**) and then continue on.

- Once finished with the shape on the left, use *[ENTER]* to exit the **Line** Command.

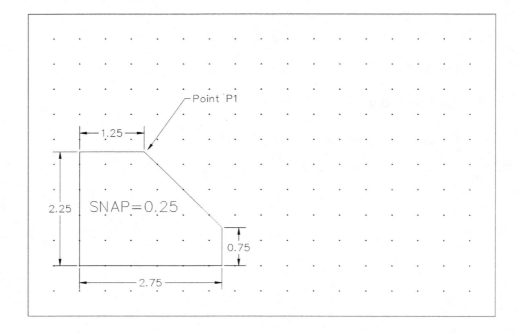

- Set **Grid** to *0.2* and **Snap** to *0.1*.

- Start a **Line** at **P2** having coordinates of *6.2,3.3* then *[ENTER]*.

- While tracking your coordinates, continue drawing the shape on the right in a counterclockwise order as you did with the previous shape.

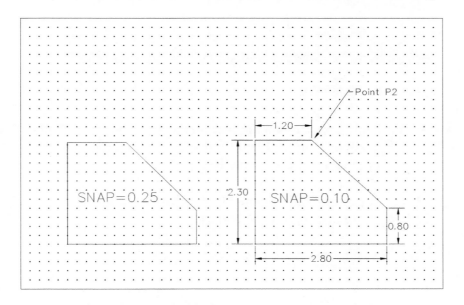

- Once finished, *[ENTER]* to exit the **Line** Command.

Note: In the case of the shape on the right, due to the 0.1 **Snap** resolution, it takes a more steady hand to construct the horizontal and vertical lines. In such cases, the **Ortho** Command can help force lines to be drawn orthogonally. **Ortho** can be Toggled *On* by pressing **F8** or by selecting it from the **Status Line**.

- **Erase** the shape on the right.

- Turn **Ortho** *On* by pressing **F8** or by selecting **Ortho** from the **Status Line**.

- Draw the shape on the right again by starting a **Line** at **P2** (**6.2,3.3**) and construct the four horizontal and vertical sides of the shape in the counter clockwise order.

- Turn **Ortho** *Off* by pressing **F8**.

- Use the **Close** option to construct the last edge.

- **Erase** the two shapes from the screen.

1. Use **Dynamic** Input to construct geometry by doing the following

    - From the **Status Line**, make sure that **Dynamic Input** is set to *On* as shown below.

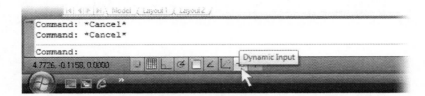

    - Select the **Line** tool.

    - As the Tooltip appears on the screen, use the mouse to select a point at a User Specified location. {Tooltip displays the prompt on screen as opposed to the usual Command line.}

    - Move the cursor to a User specified location as shown below. {Distance and angle are displayed on screen..}

    - Click for endpoint of the line.

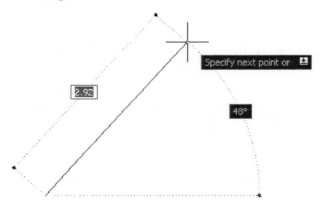

Note: In the beginning stages of learning AutoCAD, the **Dynamic Input** option and the tool tip may serve as a convenient tool. However, as you progress with AutoCAD, you will find that a clean screen makes for a better design environment. For the purpose of this book, you will work with **Dynamic Input** set to *Off*.

    - Set **DYN** to *Off*

    - **Exit** AutoCAD without saving changes.

Templates

A **Template** file basically allows for having a preset working environment. As an example, you may have a preferred type of **Units,** a particular size for your **Limits**, certain initial preferred values for **Grid** and **Snap**, and even a title block that you often like to start with. These settings can be placed in a Template file, and used to initialize Drawing files. In fact, every time you Launch AutoCAD and are placed in a blank Drawing, the software uses the settings of a Template file known as **acad.dwt** to begin your Drawing.

AutoCAD furnishes you with many Templates and a variety of title blocks and sheet sizes which you will be exposed to later in the book. In Chapter 12, you will learn about **Paper Space** and **Model Space**. There, you will be able to fully benefit from the Templates that are available within the Templates folder. For now, you will be creating your own basic Template.

1. Create a **Template** by doing the following:

    - Launch AutoCAD. {You will be placed in a blank Drawing.}

    - Make sure that in the **Status Bar**, your **Snap**, **Grid**, **Ortho**, **Polar**, **Osnap**, **Otrack**, **Ducs**, **Dyn**, and **Lwt** are set to *Off*

    - Set **Units** to **Decimal** with **Precision** of two decimal places *0.00*. Set **Angle Decimal Degrees Precision** to one decimal place *0.0*.

    - Set **Limits** to lower left corner of *0,0* and upper right corner of *9,6*.

    - Set **Grid** to *0.5* .

    - Set **Snap** to *0.25* .

    - Command: *Zoom* then *[ENTER]*.

    - Type *All* then *[ENTER]*.

    - Using the **Line** Command, create a 9 x 6 rectangle at the boundary of your **Limits** as you did in the earlier section.

    - Command: *Line* then *[ENTER]*.

    - Start point: *0.0,0.4* then *[ENTER]*.

    - Next point: *9.0,0.4* then *[ENTER]*.

118

- *[ENTER]*. {**Line** Command is cancelled.}

- Command: *Text* then *[ENTER]*.

- Start point: *0.2,0.1* then *[ENTER]*.

- Height: *0.2* then *[ENTER]*.

- Rotation angle: *0* then *[ENTER]*. {A blinking cursor appears.}

- Enter Text: "YOUR NAME COURSE SECTION LESSON   SCALE 1=1".

- *[ENTER]* twice to exit the **Text** Command.

Note: Consult with your instructor for the proper title format. You may have to abbreviate the title to fit Text on screen.

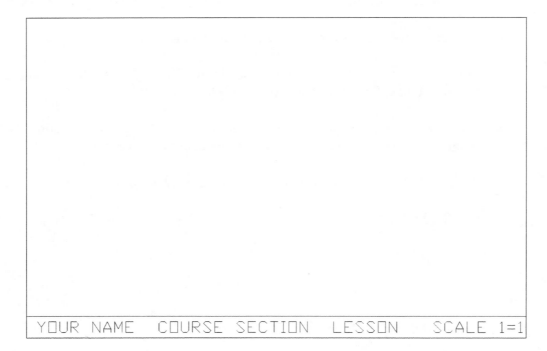

- From the **Status Line**, make sure that **Snap**, **Ortho**, **Polar**, **OSnap**, **OTrack**, **Ducs**, **Dyn, and Lwt** are set to the *Off* position, and that **Grid** is set to *On*.

Note: When a drawing file is saved as a **Template** file, it can later be used to help initialize other drawing files.

- From the Menu Bar, select **File** then **Save As...** {The **Save Drawing As** dialog box will appear.}

- Use the **Files of type** pull-down menu to change the file type to **AutoCAD Drawing Template File (*.dwt)**. {**Save in** Folder changes to **Template**.}

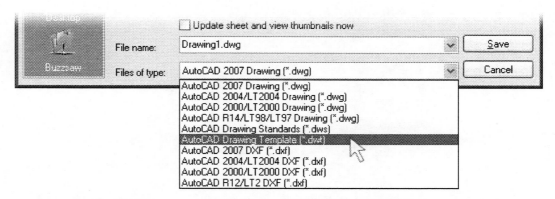

- In the **File name** field type in *"My Template."* Do not press *ENTER*.

- In the **Save in** pull-down menu, locate and select your **My CAD Folder** as opposed to the preset **Template** folder.

- Click **Save**. {The **Template Description** dialog box will appear as shown below.}

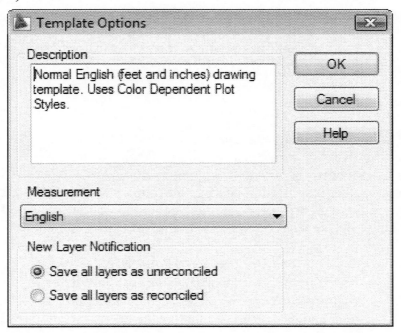

- Leave **Description** as is and click on **OK**.

- **Exit** AutoCAD.

120

2. Use a **Template** to begin a Drawing by doing the following:

- Launch AutoCAD. {You will be placed in a blank Drawing.}

- From the Menu Bar select **File**, then **New**. {The **Select Template** dialog box will appear as shown below.}

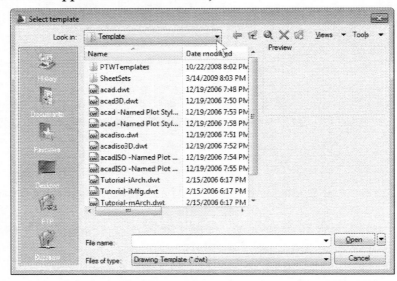

Note: As shown above, AutoCAD directs you to the **Template Folder** and pre-selects a **Template** file.

- Use the **Look in** pull-down menu to locate and select your **My Template** file from your **My_CAD_Folder**.

- Click **Open**.

Note: The above technique is the proper way of starting a Drawing by means of a Template file. Keep in mind that opening a Template file by selecting **File**, **Open** and changing the **File of type** to ***.dwt** is interpreted by AutoCAD as if you plan to modify the Template rather than use it to start up a **Standard Drawing**. So unless you intend to update or modify a **Template**, do not use the **Open** option from the **File** Menu Bar, but rather use the **File, New** option to begin a standard Drawing file.

- On the Menu Bar click on **File** then on **Save As...** {The **Save Drawing As** dialog box will appear. Note that the File extension automatically has changed to ***.dwg**. This is an automated process so that **Template** files remain unchanged and that the new file is saved in a ***.dwg** file format.}

- Click **Cancel**. There is no need to save the Drawing.

Circle Basics

1. Create a circle by doing the following:

   - From the **Status Line** make sure that **Snap**, **Grid**, **Ortho**, **Polar**, **OSnap**, **OTrack, Ducs** and **Dyn** are set to *Off*.

   - In the **Draw** toolbar, click on the **Circle** button.

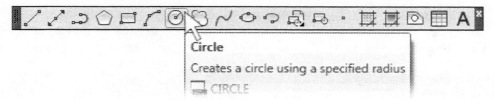

   - Enter the **Center point** as *4.5,3.25* then *[ENTER]*.

   - Enter Radius as *1.5* then *[ENTER]*.

   - Select the **Circle** button again.

   - Use the same center of *4.5,3.25* then *[ENTER]*.

   - Type *D* (for **Diameter**) then *[ENTER]*.

   - Type *2.0* then *[ENTER]*.

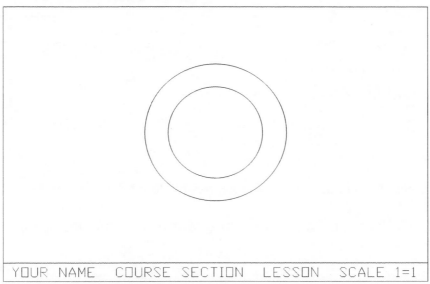

   - When finished, **Erase** the two **Circles** while keeping the border and title box.

122

Layers

When working on large scale projects where there are many different types of Objects using many different Linetypes, Drawing organization becomes even more essential. As an example, in an architectural Drawing, the Floor plan, the Piping and Electrical information may be placed on separate **Layers** of the same Drawing so that the information can be separated, managed, and channeled properly.

Before creating any Objects, make sure that in the **Properties** Toolbar your **Color**, **Linetype**, and **Lineweight** drop-down menus are all set to **ByLayer** as shown below. This way, Objects receive the properties of the layer that they are placed on.

If these settings are set to other than **ByLayer**, make sure to use the drop-down menus to reset all three settings to **By Layer** as shown below.

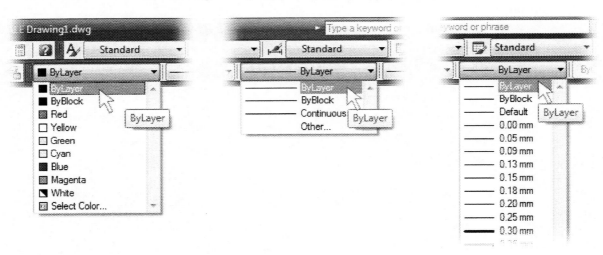

1. Create new **Layers** and assign **Properties** by doing the following:

- Click on the **Layer Properties Manager** button on the **Layers** toolbar.

{The **Layer Properties Manager** dialog box will appear as shown below.}

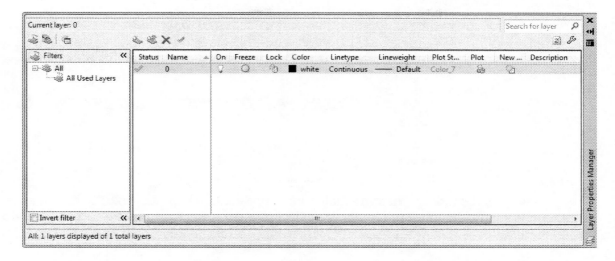

Note: **Layer 0** is the AutoCAD default **Layer**. It is considered good practice to keep the settings such as **Linetype, Color**, etc., of **Layer 0** unchanged.

- Click on the **New Layer** button. {A new **Layer** appears temporarily titled and highlighted as **Layer1**.}

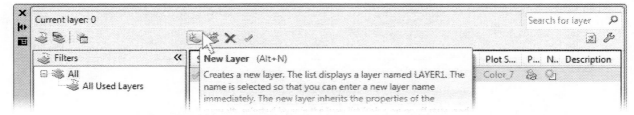

- Name the new **Layer** as *HID,* then *[ENTER]*.

- Create two more **Layers** named *CEN* and *OBJ*.

Note: You can **Rename** a **Layer** at any time by highlighting and again single-selecting the name, then typing in a new name.

- In the **Linetype** column, select the default **Linetype** of **Layer HID** as shown below.

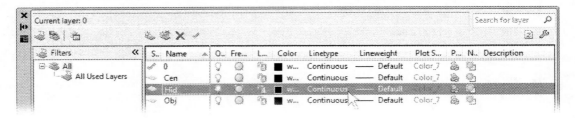

- As the **Select Linetype** dialog box appears, Click on the **Load...** button as shown below.

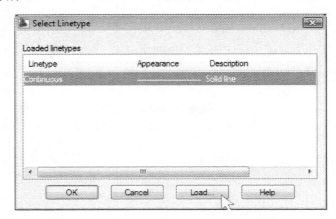

- Note that the **Load or Reload Linetypes** dialog box will appear.

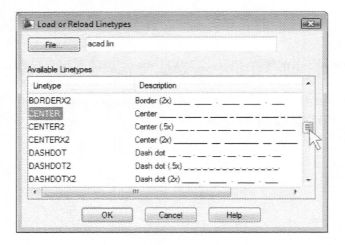

- Scroll through the **Available Linetypes** and select the **CENTER** Linetype. {**CENTER** Linetype is highlighted.)

- Scroll further down to see the **Hidden** Linetype listed.

- Hold down the **Ctrl** key while selecting the **HIDDEN Linetype** from the list. {Here **Ctrl** allows you to add or subtract multiple Linetypes to your selection list.}

- Click **OK**. {Both Linetypes are loaded as shown below.}

- Click on **HIDDEN** in the **Select Linetype** dialog box.

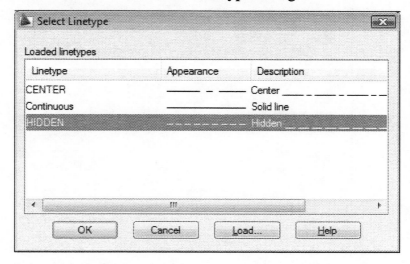

- Click **OK**. {**HIDDEN** Linetype is assigned to **Layer HID**.}

- In the **Layer Properties Manager** dialog box click on **Continuous Linetype** of **Layer CEN**, just as you did with **Layer HID**.

- Select **CENTER** from the **Select Linetype** dialog box.

- Click on **OK**. {**Center** Linetype is assigned to the **CEN Layer**.}

- Select the **Color** of the **Layer HID** by clicking on the color box as shown below.

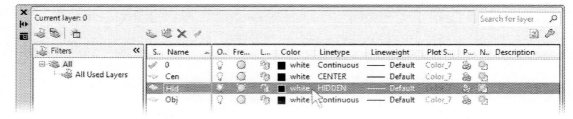

126

{The **Select Color** dialog box will appear.}

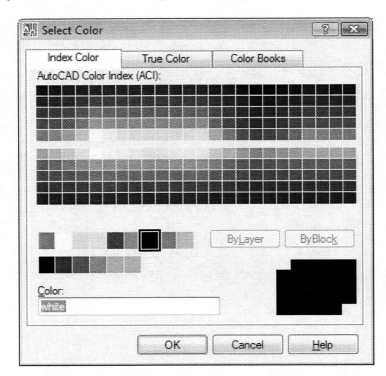

- Choose one of the 9 standard colors other than the color white.

- Click on **OK**.

- Repeat the procedure above to assign colors to **Layer CEN** and **OBJ**.

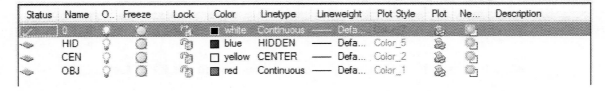

- Select the **Default Lineweight** for **Layer HID** as shown below.

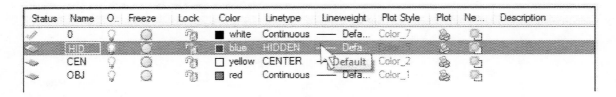

- In the **Lineweight** dialog box select **0.13 mm** as shown below.

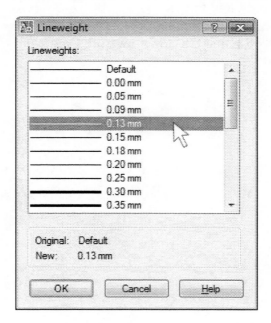

- Click **OK**.

- Change **Lineweight** for Layer **CEN** to **0.13 mm**, and Layers **0** and **OBJ** to **0.25 mm** as shown below. {Not all digits of your **Lineweights** may appear within the **Lineweight** column. This can be fixed by dragging/expanding the Lineweight column header to the right.}

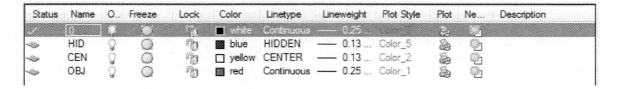

Note: The **Lineweight (LWT)** button in the **Status Line** is used to display **Lineweights** on your monitor; however, not all **Lineweights** appear properly, so it is best to keep the **LWT** Toggle set to *Off*. In any event, the **Lineweights** will apply when **Plotting**.

2. Create Objects on numerous **Layers** by doing the following:

- Select **Layer OBJ**.

- Click on the **Set Current** button. {**Layer OBJ** becomes the **Current Layer**.}

- Select the **[X]** button to **Close** the **Layer Propertied Manager** dialog box.

128

- Set **Snap** and **Grid** to *On*.

- Create a 3 x 2 rectangle using the **Line** Command starting at **1.00,2.00**.

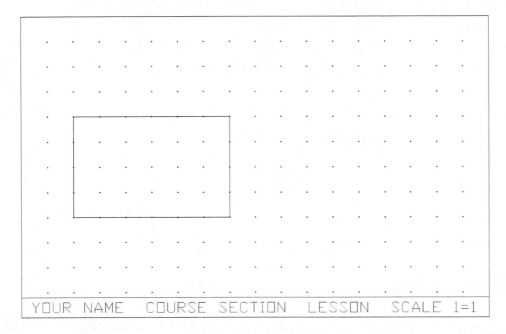

Note: The rectangle is on **Layer OBJ** and therefore takes on the properties of **Layer OBJ**.

- Create a Circle with the **Center** located at **6.5,3.0** having a **Radius** of **1.0**.

- Create a second Circle with the same center point as the first with a **Diameter** of **1.5**. Make sure to use the **Diameter** option.

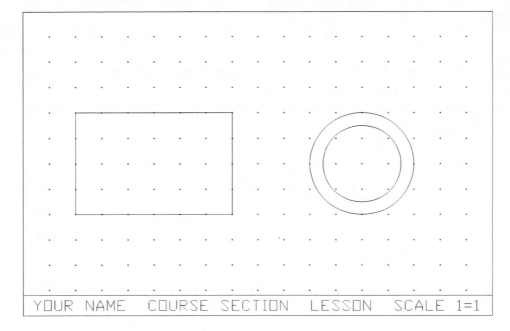

3. Draw **Hidden** lines by doing the following:

- Make **HID** your **Current** Layer.

- From the **Status bar**, Toggle **Ortho** to **On**.

- Draw the two lines **L1** and **L2** such that they line up with the 12 o'clock and 6 o'clock position of the inner circle.

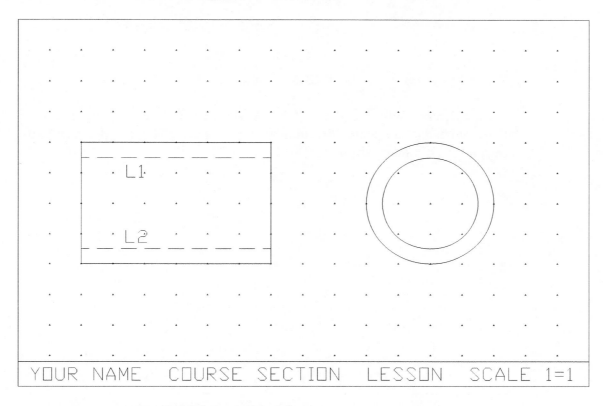

YOUR NAME   COURSE SECTION   LESSON   SCALE 1=1

4. Adjust **Linetype Scale** by doing the following.

- Command: *Ltscale* then *[ENTER]*.

- Type *0.4* and then *[ENTER]*. {**HID Layer** line spacing of the dashes will decrease.}

Note: **Linetype Scaling (LTscale)** allows you to change the scaling of the non-continuous Linetypes. Pay special attention to the dash size of the **Hidden** lines. Next you will change the **LTscale** value to decrease the **Dashed** line gap.

5. Draw the **Center** Lines by doing the following:

- On the **Layers** toolbar click on the drop-down menu.

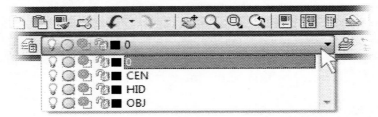

- Select **Layer CEN**. {**Layer CEN** becomes the **Current Layer**.}

- Draw the remaining three lines (**L3**, **L4**, and **L5**) as shown. {These center lines represent the center location of the cylindrical tube and are drawn beyond the boundary of the Object.}

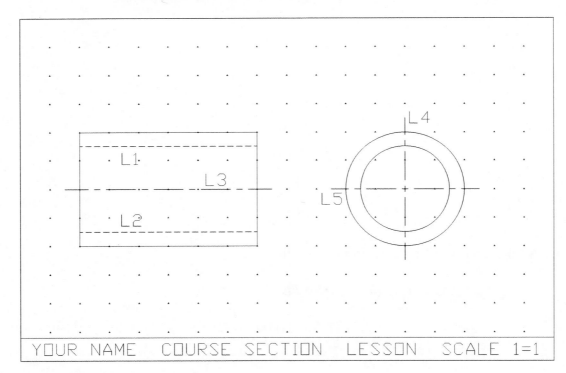

6. Change the **Layer Property** of an Object by doing the following:

- While outside of any Command, select lines **L1** and **L2**. {Lines are selected and several square markers known as **Grips** appear.}

Note: You will learn more about **Grips** in later chapters. However, if **Grips** do not appear, consult with your instructor. This problem can be fixed by setting the **Grips system variable** to **1**.

- On the **Layers** toolbar, click on the drop-down menu again.

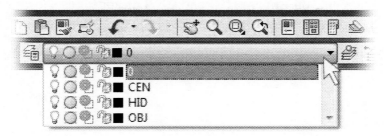

- Select **Layer 0**. {Lines **L1** and **L2** will **Change** to **Layer 0** and take on that **Layer's** properties.}

- Press the **Esc** (escape) key.

Note: As you can see, the above technique allows for moving entities from one **Layer** to another. Changing the Layer property of an Object is a very useful technique and will be used frequently in later chapters.

- Command: *U* then *[ENTER]*. {Lines **L1** and **L2** are placed back on to **Layer HID**.}

Note: At times it is helpful to avoid displaying a group of Objects. As an example, if you are working on the electrical layout portion of an architectural design, you may not need to see the piping layout within the same drawing. This can be accomplished by **Turning Off** those respective Layers. This technique also allows for selective editing and plotting.

7. Turn **Layers *On*** and ***Off*** by doing the following:

- Click on the **Layer Properties Manager** button to load the dialog box.

- Make the **OBJ Layer Current**.

- Pick the **CEN Layer**.

- Hold down the **Ctrl** key and Pick the **HID Layer**. {Both layers are highlighted.}

- On either of the two selected **Layers**, click in the *On* column (the light bulb) as shown below. {The Light bulb symbols are turned *Off*.}

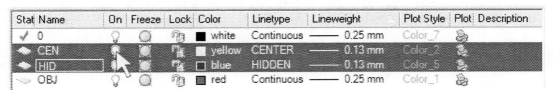

Stat	Name	On	Freeze	Lock	Color	Linetype	Lineweight	Plot Style	Plot	Description
✓	0				■ white	Continuous	—— 0.25 mm	Color_7		
	CEN				□ yellow	CENTER	—— 0.13 mm	Color_2		
	HID				□ blue	HIDDEN	—— 0.13 mm	Color_5		
	OBJ				▩ red	Continuous	—— 0.25 mm	Color_1		

132

- Select **[X]** to close the **Layer Properties Manager** dialog box. {Objects that reside on **Layers HID** and **CEN** disappear as shown below.}

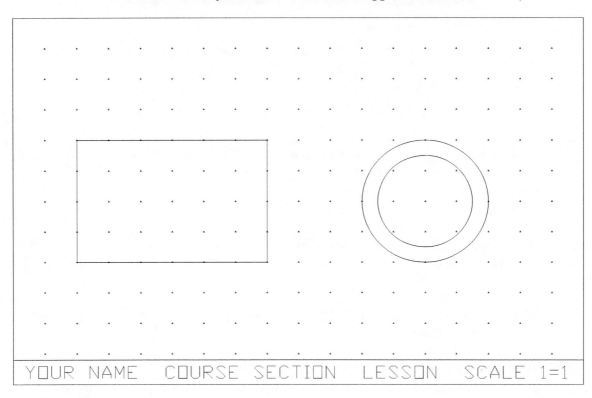

Note: Although the system will permit it, do not attempt to turn *off* the **Current Layer**. It is not a practical move. If you try, you will get the warning below.

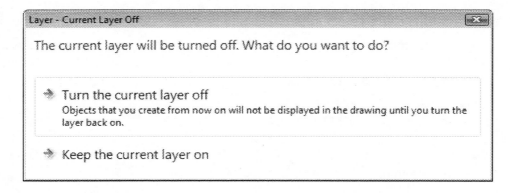

- Open the **Layer Properties Manager** dialog box again.

- Turn all **Layers** back to *On* by toggling the light bulb icon of those **Layers** and remain in the **Layer Properties Manager** dialog box.

- **Lock Layer OBJ** by clicking on the icon in the **Lock** column of the **OBJ** layer. {**OBJ Layer** is set to **Locked** mode.}

Status	Name	O..	Freeze	Lock	Color	Linetype	Lineweight	Plot Style	Plot	Ne...	Description
✓	0	♀	○	🔓	■ white	Continuous	—— 0.25 ...	Color_7	🖨	🗐	
◈	CEN	♀	○	🔓	□ yellow	CENTER	—— 0.13 ...	Color_2	🖨	🗐	
◈	HID	♀	○	🔓	■ blue	HIDDEN	—— 0.13 ...	Color_5	🖨	🗐	
◈	OBJ	●	●	🔓	□ red	Continuous	—— 0.25 ...		🖨	🗐	

- Select **[X]** to **Close**. {All Objects display again and **Layer OBJ** is **Locked**.}

- In the **Modify** toolbar, click on the **Erase** button.

- Use the **Crossing** to select all of the geometry related to the cylindrical tube and *[ENTER]*. {The **OBJ Layer** is **Locked** and Objects that reside on that **Layer** cannot be **Erased**.}

- Type *U* then *[ENTER]* to bring back the **Erased** Objects.

Note: The locking process is a very suitable option for making changes to one group of Objects and keeping others unchanged.

- Open the **Layer Properties Manager** dialog box.

- Select **Layer 0**.

- Hold down [**Shift**] key and select **Layer OBJ**. {All **Layers** are selected.}

- Hold down [**Ctrl**] key and select **Layer 0**. {**Layer 0** is deselected.}

Note: When you use the [**Shift**] key to select two **Layers**, all the in-between **Layers** are also selected. The [**Ctrl**] key allows you to add or subtract from your selection.

- Pick the color selection box in any of the selected **Layers**. {**Select Color** dialog box appears.}

- Select the **Color White** and click **OK**. {All selected **Layers** turn white.}

- Select **Layer OBJ** so that it becomes the only selected **Layer** and then **Unlock** it.

134

- **Freeze Layer HID** by clicking the icon under the **Freeze** column in the **HID** row. {The icon will turn to a snowflake as shown below.}

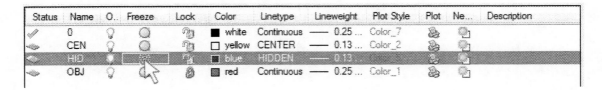

Status	Name	O..	Freeze	Lock	Color	Linetype	Lineweight	Plot Style	Plot	Ne...	Description
	0				■ white	Continuous	—— 0.25 ...	Color_7			
	CEN				□ yellow	CENTER	—— 0.13 ...	Color_2			
	HID				■ blue	HIDDEN	—— 0.13 ...				
	OBJ				■ red	Continuous	—— 0.25 ...	Color_1			

- Click on the **[X]** to **Close** the **Layer Property Manager** .

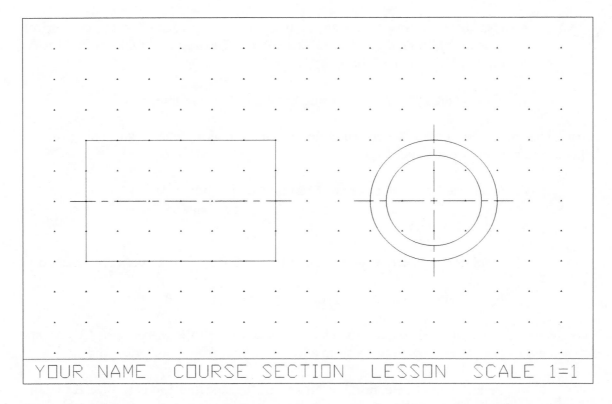

YOUR NAME   COURSE SECTION   LESSON   SCALE 1=1

Note: The **On/Off** and the **Freeze/Thaw** Toggle buttons appear to do the same thing. For the scope of this book, the difference of the two is insignificant.

- From the **Layer** drop-down menu, select and **Thaw** the **Layer HID** as shown below.

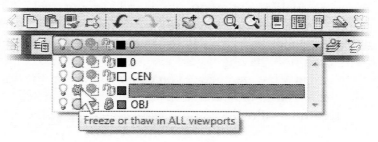

- Press the **Esc** key. {**Layer** drop-down menu is closed.}

Note: From the **Layer** pull-down menu, you can also Toggle **On/Off**, **Freeze/Thaw**, and **Lock/Unlock**. This method is faster than opening the **Layer Property Manager**.

8. Delete **Layers** by doing the following:

- Open the **Layer Properties Manager** dialog box.

- Make **Layer 0 Current**.

- Select **Layer CEN**.

- Click on the **Delete Layer** button in the **Layer Properties Manager** dialog box. {A warning box will pop up stating that "The selected **Layer** was not deleted."}

- Close warning box by selecting **Close**.

- Select the **[X]** to **Close** the **Layer Property Manager**.}

- **Erase** all 3 centerlines. {**Layer CEN** has no entities.}

- Go back to the **Layer Properties Manager**. Select **CEN Layer** and pick the **Delete Layer** button. {**Center Layer** is successfully deleted.}

- **Close** the **Layer Property Manager**.

Note: AutoCAD does not allow the user to delete **Layers** such as **Layer 0**, **Defpoints**, the **Current Layer**, **Xref-Dependent Layers**, and as you have already witnessed, **Layers** which contain Objects.

- **Erase** all geometry from the screen.
- Make **Layer 0 Current** and then **Delete Layers HID** and **OBJ**.

Note: When working on large scale projects, you are often confronted with working with many layers; therefore, making the modification and keeping track of all Layers and their Properties becomes a large task. In such cases, **Filtering** allows for selective viewing of the Layer's list. As an example, in the case of an architectural design project containing several floors with each floor having layers assigned to Electrical, Piping, HVAC.... in addition to the basic Plan View geometry, you can imagine that the number of layers can quickly grow into the tens if not hundreds. In such cases Filtering can help reduce the Layer list at any given time, allowing for a selective viewing of the list.

1. Filter Layers by doing the following:

   - From the **Layers Property Manager** dialog box, create the following 12 layers.

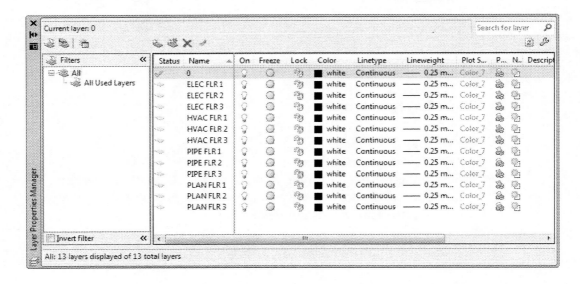

   - From the upper left side of the dialog box, select the **New Property Filter** button as shown below.

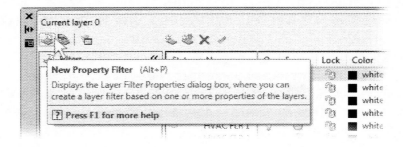

- As the **Layer Filter Properties** dialog box appears, give it the Filter name **Floor 1 all.**

- In the **Filter definition** area, in the **Name** column, to the right of the *, as shown below, type **FLR 1** {All layer names ending with "FLR 1" will be isolated and displayed in the Filter Preview as shown below.}

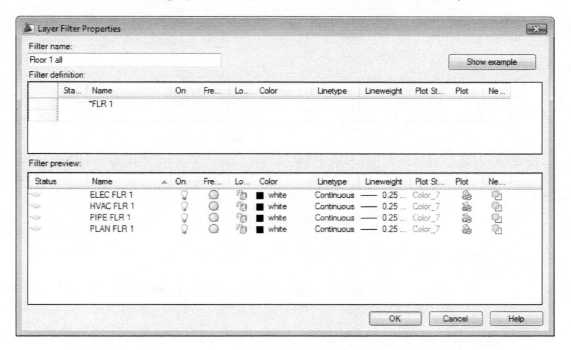

- Select **OK**.

- Select the **New Property Filter** button again.

- As the **Layer Filter Properties** dialog box appears, enter the Filter name **Electrical all.**

138

- In the **Filter definition** area, in the **Name** column, to the left of the * as shown below, enter **ELEC** {All layer names containing ELEC will be isolated and displayed in the Filter Preview as shown below.}

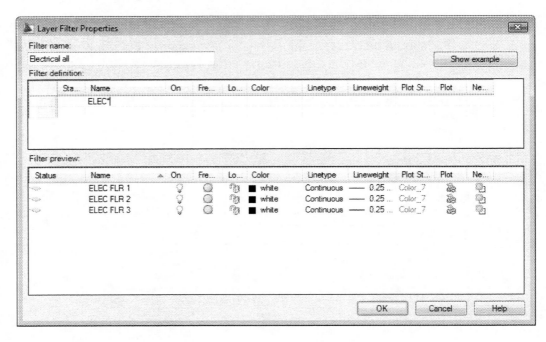

- Select **OK**. {The two filters **Floor 1 all** and **Electrical all** are created in the list of filters.}

2. **Manage Layer States** by doing the following:

- In the **Filters** area of the **Layer Property Manager** select **All** located at the top of the tree. {All layers appear.}

- From the **Layers Property Manager** dialog box, select the **Layer States Manager** button in the upper left hand corner as shown below.

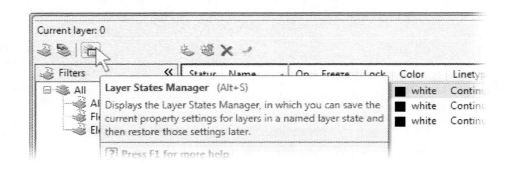

- As the **Layer States Manager** dialog box appears, select **New** as shown below.

- As the **New Layer State to Save** dialog box appears, name it **Layers Default Settings** and then select **OK.**

- Select **[X]** to **Close** the **Layer States Manager** dialog box.

- Go back and set your **Layer Properties** as that shown below. Pay special attention to the **Freeze** and **Lock** columns' settings as well as the **Current Layer**.

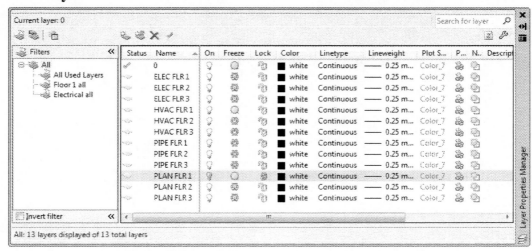

- Select the **Layer States Manager** button again and then select **New.**

- As the **New Layer State to Save** dialog box appears, name it **HVAC and Plan 1** and then select **OK.**

- Select **Layers Default Settings** and then **Restore**. {Layers refer back to the default state.}

- Select **Layer States Manager** button and highlight the **HVAC and Plan 1** state and select **Restore.** {Layers Property settings change to the HVAC and Plan 1 state.}

- Select **[X]** to **Close** the **Layer Properties Manager**.

Note: In the previous exercise you learned to draw Objects using the **ByLayer** option on the **Properties** toolbar, where entities/Objects having different **Linetypes** were placed on different **Layers**, and where each **Layer** was assigned a different Color for clarity. In AutoCAD you can also assign Properties using the **ByObject** option, where you can apply different **Colors**, **Linetypes**, and **Lineweights** to Objects as opposed to Layer as shown below.

However, the method discussed above is mostly used in special cases only, and can make the management of Objects cumbersome. These tutorials will move forward using the default ByLayer option as shown below.

10. **Exit** AutoCAD without saving the changes.

AutoCAD Standard Lineweights

mm	inch		ISO
0.05	.002		
0.09	.003		
0.13	.005		
0.15	.006		
0.18	.007		X
0.20	.008		
0.25	.010		X
0.30	.012		
0.35	.014		X
0.40	.016		
0.50	.020		X
0.53	.021		
0.60	.024		
0.70	.028		X
0.80	.031		
0.90	.035		X
1.00	.039		
1.06	.042		
1.20	.047		X
1.40	.056		
1.58	.062		
2.00	.078		X
2.11	.083		

142

<u>Aliases and Hot Keys</u>

CIRCLE C

LTSCALE .... LTS

TOGGLES GRID MODE.. CTRL+G OR F7

TOGGLES ORTHO MODE..CTRL+L OR F8

TOGGLES SNAP MODE ....CTRL+B OR F9

Assignment 3

Objective:

1. To practice Using **Template** Files.
2. To practice naming your Drawing file and **Saving** to the designated Folder.
3. To practice setting **Snap** and **Grid** to suitable values.
4. To practice working with **Layers**.
5. To practice **Plotting**.

Instructions:

1. Launch AutoCAD and use your **My Template** to begin a **New** Drawing.
2. **Save As** the Drawing file to your folder. Name it **"ASSIGN03_ _ _.dwg"** where the 3 blanks are your initials.
3. Create **New Layers HID, CEN** and **OBJ**.
4. Assign **Hidden** and **Center Linetypes** to the **Layers HID** and **CEN** respectively.
5. Assign suitable **Colors** to these three **Layers**
6. Assign **Lineweight** of *0.25mm* to **Layer OBJ**. Assign **Lineweight** of *0.13mm* to **Layers HID** and **CEN**. Keep the **Properties** of **Layer 0** as default.
7. Set the **Ltscale** value to *0.3*.
8. Set **Snap** and **Grid** to suitable values. Make your decision based on the given dimensions. Also set **Ortho**, **Polar**, **Osnap**, **Otrack,** and **Dyn** to **Off**.
9. Make good use of Coordinate Tracking.
10. Draw the three-view orthographic projection shown below using the given dimensions. Do not **Dimension** the Drawing.
11. All Objects are drawn using the **Line** and **Circle** tools.
12. Front and Top Views are *0.8* units apart. Front and Right View are *0.8* units apart.

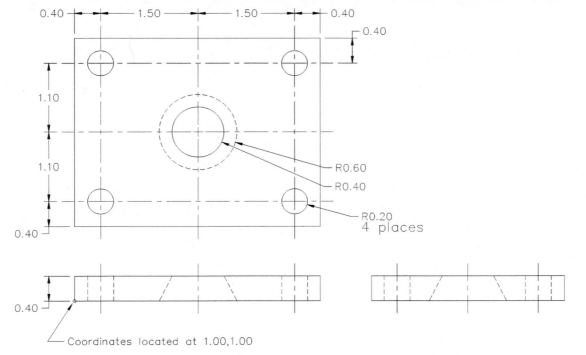

144

13. The 3D sectioned Drawing below is not to be drawn. It is to help you better visualize the Object.

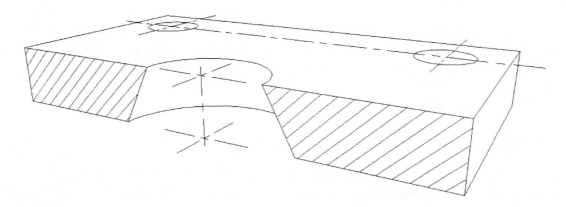

14. Check your geometry to match that of the next page.
15. Double Click on the Text Block in the title box and add lesson number using the **Edit Text** dialog box.
16. **Save** the Drawing.
17. Preview and Plot Drawing using the following settings:

- Paper size: Letter (8.50x11.00 **inches)**
- Plot area: Limits
- Plot offset: Centered
- Plot scale: 1=1

18. Exit AutoCAD.

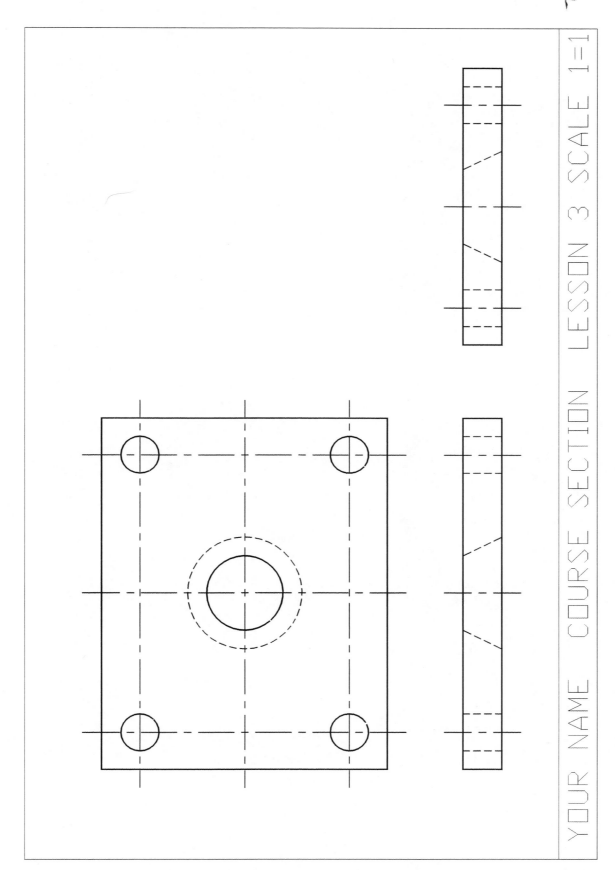

Chapter 4

Object Snap

Midpoint
Endpoint
Perpendicular
Center
Intersection
Apparent Intersection
Tangent
Shortcut Menu
Running Mode
Quadrant

Polar Tracking

Alignment path

Object Tracking

Alignment path
Acquire point

148

Object Snap

One of the main advantages and strengths of design and drafting using AutoCAD is its high degree of precision. Below, you will go through the **Object Snap** Tools which will allow for great accuracy and precision in geometric construction.

1. Launch AutoCAD and use your **Template** to begin a **New** Drawing.

2. From the **Status Line** make sure that **Snap**, **Grid**, **Ortho**, **Polar**, **OSnap**, **OTrack**, **Ducs** and, **Dyn** are set to *Off*.

3. Draw Lines **L1**, **L2** and **L3** and Circles **C1**, **C2** and **C3** at user-specified Sizes and Locations as shown below.

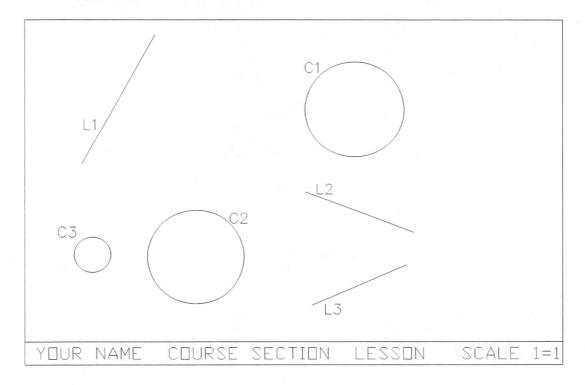

YOUR NAME   COURSE SECTION   LESSON   SCALE 1=1

4. Open and then dock the **Object Snap** Toolbar by right-clicking on any tool and selecting Object Snap from the shortcut menu list.

150

5. Draw a Line to the **Midpoint** of another Line by doing the following:

- Start a **Line** at about point **P1**.

- In the **Object Snap** toolbar, click on the **Snap to Midpoint** button.

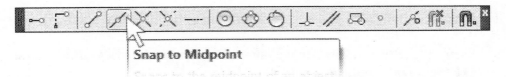

Snap to Midpoint

- Move the cursor near the midpoint of Line **L1** as shown below. As the **AutoSnap Marker** appears, click.

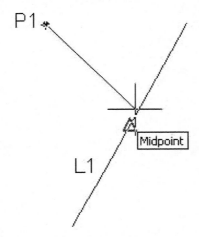

P1

Midpoint

L1

- *[ENTER]*. {Exits the **Line** Command.}

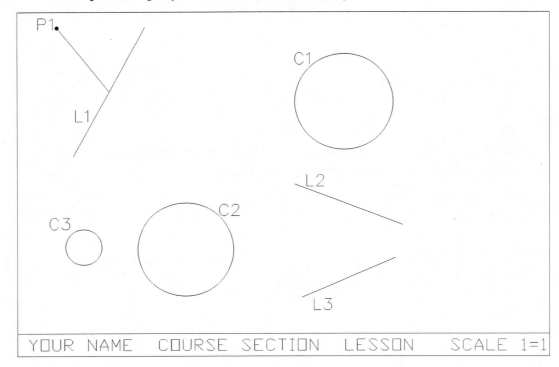

P1

C1

L1

L2

C3

C2

L3

YOUR NAME   COURSE SECTION   LESSON   SCALE 1=1

6. Draw a Line to the **Endpoint** of another Line by doing the following:

- Start a **Line** at about point **P2**.

- In the **Object Snap** toolbar, click on the **Snap to Endpoint** button.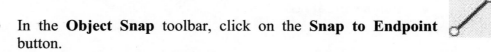

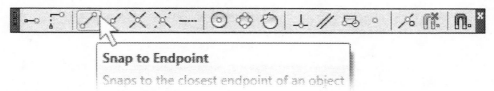

- Move the cursor close to the lower end of Line **L1** as shown below. As the **AutoSnap Marker** appears, click mouse on the screen.

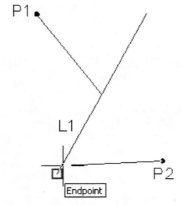

- *[ENTER]*. {Exits the **Line** Command.}

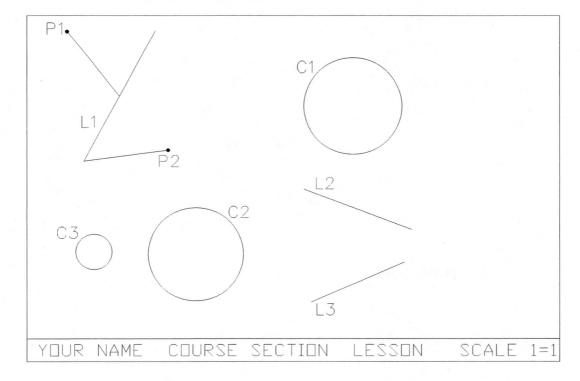

7. Draw a Line **Perpendicular** to another line by doing the following:

- Start a **Line** at about point **P3** as shown below.

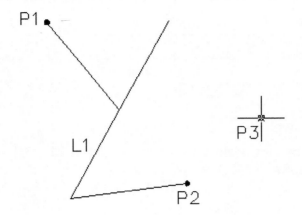

- In the **Object Snap** toolbar, click on the **Snap to Perpendicular** button.

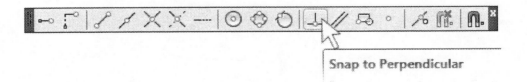

- Move the cursor near Line **L1** as shown below. As you see the **AutoSnap Marker** appear, click on the screen.

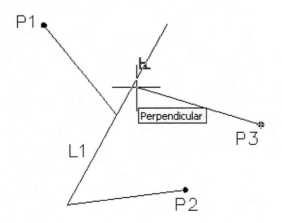

- *[ENTER]*. {Exits the **Line** Command.}

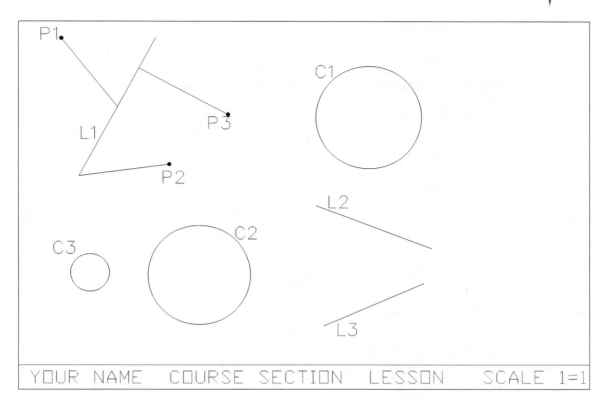

```
P1
        L1    P3
           P2
                        C1
        C3                      L2
              C2
                              L3
YOUR NAME   COURSE SECTION   LESSON   SCALE 1=1
```

8. Draw a **Line** to the **Center** of a Circle by doing the following:

- Start a **Line** at about Point **P4** as shown below.

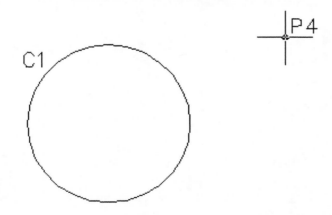

- In the **Object Snap** toolbar, click on the **Snap to Center** button.

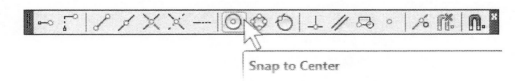

Snap to Center

154

- Move the cursor near Circle **C1** as shown below. As you see the **AutoSnap Marker** appear, click on the screen.

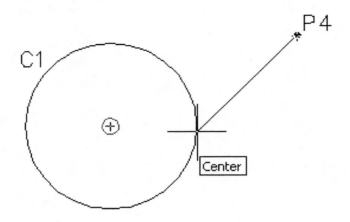

- *[ENTER]*. {Exits the **Line** Command.}

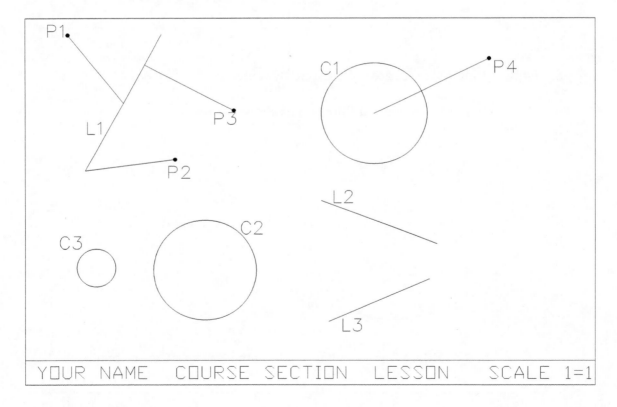

9. Draw a Line to the **Intersection** of two Objects by doing the following:

- Start a **Line** at about point **P5** as shown below.

- In the **Object Snap** toolbar, click on the **Snap to Intersection** button.

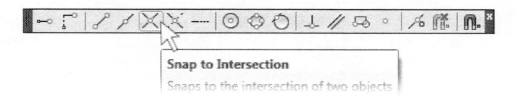

Snap to Intersection

Snaps to the intersection of two objects

- Move the cursor to the intersection of Circle **C1** and Line **L4** as shown below. As the **Intersection Auto Snap Marker** locks onto the intersection, click on the screen.

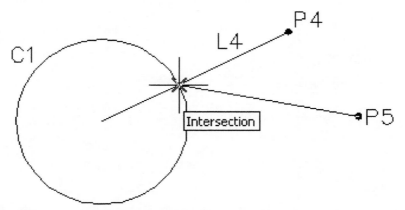

- *[ENTER]*. {Exits the **Line** Command.}

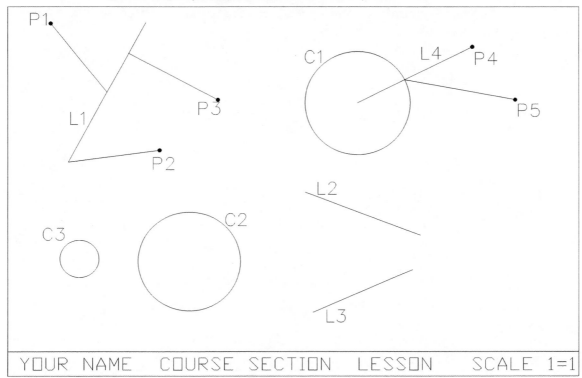

10. Draw a Circle at the **Apparent Intersection** of two Lines by doing the following:

- Select the **Circle** tool.

- In the **Object Snap** toolbar, click on the **Snap to Apparent Intersection** button.

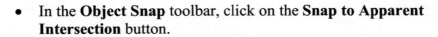

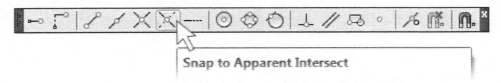

- Pick Line **L2** as shown below on the left, and then Pick Line **L3** as shown below on the right.

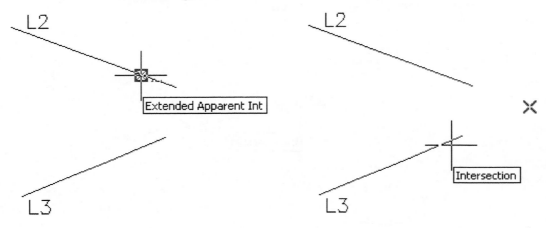

- As your **Dynamic Circle** appears at the **Apparent Intersection**, enter a radius of *0.5* then *[ENTER]*.

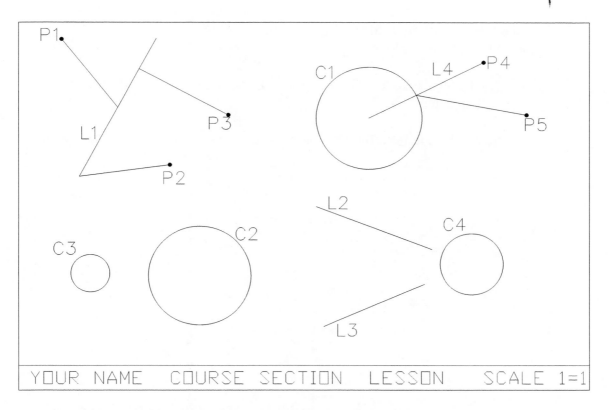

11. Draw a Line **Tangent** to a Circle by doing the following:

- Start a **Line** at about point **P6**.

- In the **Object Snap** toolbar, click on the **Snap to Tangent** button.

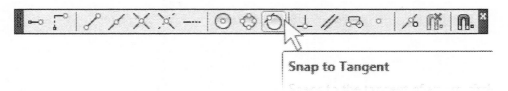

- Pick a point on circle **C4** as shown below, then *[ENTER]*.

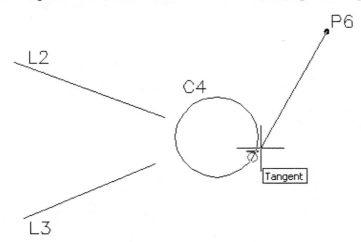

12. Use the **OSnap Shortcut Menu** by doing the following:

- Start a **Line** at about point **P7**.

- Hold down the **SHIFT** key and right-click the mouse. {Shortcut Menu will appear.}

- Select the **Tangent** option from the **Shortcut Menu** as shown below.

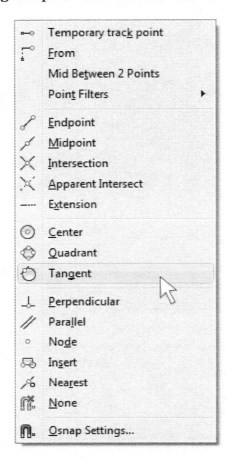

- Pick **Circle C4** near 6 o'clock as shown below, then *[ENTER]*.

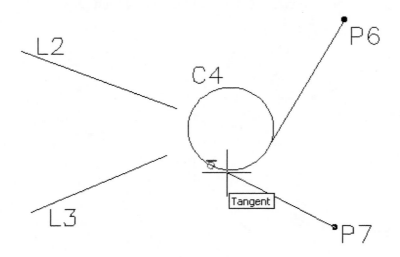

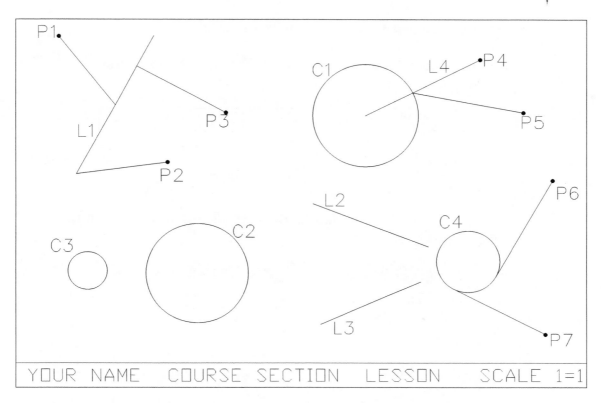

YOUR NAME   COURSE SECTION   LESSON   SCALE 1=1

Note: Once a Command is activated, to use the **Osnap** options, you may also type in the first three letters of the **OSnap** option and then *[ENTER]*.

Endpoint	*END*
Midpoint	*MID*
Intersection	*INT*
Apparent Intersection	*APPINT*
Extension	*EXT*
Center	*CEN*
Quadrant	*QUA*
Tangent	*TAN*
Perpendicular	*PER*
Parallel	*PAR*
Node	*NOD*

Also, when Drawing Objects that require the use of the same **Snap** mode a repeated number of times, it is best to put **Object Snap** in the **Running Mode** as shown in the next exercise.

13. Draw multiple **Tangent Lines** by doing the following:

- In the **Object Snap** toolbar, click on the **Object Snap Settings** button.

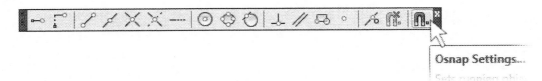

Osnap Settings...

- Notice that as the **Drafting Settings** dialog box opens, the **Object Snap** tab is already selected.

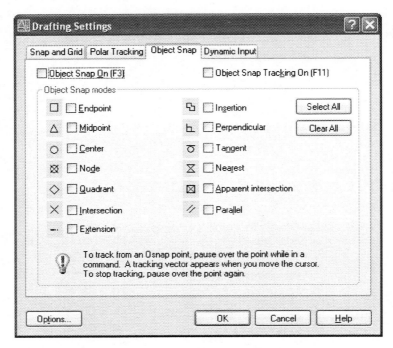

- Toggle **Object Snap On** to *On* mode.

- In the **Object Snap modes** area, click **Clear All**.

- Toggle *On* the **Tangent** option.

- Click **OK**.

Note: OSnap Running Mode is now set to **On**. As you are creating geometry, the cursor attempts to snap to the **Tangent** of nearby Objects just as it did after clicking on the Tangent tool. The difference is that in **Running Mode,** the user does not have to repeatedly activate the **Object Snap** mode. The process is automatic.

- Select the **Line** tool.

- Pick a point near 11 o'clock on Circle **C2** as shown below.

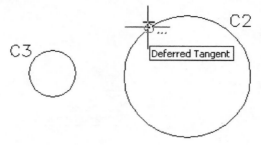

- Pick a point near 11 o'clock on Circle **C3** as shown below.

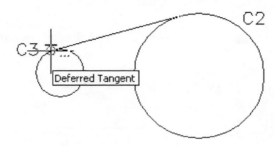

- *[ENTER]* {Exits the **Line** Command.}

- *[ENTER]* *again* to activate the **Line** Command.

Note: An *[ENTER]* at the blank **Command Prompt** always reactivates the previous Command.

- Pick a point near 1 o'clock on Circle **C3** as shown below.

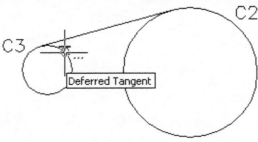

162

- Pick a point near 7 o'clock on Circle **C2** as shown below.

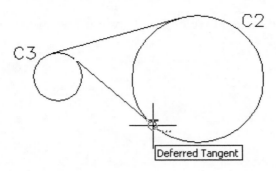

- *[ENTER]*. {Exits the **Line** Command.}

- *[ENTER]*. {Activates the **Line** Command.}

- Pick a point near 11 o'clock on Circle **C2** as shown below.

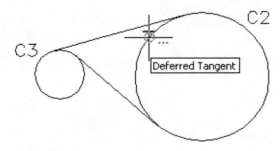

- Pick a point near 5 o'clock on Circle **C3** as shown below.

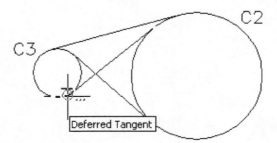

- *[ENTER]*. {Exits **Line** Command.}

- *[ENTER]*. {Activates **Line** Command.}

- Pick a point near 7 o'clock on Circle **C2** as shown below.

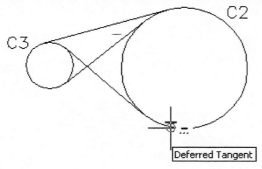

- Pick a point near 7 o'clock on Circle **C3** as shown below.

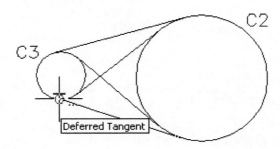

- *[ENTER]*. {Exits the **Line** Command.}

164

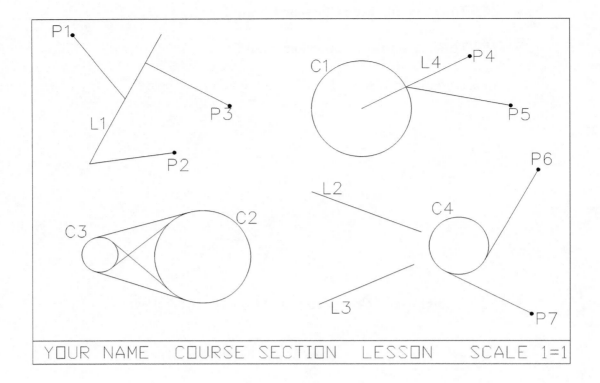

YOUR NAME   COURSE SECTION   LESSON   SCALE 1=1

Note: The **Quadrant** mode of **Object Snap** allows the user to locate the 3, 6, 9, and 12 o'clock positions on a Circle.

14. Draw Lines to the **Quadrants** of a Circle by doing the following:

- From the Menu Bar, select **Tools** , and then open the **Drafting Settings** dialog box.

- Select **Object Snap** tab. Make sure that the **Object Snap On** is Toggled to the *On* position.

- Click **Clear All**.

- Toggle *On* **Quadrant**.

- Click **OK**.

- Start a Line near the 3 o'clock position of Circle **C1** as shown below.

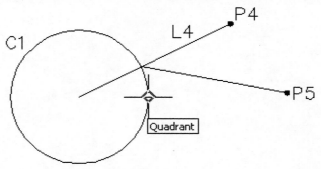

- Pick a point near the 6 o'clock position of Circle **C1** as shown below.

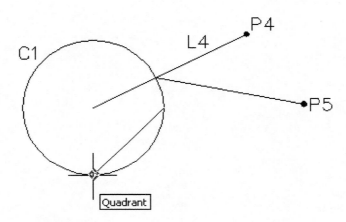

- Pick a point near the 9 o'clock position of Circle **C1** as shown below.

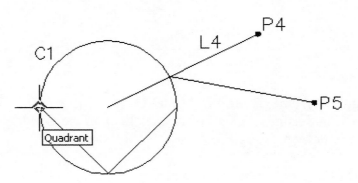

166

- Pick a point near the 12 o'clock position of Circle **C1** as shown below.

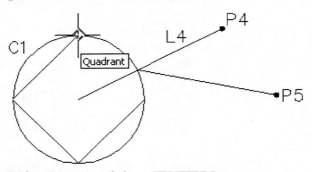

- Type *C* (for **Close**) and then *[ENTER]*.

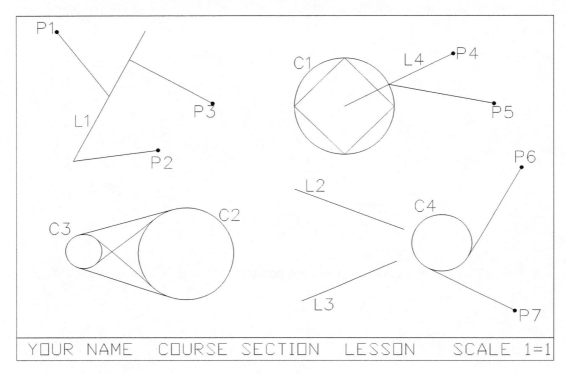

- Toggle *Off* the **Running Mode Object Snap** either by opening the **Drafting Settings** dialog box and clicking on the **Object Snap On** Toggle button, or by pressing **F3**.

- When finished, **Erase** all geometry.

Polar Tracking

1. Draw a shape using **Polar Tracking** by doing the following:

    *   From the Menu Bar, select **Tools** then **Drafting Settings** as shown below.

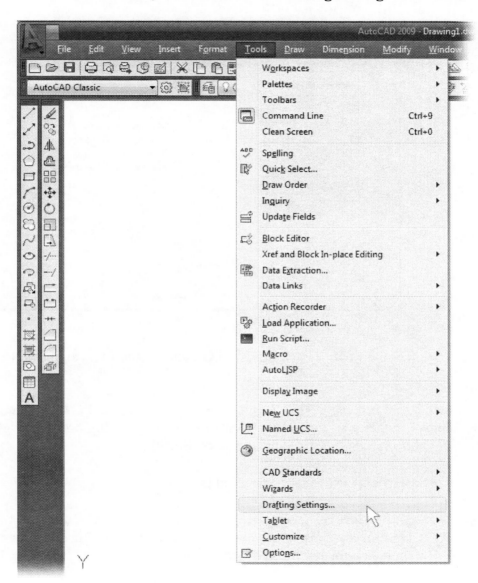

{The **Drafting Settings** dialog box will appear.}

- Click on the **Polar Tracking** tab of the **Drafting Settings** dialog box as shown below.

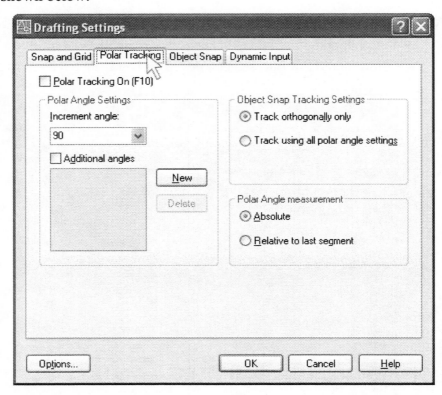

- Toggle **Polar Tracking *On*** to **On** and set the **Increment angle** to *30,* then click **OK**.

Note: **Polar Tracking** can also be toggled *On* by selecting the **POLAR** button from the **Status Line**. Another way to load the **Drafting Settings** dialog box is to right-click on the **POLAR** button in the **Status Line** and select **Settings**.

- Start a **Line** at a user-specified location.

- Slowly revolve your cursor around the start point of this line. Notice how the cursor snaps to 30 degree increments using an **alignment path**, as shown below by the 60 degree angle.

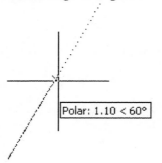

Note: You can benefit from **Polar Tracking** by moving the cursor to the desired angle and using the keyboard to enter a specific length.

- Use **Polar Tracking** to align the cursor along a *30*-degree angle.

- Type *2.0* (for Length) then **[ENTER]**. {**Line** is constructed at a *30*-degree angle with a length of 2 units.}

- Use **Polar Tracking** to move the cursor along a *150*-degree angle as shown below.

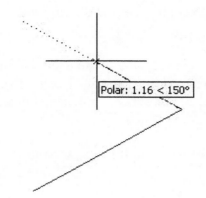

- Type *2.0* then *[ENTER]*.

- Move the cursor along a *210*-degree angle as shown below.

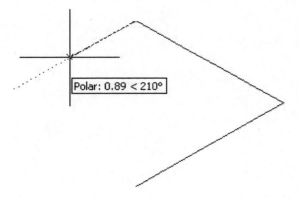

- Type *2.0* then *[ENTER]*.

170

- Type *C* (for **Close**) then *[ENTER]*.

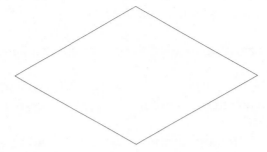

2. Set **Polar Tracking** to *Off* either by opening the **Drafting Settings** dialog box and clicking the **Polar Tracking On** toggle button, or by selecting **POLAR** from the **Status Line**.

Note: The technique mentioned above, where you use the mouse to define your direction first, and then use the keyboard to define distance, is an efficient method of coordinate entry in **Relative Polar** mode. Make sure to practice this technique as it will be used frequently in the book.

3. Erase all geometry and move on to the next section.

Object Tracking

Note: Object tracking is a method for tracking Objects by combining the **Object Snap** and the **Polar** settings together in one operation. As you place the mouse on what is known as an **Acquired Point** and then move the mouse in a particular direction, alignment paths will appear, thus aiding you in creating your geometry. Refer to the two cases shown below.

1. Create geometry while tracking Objects by doing the following:

   - Make sure that **Snap**, **Grid**, **Ortho**, **Polar**, **Osnap**, **Otrack**, **Ducs** and **Dyn** are set to *Off*.

   - Create the geometry shown below at a user-specified size and location.

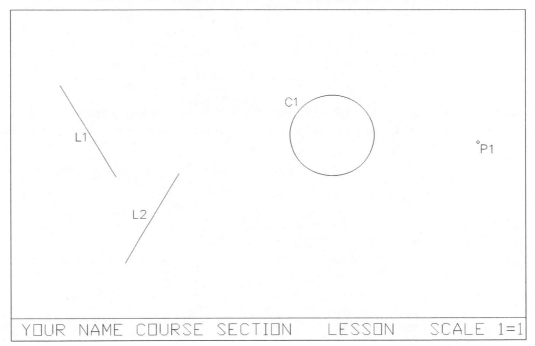

   - In the **Status Line, Right-click** on the **Polar** button and then select the **Settings** button. {The **Drafting Settings** dialog box appears.}

172

- Make sure that the **Increment angle** is set to **30** and that the **Object Snap Tracking Settings** is set to **Track orthogonally only** as shown below.

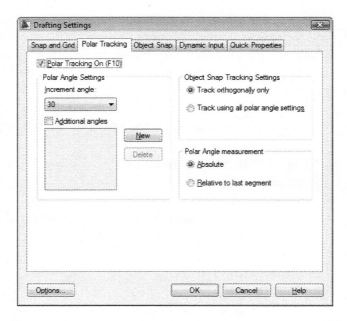

- Select the **Object Snap** tab and as the **Osnap** options appear, set the mode of **Osnap** to **Endpoint** and **Center** with all other **Osnap** modes set to *Off* as shown below.

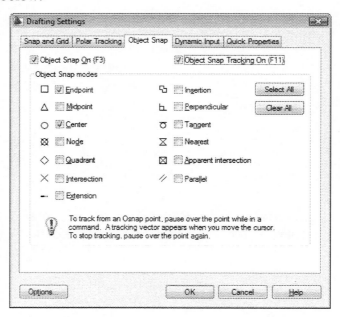

- Select **OK.**

- In the **Status Line,** make sure that **Polar, Osnap**, and **Otrack** are set to **On**.

- Start a **line** at the lower endpoint of **L1.**

- Move the cursor to the upper endpoint of **L2,** known as an acquired point, but do not click. {The **OTrack** marker recognizes the endpoint signified by a **(+)** symbol.}

- Move cursor slightly upwards, {A vertical alignment path appears as shown below.}

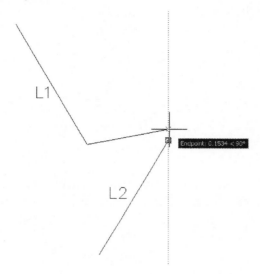

- Move the cursor upwards along the alignment path and notice that a second alignment path appears. {The text box displays the angles of 30 and 90 from the two endpoints respectively.}

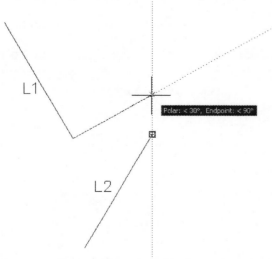

- Start a **line** at that point and then make its endpoint to be the upper endpoint of line **L1** and then *[Enter].*

- From the **Status Line**, **Right-click** on the **Polar** button and then select **Settings**. {The Polar Settings dialog box appears.}

- In the **Object Snap Tracking Settings** area, select **Track using all polar angle settings.**

- Select **OK.**

- Start a **line** at about point **P1** as shown below and move the cursor to the **center** of Circle **C1**.

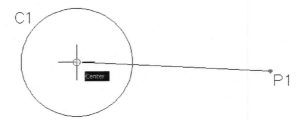

- Once the center is recognized as signified by the **(+)** symbols, move the cursor along a **30** degree alignment path as shown below.

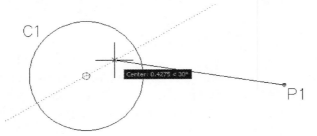

- Follow the alignment path to the right as shown until a second alignment path is displayed. Note that based on your settings, your alignment paths may not necessarily extend to the edge of the screen as shown.

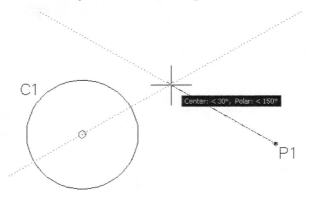

- With the cursor still in this position, **Click** to specify the next point of the line.

- For the endpoint of the line, select the center of the circle and then type in **Close**. {A triangle is constructed.}

Note: Although **Otrack** can be useful in special cases, it is usually cumbersome and the technique is often replaced by creating construction lines for geometric construction purposes.

Aliases and Hot Keys

APPARENT INTERSECTION ....APPINT

CENTER ....CEN

ENDPOINT..END

EXTENSION ....EXT

INTERSECTION ....INT

MIDPOINT..MID

NODE ....NOD

PARALLEL ....PAR

PERPENDICULAR ....PER

QUADRANT ....QUA

TANGENT.. TAN

TOGGLES OSNAP RUNNING MODE F3

TOGGLES POLAR TRACKING MODE F10

OBJECT SNAP SHORTCUT MENU...SHIFT+RIGHT-CLICK

Assignment 4

Objective:

1. To practice using **Template** Files.
2. To practice working with all previously learned **Tools**.
3. To practice the **Object Snap** options and Geometric construction.
4. To practice setting regular **Snap** and **Grid** to suitable values.
5. To practice **Plotting**.

Instructions:

1. Launch AutoCAD and use your **My Template** to begin a **New** Drawing.
2. **Save As** the Drawing file to your folder. Name it **ASSIGN04_ _ _.dwg** where the 3 blanks are your initials.
3. Turn **Snap, Grid, Ortho, Polar,** *Otrack and Dyn to Off*.
4. Draw Line **L1** using the given coordinates below.

   - **P1** is located at *2.03,5.27*.
   - **P2** is located at *2.50,4.18*.

5. Draw Line **L2** using the given coordinates below.

   - **P3** is located at *3.40,5.80*.
   - **P4** is located at *2.80, 4.40*.

   Construct Circle **C1** such that the **Center** is located at the **Apparent Intersection** of **L1** and **L2**, and that the Circle goes through the **Midpoint** of **L2**.

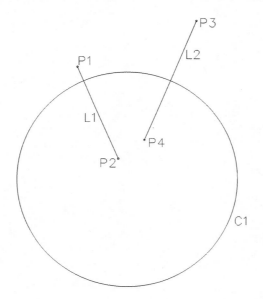

6. Draw the two Circles **C1** and **C2** with the **Centers** and **Radii** as given below.

- **Center** of **C1** is located at *1.50,1.30* with **R1** = *0.45* .
- **Center** of **C2** is located at *3.80, 1.80* with **R2**= *0.85* .

L1 connects the two **Centers** and Lines **L2** and **L3** are **Tangent** to Circles **C1** and **C2**.

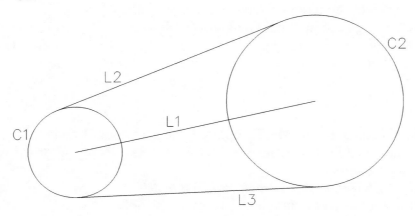

7. The horizontally positioned equilateral triangle has a corner at **P1** and Side **L1** such that **P1** is located at *5.0,3.0* and **L1**=*3.00*.

- Construct the larger of the two Circles knowing that it is inscribed by the triangle. Draw any construction lines needed to find the **Center** of the triangle, and then **Erase** the construction lines.
- Construct the Square knowing that its corners are located at the **Quadrant**, of the Circle.
- Construct the inner Circle knowing that it is inscribed by the square.

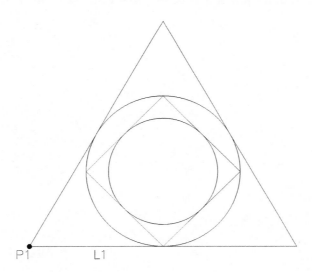

8. Use the **Line** Command in conjunction with **Polar Snap** Settings to construct the five point star knowing that:

- **P1** is located at *5.75,0.75* .
- Keep in mind that each line falls on a *36*-degree **Polar Snap** and is *2 units* in length.

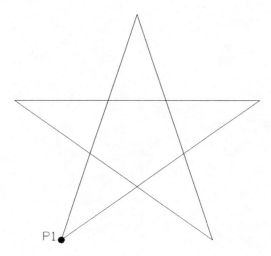

9. Add lesson number to the title page.
10. Check your work to match that of the next page and **Save** the Drawing.
11. **Preview** and **Plot** Drawing using the following settings:

- Paper size: Letter (8.50x11.00 **inches**)
- Plot area: Limits
- Plot offset: Centered
- Plot scale: 1=1

180

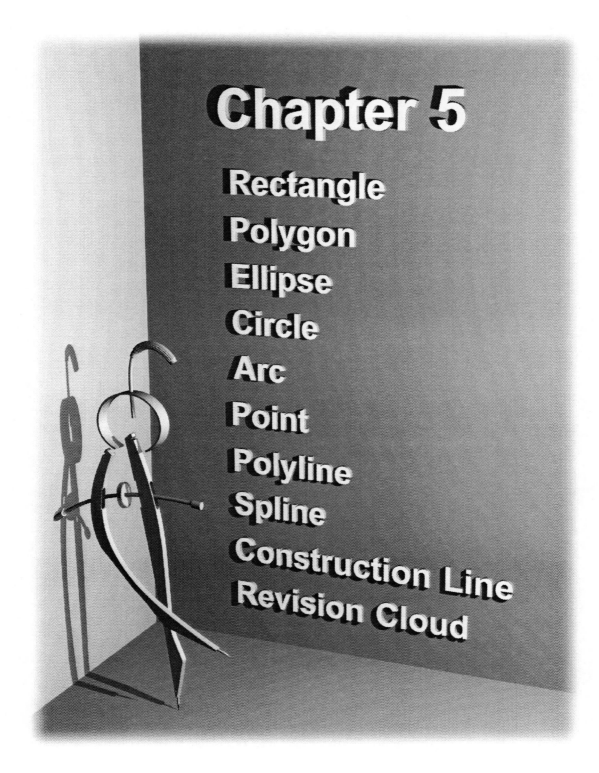

Chapter 5

Rectangle
Polygon
Ellipse
Circle
Arc
Point
Polyline
Spline
Construction Line
Revision Cloud

Rectangle

1. Launch AutoCAD and use your **My Template** to begin a **New** Drawing.

2. From the **Status Line** set **Snap** and **Grid** to *On*. Set **Ortho**, **Polar**, **OSnap**, **OTrack, Ducs** and **Dyn** to *Off*.

3. Create Rectangle **R1** by doing the following:

   - In the **Draw** toolbar, click on the **Rectangle** button.

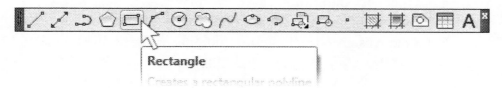

   - Pick the two points **P1** & **P2** using the mouse as shown below to create the 3 x 2 unit rectangle.

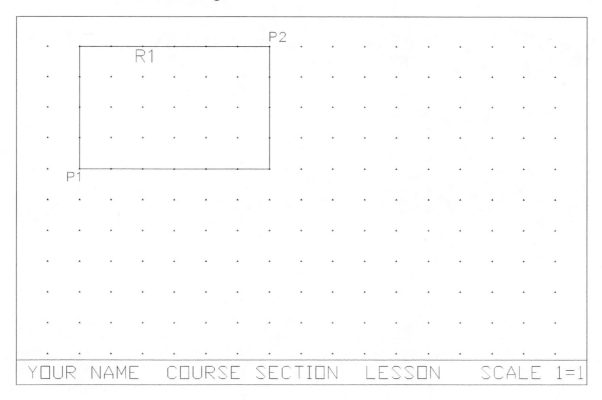

184

4. Create Rectangle **R2** by using the **Absolute Rectangular Coordinate System**.

- Click on the **Rectangle** button in the **Draw** toolbar again.

- When asked for the **first corner or point,** type *1,1* and then *[ENTER]*.

- When asked for the **other corner or point,** type *3,3* and then *[ENTER]*.

5. Create Rectangle **R3** using the **Relative Rectangular Coordinate System** by doing the following:

- Select the **Rectangle** tool.

- Enter the **Absolute Rectangular** coordinates for the first point: *5.23,0.77* and then *[ENTER]*.

- For the other corner, type in the **Relative Rectangular** coordinates *@3,2* and *[ENTER]*.

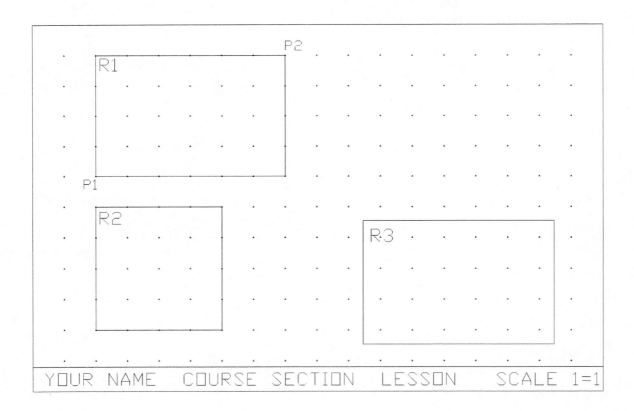

6. Create Rectangle **R4** by doing the following:

   • Turn **Snap** *Off*.

   • Draw Line **L1** at a user-specified Location as shown below. This line will
     serve as the diagonal line of a rectangle.

   • Select the **Rectangle** tool.

   • Using the **Object Snap to Endpoint** button, **OSnap** to the two
     Endpoints of Line **L1**.

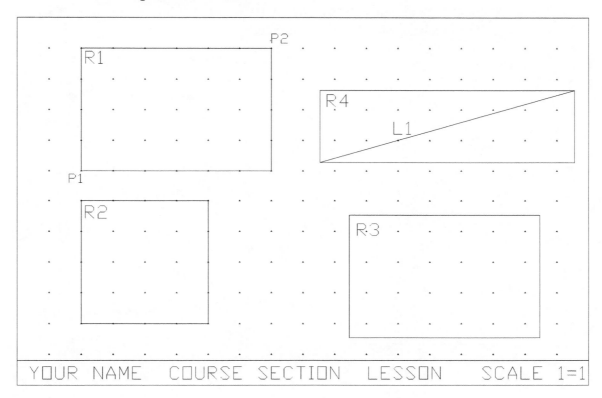

7. When finished, **Erase** all geometry.

1. Create a **Rectangle** by using the **Area** option.

   - Select the **Rectangle** tool.

   - For the first corner, type **1,1** and then *[ENTER]*.

   - When asked to specify other corner, Type **A** (for Area) and *[ENTER]*.

   - Type in **6.75** and then *[ENTER]*.

   - Type in **L** (for length) and then *[ENTER]*.

   - Type in **3.25** and then *[ENTER]* {A Rectangle having an area of 6.75 sq units and a base of 3.25 units is created.}

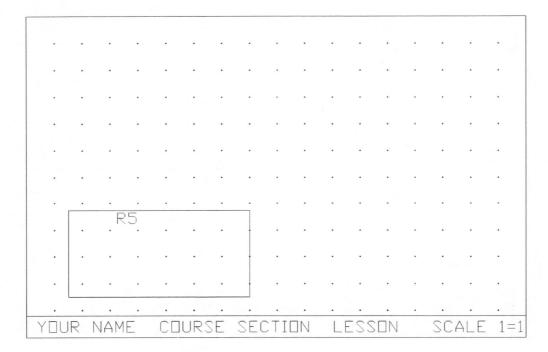

2. Create Rectangle **R6** by doing the following:

   - Select the **Rectangle** Tool.

   - For the first corner, use the mouse to select point **P3** at a user-specified location as shown on the next page.

   - For the second corner, type **R** (for Rotation) and then *[ENTER]*.

   - For the rotation angle, type **30** and then *[ENTER]*.

- To specify the other corner, use the mouse to pick point **P4** at a user-specified Location as shown below.

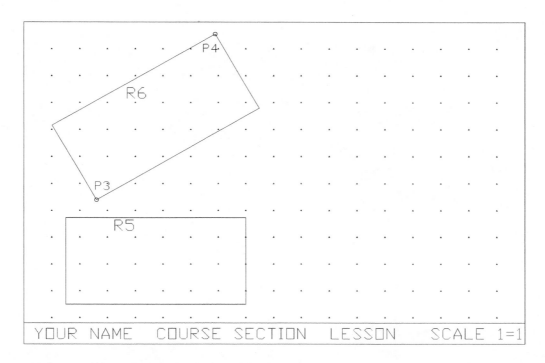

3. Create Rectangle **R7** by doing the following:

- Command: **Rec** (for Rectangle) and then *[ENTER]*.

- For the first corner, type in **4.8,1.2** .

- When asked to specify other corner, type **R** (for rotation) and set rotation angle back to **0.0** and then *[ENTER]*.

- To specify other corner type in **D** (for Dimensions) and then *[ENTER]*.

- For length enter a value of **3.5** and then *[ENTER]*.

- For width enter a value of **4.0** and then *[ENTER].*

188

- Move the mouse up and down and also to the left and right to see the four possible solutions for the rectangle and then click the mouse to result in the one that fits on the screen.

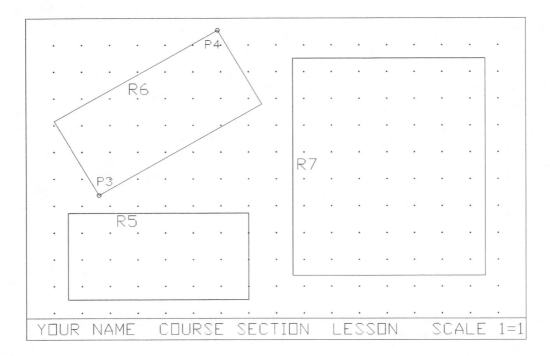

- When finished, **Erase** all geometry on the screen.

Polygon

1. Create Polygon **Pg1** by doing the following:

   - In the **Draw** toolbar, click on the **Polygon** button.

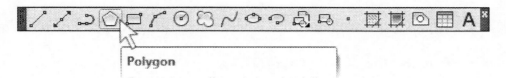

Polygon

   - When asked for the **number of sides**, enter *6* then *[ENTER]*.

   - Enter the Center Point *2,3* then *[ENTER]*.

   - Type *I* (for **Inscribed in Circle**) and *[ENTER]*.

   - Specify the **Radius** as *1.5* and then *[ENTER]*.

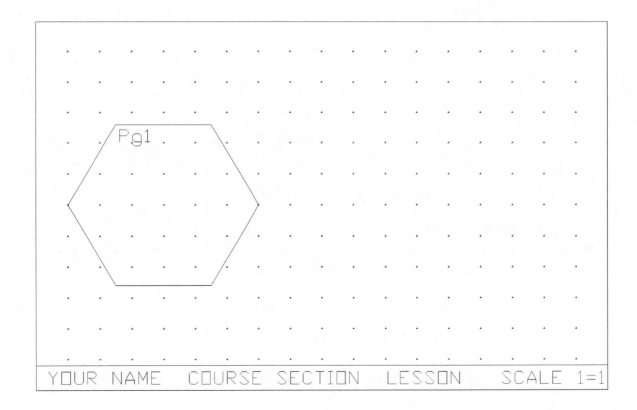

190

2. Create Polygon **Pg2** by doing the following:

- Click on the **Polygon** button.

- Enter number of sides: *5* and then *[ENTER]*.

- Enter center point of *6,3*.

- Type *C* (for **Circumscribed About Circle**) and then *[ENTER]*.

- Enter **Radius** of *1.5* then *[ENTER]*.

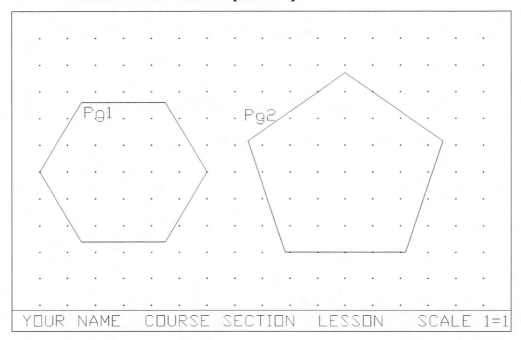

3. Create Polygon **Pg3** by doing the following:

- Set **Snap** to **On**.

- Command: **Pol** and then *[Enter]*.

- Enter number of sides: *5* then *[ENTER]*.

- Type *E* (for **Edge**), then *[ENTER]*.

- Pick points **P1** and then **P2** as shown on the next page. Both points are on **Snap**.

4. Repeat Step 3 again; however, this time Pick **P2** first, and then **P1**.

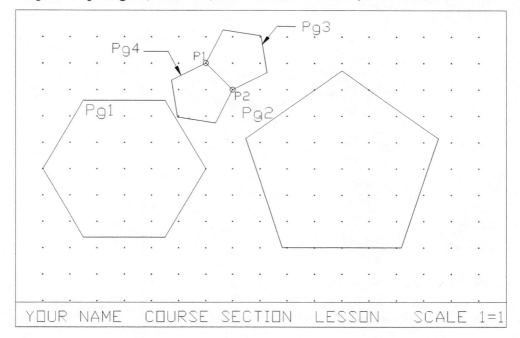

Note: When using the **Edge** option, the **Polygon** is drawing in Counter-Clockwise order.

5. When complete, **Erase** the screen.

Note: In order for you to successfully grasp the construction of a Polygon, you need to think in terms of an imaginary circle. As demonstrated below, AutoCAD constructs Polygons in relation to a Circle in one of two methods: **Inscribed** and **Circumscribed**.

Furthermore, keep in mind that an equilateral triangle can be thought of as a 3-sided Polygon and a Square can be though of as a 4-sided Polygon. In AutoCAD, a Polygon can have up to 1024 sides.

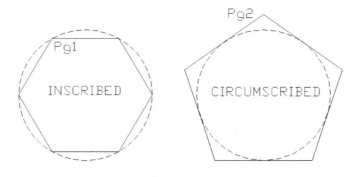

192

 **Ellipse**

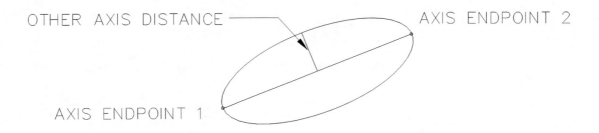

OTHER AXIS DISTANCE ———— AXIS ENDPOINT 2

AXIS ENDPOINT 1

1. Set **Grid** and **Snap** to *Off*.

2. Create Ellipse **El1** by doing the following:

   - In the **Draw** toolbar, click on the **Ellipse** button.

   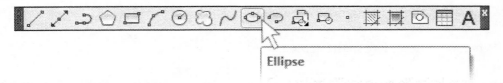

   Ellipse

   - Pick **Axis Endpoint 1** at about **P1** and **Axis Endpoint 2** at about **P2** as shown.

   - Enter **Distance to Other Axis** of *.5* then *[ENTER]*.

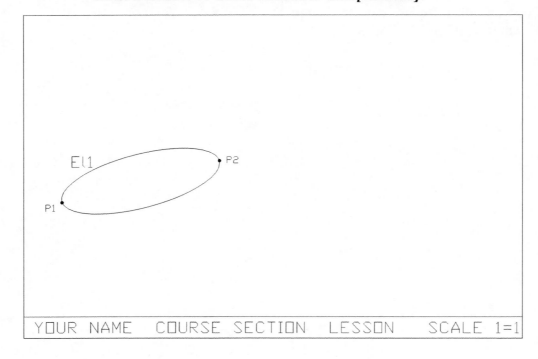

El1

P2

P1

YOUR NAME   COURSE SECTION   LESSON   SCALE 1=1

3. Create Ellipse **El2** by doing the following:

- Select the **Ellipse** button.

- Type *C* (for **Center**), then *[ENTER]*.

- Pick at about **P3**.

- Pick at about **P4**.

- Enter **Other Axis Distance** of *0.5* then *[ENTER]*.

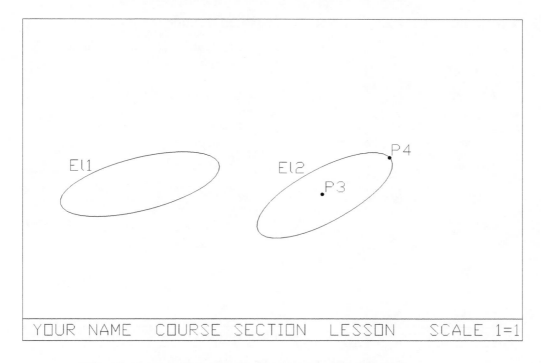

- When complete, **Erase** all geometry from screen.

Note: Just like the Circle, the Ellipse has 4 **Quadrants** that can be located using the **Quad** option of the **Object Snap** menu. These 4 **Quadrants** pertain to the **Endpoints** of the Major and Minor Axes.

194

 **Circle**

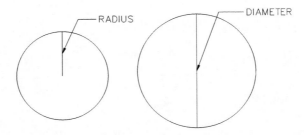

1. Create Lines **L1**, **L2**, and **L3** at user-specified locations as shown below.

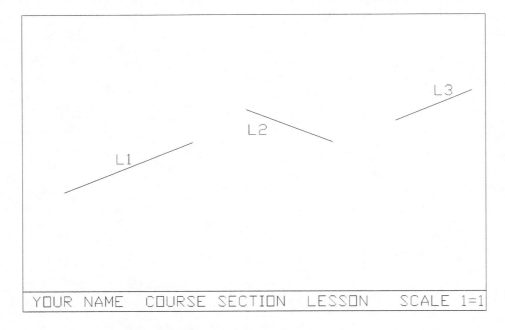

2. Use **Blips** as a visual aid by doing the following:

   - Type *Blipmode* and *[ENTER]*.

   - Type *On* and *[ENTER]*. {**Blips** will show when picking points.}

3. Create the **2 Point Circle C1** by doing the following:

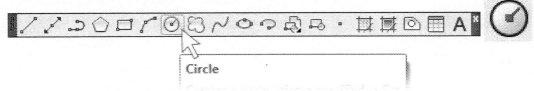

   - In the **Draw** toolbar, click on the **Circle** button.

- Type *2P* and then *[ENTER]*.

- **OSnap** to the left **Endpoint** of **L1**. {**Circle** is dragging on screen.}

- **OSnap** to the right **Endpoint** of **L1**.

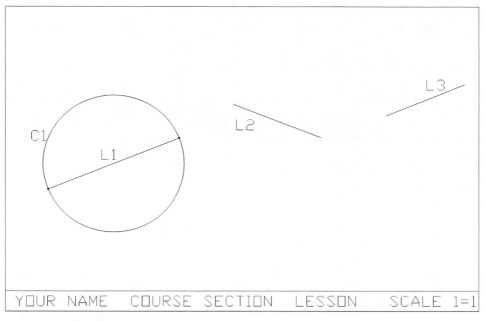

4. Create the **2 Point Circle C2** by doing the following:

- Select the **Circle** tool.

- Type **2P** and then *[ENTER]*.

- Use **OSnap** to select the **Midpoint** of **L2** and then the **Endpoint** of **L3**.

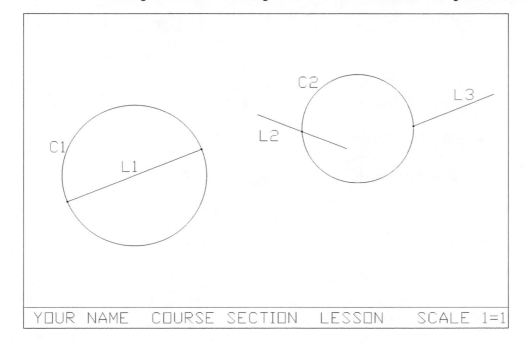

196

- When complete, **Erase** the screen.

- Command: *Regen* then *[ENTER]*. {Blips are cleared.}

5. Create the **3 Point Circle C1** by doing the following:

- Select the **Circle** tool.

- Type *3P* then *[ENTER]*.

- Pick two points at about **P1** and **P2** as shown below. Move the cursor and observe how the **3 Point Circle** is dragging then Pick **P3**. {Circle is going through **P1**, **P2**, and **P3** as shown by your Blips.}

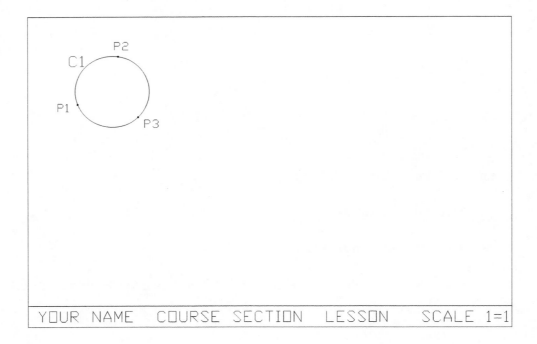

- Use the **Center, Radius** option to create the 3 small Circles at user-specified locations as shown on the next page.

- Select the **Circle** button to create **Circle C2**.

- Type *3P* then *[ENTER]*.

- **OSnap** to the Centers of each of the 3 small Circles.

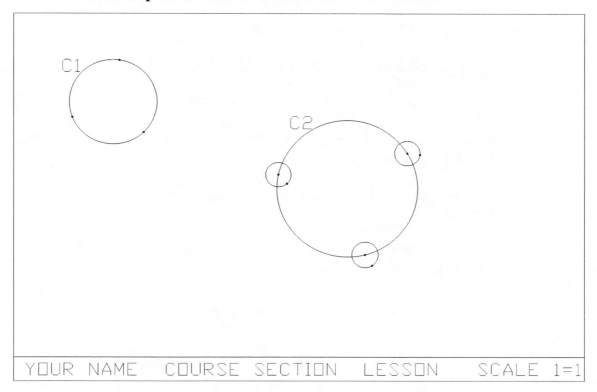

- When complete, **Erase** all geometry.

- Set **Blipmode** to *Off* and then **Regen** (for Regenerating) the screen. {Once **Regen** is used, **Blips** disappear from Drawing.}

Note: Here is another example of the **Circle 3Point** option where Circle **C2** is passing through the Center of **C1** and the two **Endpoints** of **L1**.

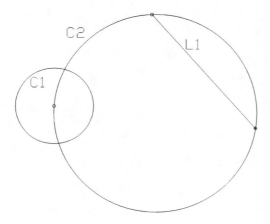

198

6. Create a **TTR** (for **Tangent Tangent Radius) Circle** by doing the following:

- Create Line **L1** with **Endpoints** located at *2.5,5* and *6,4*.

- Create Line **L2** with **Endpoints** located at *2.5,2.5* and *6,3.5*.

- Select the **Circle** Tool and type *TTR* then *[ENTER]*.

- Move cursor to Line **L1**; as you see the **Deferred Tangent** marker, Pick Line **L1**.

- Move cursor to Line **L2;** as you see the **Deferred Tangent** marker, Pick Line **L2**.

- Enter the **Radius** of *0.75*. {Circle **C1** has a specified **Radius** and is **Tangent** to both Lines **L1** and **L2**.}

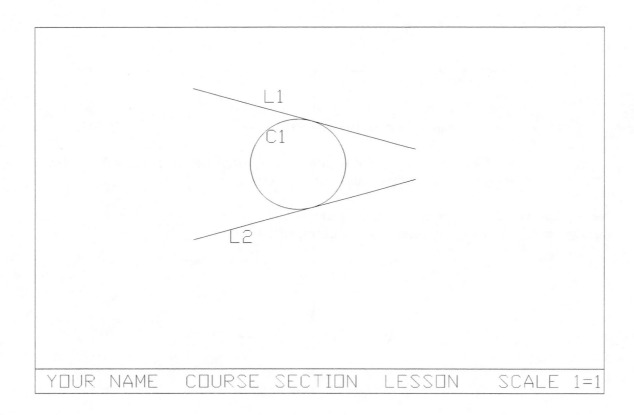

7. Create **TTR Circle C2** by doing the following:

   • Create a **TTR Circle** so that it is tangent to both Lines **L1** and **L2** with the radius of **0.5**.

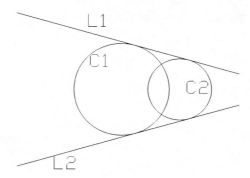

8. Create **TTR Circle C3** by doing the following:

   • Create a **TTR Circle** that is tangent to both Lines **L1** and **L2** by picking the two lines closer to the left Endpoints of **L1** and **L2**. Enter a radius of **1.0**.

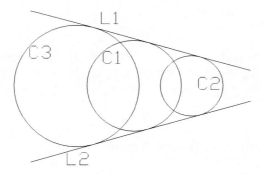

9. Create **TTR Circle C4** by doing the following:

   • Create a **TTR Circle** tangent to both lines **L1** and **L2** and a radius of **0.1**.

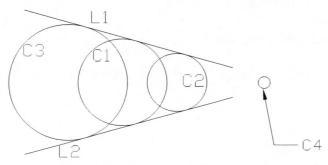

Note: Not all solutions are obvious. Next you will look at some of these solutions.

10. Create **TTR Circle C5** by doing the following:

- Create a **TTR Circle** tangent to both Lines **L1** and **L2** by picking lines **L1** and **L2** near the right-most endpoints, with **L2** selection being closer to the endpoint than that of **L1**, as shown below by the arrowheads.

- Set the radius to *1.0*.

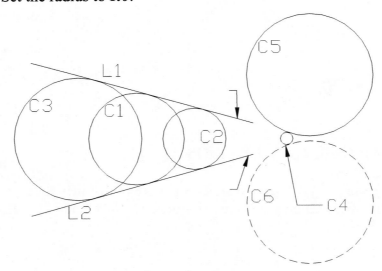

Note: If you had chosen your **Deferred Tangents** with the tangent on **L1** being closer to the Endpoint than the **Deferred Tangent** on **L2**, you would have constructed Circle **C6**. Note that if you would extend **L1** and **L2** to the Circles, they both would be tangent Lines to **C5** and **C6**.

- When complete, **Erase** the screen.

11. Create two different size circles **C1** and **C2** similar to diagram on the next page. Exact position and size are User Specified.

12. Create **TTR Circle C3** by doing the following:

- Select the **Circle** button again.

- Type *TTR* then *[ENTER]*.

- Select the first **Deferred Tangent** at about the 1 o'clock position on Circle **C1**.

- Select the second **Deferred Tangent** at about the 11 o'clock position on Circle **C2**.

- Enter a **Radius** of *10*. (Use this radius for the rest of the **TTR** exercises.)

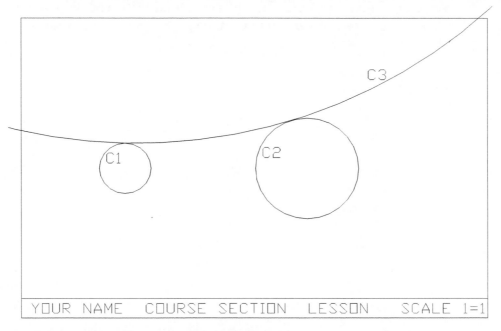

13. Create **TTR Circle C4** by doing the following:

- Create a **TTR Circle** with the first **Deferred Tangent** at about the 11 o'clock position on Circle **C1**, and the second **Deferred Tangent** at about the 1 o'clock position on Circle **C2**.

- Use the same **Radius** as before in the following examples:

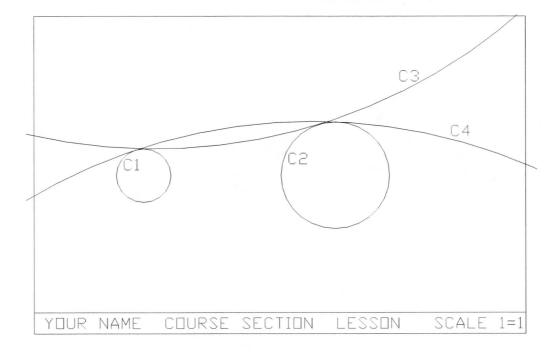

14. Create **TTR Circle C5** by doing the following:

- Create a **TTR Circle** with the first **Deferred Tangent** at about the 5 o'clock position on Circle **C1**, and the second **Deferred Tangent** at about the 7 o'clock position on Circle **C2** then *[ENTER]* for the **Radius**.

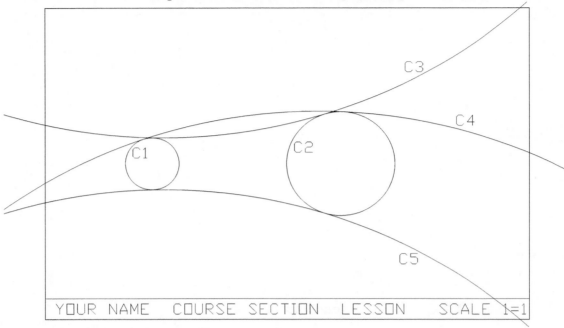

YOUR NAME   COURSE SECTION   LESSON   SCALE 1=1

15. Create **TTR Circle C6** by doing the following:

- Create a **TTR Circle** with the first **Deferred Tangent** at about the 7 o'clock position on Circle **C1** (make sure not to select **C5** by error), and the second **Deferred Tangent** at about the 5 o'clock position on Circle **C2.** Use the same **Radius** as before.

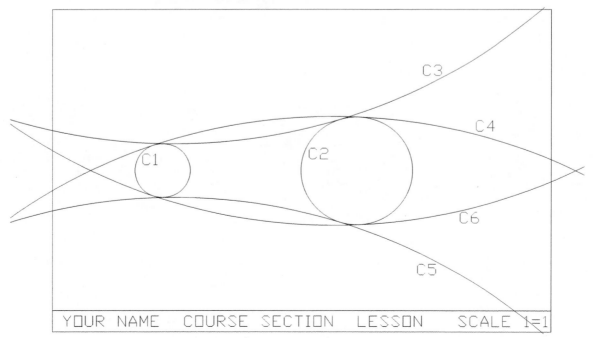

YOUR NAME   COURSE SECTION   LESSON   SCALE 1=1

16. Create **TTR Circle C7** by doing the following:

- Create a **TTR Circle** with the first **Deferred Tangent** at about the 5 o'clock position on Circle **C1**, and the second **Deferred Tangent** at about the 11 o'clock position on Circle **C2**.

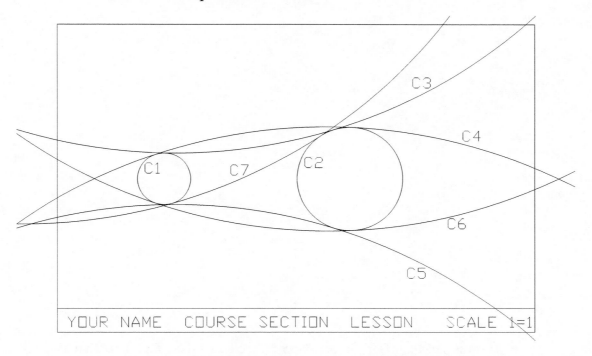

Note: Three additional possible solutions exist for this **TTR Circle** scenario; it is up to you to find them.

- When complete, use the **Crossing** option to **Erase** all Objects within the Drawing area, leaving the border and title Block.

1. Create a Circle Tangent to 3 Objects by doing the following:

    •   Create Line **L1**, Circle **C1**, and **C2** similar to the diagram below. Exact
        size and position are user-specified.

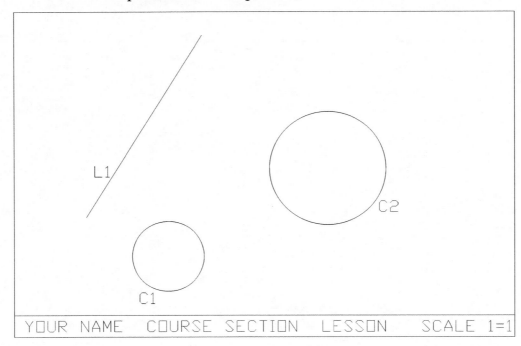

    •   From the Menu Bar, Select **Draw**, **Circle** and then **Tan Tan Tan** as
        shown below.

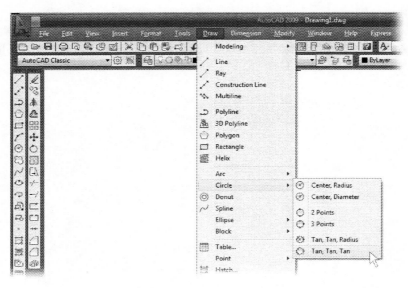

    •   Select the **1st Tangent point** of Circle at about Point **P1** on Line **L1** shown
        on the next page.

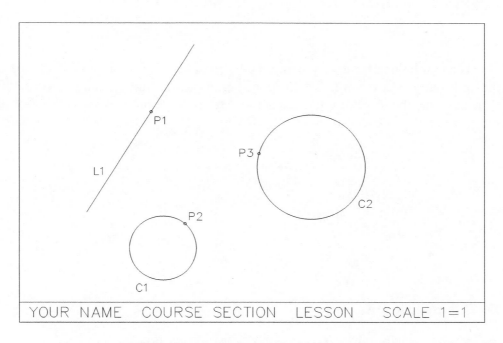

- Select the **2nd Tangent point** of Circle at about Point **P2** on Circle **C1**.

- Select the **3rd Tangent point** of Circle at about Point **P3** on Circle **C2**.

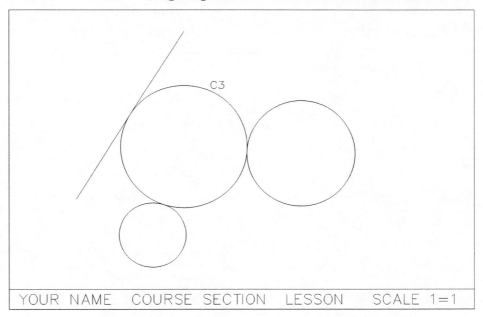

Note: Circle **C3** is constructed such that it is tangential to all three objects. Also note that you are not prompted for the radius of the circle since this value is fixed.

- When finished, **Erase** all geometry from the screen.

206

 **Arc**

An **Arc** can be positioned by using a combination of three inputs as identified by one of the following: **S**tart point, **C**enter point, **E**nd point, **A**ngle, **L**ength, **D**irection, or **R**adius. In general, the system will create the Arc in a counterclockwise fashion when possible.

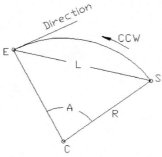

1. Set **Blipmode** to **On**.

2. Create an **Arc** using the **3Point** option by doing the following:

    - In the **Draw** toolbar, click on the **Arc** button.

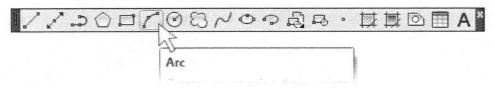

    - Pick about Point **P1**, then about **P2** as shown below.

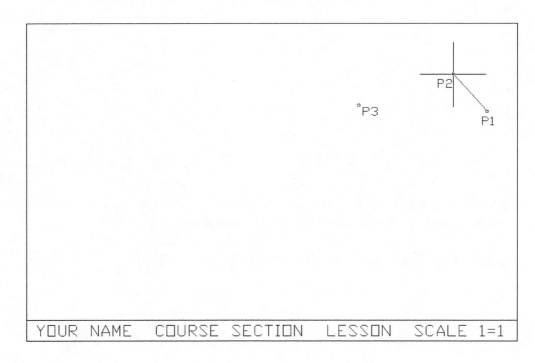

YOUR NAME   COURSE SECTION   LESSON   SCALE 1=1

Note: As you move the cursor, the dragging arc will always start at the first point selected, pass through the second point selected, and end with the cursor.

- Pick about **P3**. {An arc will be created similar to the one shown below, and the system will automatically exit out of the Command.}

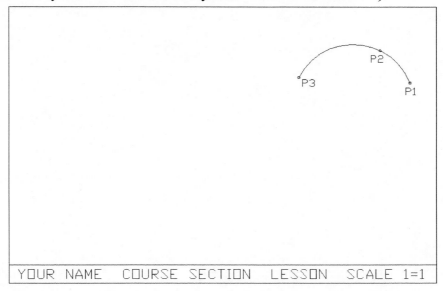

YOUR NAME   COURSE SECTION   LESSON   SCALE 1=1

Note: When using the **Arc** button on the **Draw** toolbar, the system default is to use the **3Point** option; however, as you will learn in the following exercises, when creating Arcs using other options, the preferred method is to use the Menu Bar.

3. Create an Arc using the **Start, Center, End** option by doing the following:

- From the Menu Bar select **Draw** then **Arc**, and lastly **Start, Center, End** as shown below.

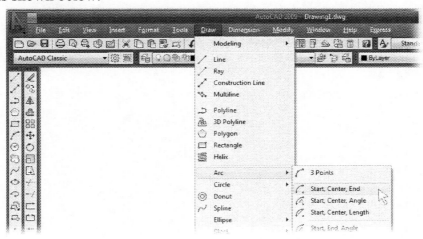

208

- Pick about Point **P4**, then **P5**. Move the cursor a distance away from **P5** as shown below.

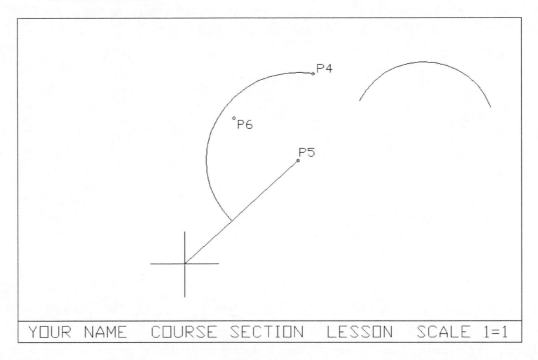

YOUR NAME   COURSE SECTION   LESSON   SCALE 1=1

Note: When using the **Start, Center, End** option of the **Arc** Command, once the **Start** and **Center** points are defined, since the radius is fixed, the end point of **Arc** is determined as the nearest point to the cursor. Also note that the arc is created in a counterclockwise order about the center point.

- Pick about Point **P6**. {An Arc will be created similar to the one shown below.}

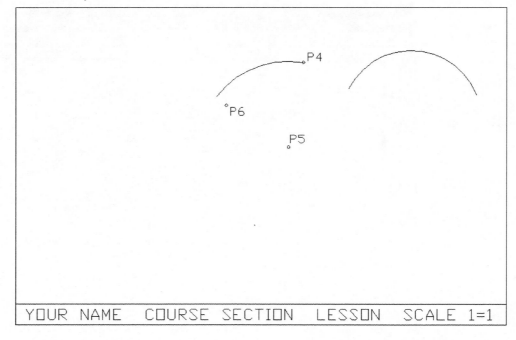

YOUR NAME   COURSE SECTION   LESSON   SCALE 1=1

4. Create an Arc using the **Start, Center, Angle** option by doing the following:

- From the Menu Bar select **Draw,** then **Arc**, and lastly **Start, Center, Angle** as shown below.

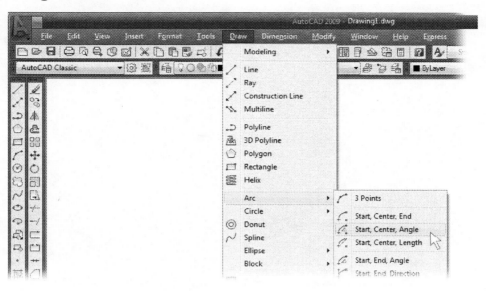

- Pick about Point **P7**, then **P8** as shown below.

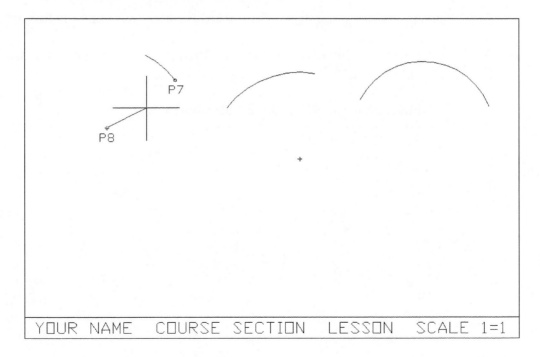

- Move the cursor around and observe that the angle of the dragging line (measured from the +X axis) is the same as the swept angle of the Arc.

210

- Specify included angle of *75*, then, *[ENTER]*. {The 75 degree **Arc** will appear similar to the one shown below.}

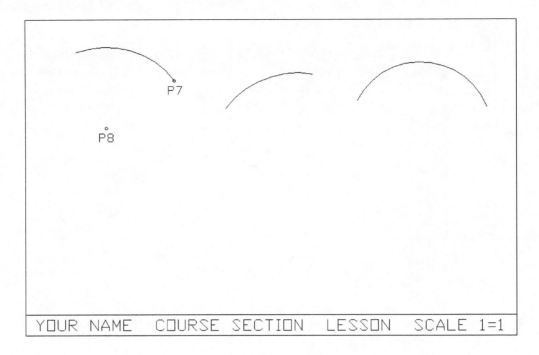

YOUR NAME   COURSE SECTION   LESSON   SCALE 1=1

5. Create an **Arc** using the **Start, End, Radius** option by doing the following:

- From the Menu Bar select **Draw** then **Arc**. Select the **Start, End, Radius** option.

- Pick about Point **P9**, then **P10** as shown below.

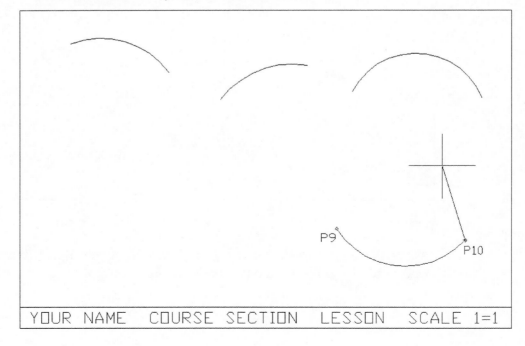

YOUR NAME   COURSE SECTION   LESSON   SCALE 1=1

Note: As you move the cursor, notice that the larger the radius, the flatter the arc.

- Specify radius of **Arc** as *1.5* then *[ENTER]*. {**Arc** is created similar to the one shown below.}

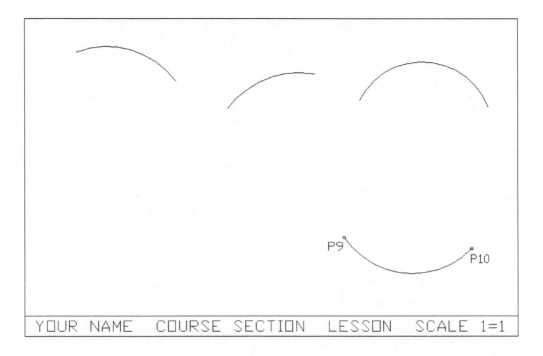

```
YOUR NAME   COURSE SECTION   LESSON   SCALE 1=1
```

6. Create an Arc using the **Start, End, Direction** option by doing the following:

- From the Menu Bar select **Draw,** then **Arc**. Select the **Start, End, Direction** option.

212

- Pick about Point **P11**, then **P12** and define your direction (of the arc) by picking about **P13** as shown below.

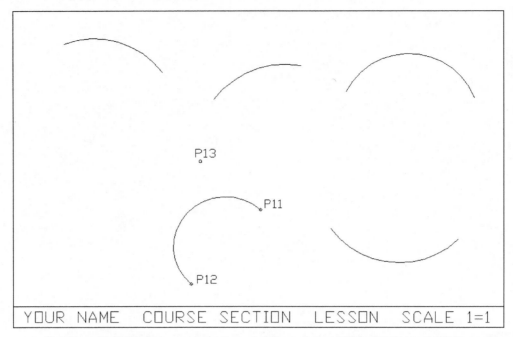

YOUR NAME   COURSE SECTION   LESSON   SCALE 1=1

- Create a **3 Point Arc** again by picking about **P14**, **P15**, and **P16** as shown below.

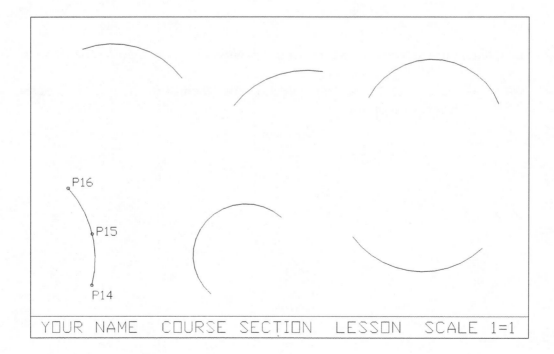

YOUR NAME   COURSE SECTION   LESSON   SCALE 1=1

- From the **Draw** Menu Bar, select **Arc** and then select **Continue**. Pick near **P17**.

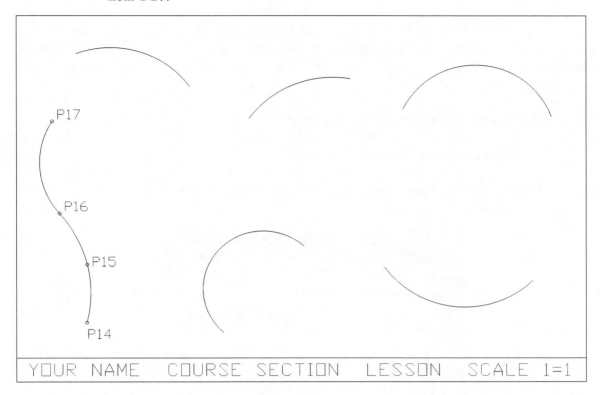

Note: Notice that the **Arc Continue** option picks up where the last arc left off, and that it is tangential to the last arc.

- Press the Enter key twice. {**Arc continue** option is activated.}

- Construct a few more arcs at user specified locations using the **Arc Continue** option. Use the Enter key to do this.

- Set **Blipmode** to *Off* and then **Regen**.

- When finished, **Erase** all geometry from the screen.

■ Point

A **Point** is just another entity such as a **Line**, **Circle**, **Arc**, **etc**., except that it is not generally used as a part of your geometry, but rather as a tool to allow for locating a specific position. With the help of **Osnap's Node** option, **Points** can be located with precision.

1. Make sure that **Grid** and **Snap** are set to *Off*.

2. Set a **Point Style** by doing the following:

   - From the Menu Bar, select **Format** and then select **Point Style...** as shown below.

   - In the **Point Style** dialog box select the **Point Type** as shown below. Set **Point Size** to *0.10*, and toggle "**Set Size in Absolute Units**" to **On**.

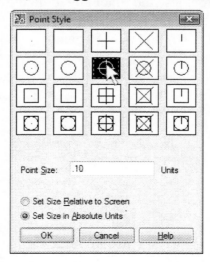

   - Click **OK**.

3. Create a Point by doing the following.

- In the **Draw** toolbar, click on the **Point** button.

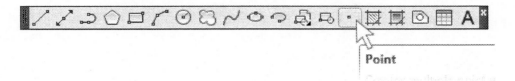

Point

- Create 3 **Points** at user-specified locations as shown below.

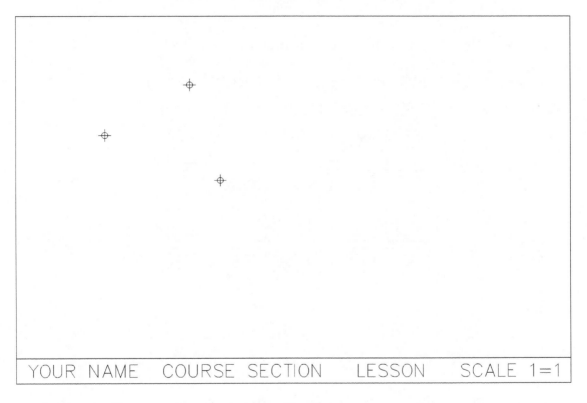

YOUR NAME   COURSE SECTION   LESSON   SCALE 1=1

4. Create an Object using the position of existing **Points** by doing the following:

- From the **Status line**, right-click on **OSnap**, select **Settings**, and set the **Object Snap Modes** to **Node** only.

- Select **OK**.

- Toggle **OSnap** to **On**.

216

- Use the **Line** Command to **OSnap** onto the three **Nodes** to create a triangle as shown below.

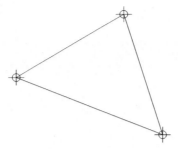

5. Change **Point Style** by doing the following:

- From the Menu Bar, select **Format** and **Point Style** again.

- In the **Point Style** dialog box, select the 2nd Icon as shown below.

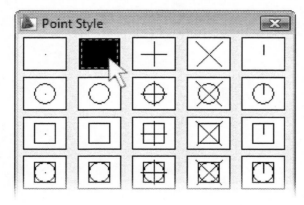

- Click **OK**. {**Points** are no longer visible because of the **Point Style** chosen.}

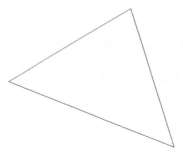

- When finished, **Erase** all geometry from the screen.

Polyline

This section is intended only to serve as an introduction to the **Polyline** Command. Although at first the **Polyline** may appear to be the same as the **Line** Command, it has certain advantages. This Command is covered in great detail in Volume 2 of the Academic Solution Textbook Series for AutoCAD.

1. Set **OSnap** to *Off*.

2. Create **Polyline** by doing the following:

    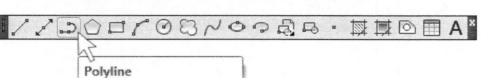

    - In the **Draw** toolbar, click on the **Polyline** button.

    - Pick 7 user-specified points to create a **Polyline** similar to the one shown below, then *[ENTER]*.

    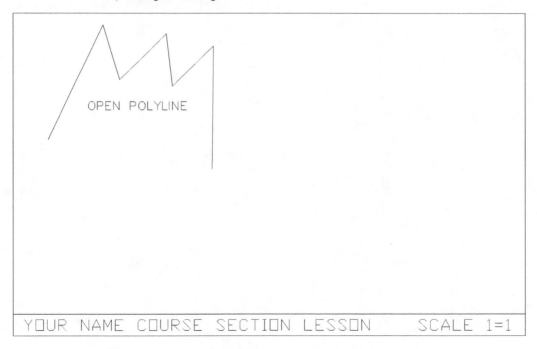

    - Type *PL* (for **Polyline**), then *[ENTER]*.

218

- Pick 7 user-specified points to create a second **Polyline** similar to the one shown below in the lower left corner.

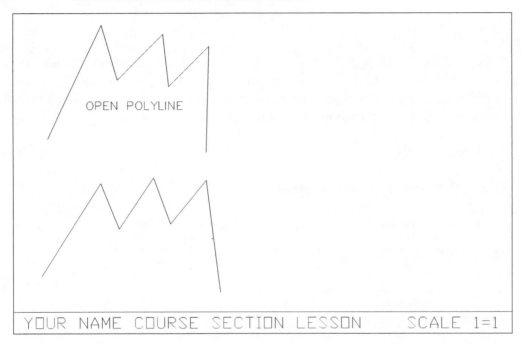

- Type *C* (for **Close**), then *[ENTER]*. {The second **Polyline** will **Close** as shown below.}

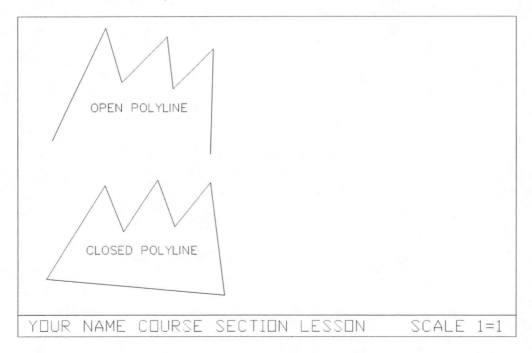

3. Continue to the next section without **Erasing** the screen.

__Spline__

This section, like the last, is intended only to serve as an introduction to the **Spline** Command; **Spline** will be covered extensively in Volume II.

1. Create a **Spline** by doing the following:

   - In the **Draw** toolbar, select the **Spline** button.

   Spline
   Creates a smooth curve that passes through

   - Select 5 User Specified points to create an Object similar to the one shown below in the upper right corner, then *[ENTER]* three times to accept the default **Start** and **End Tangent** directions.

   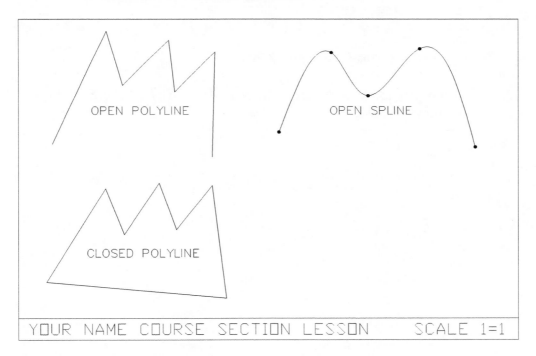

   - Type *SPL* (for **Spline**), then *[ENTER]*.

- Select 7 user-specified points to create the **Spline** similar to the one shown below in the lower right corner.

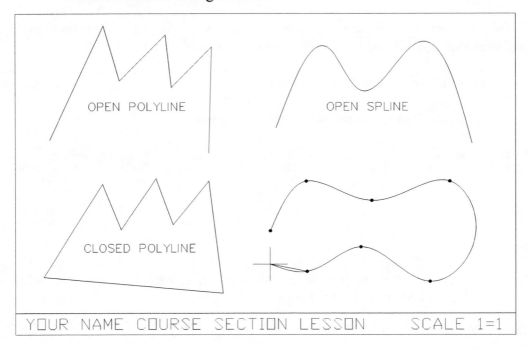

- Type *C* (for **Close**), then *[ENTER]*.

- When prompted to **Specify Tangent**, *[ENTER]*.   {The **Spline** will close as shown below.}

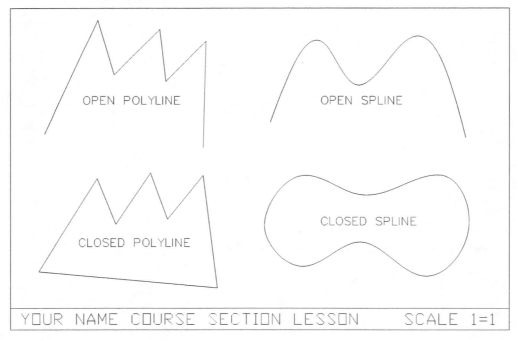

- When finished, **Erase** all geometry from the screen.

Construction Line

A **Construction Line** is simply a line that extends indefinitely in both directions. This type of a line generally serves as an aid to geometric construction; however, you can use the **Trim** or the **Break** Command (introduced in later chapters) to convert a **Construction line** to a regular **Line** that is a part of the actual geometry.

1. Create a **Construction Line** by doing the following:

   - In the **Draw** toolbar, click on the **Construction Line** button.

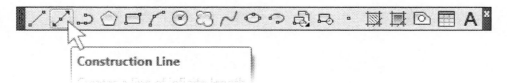

Construction Line

   - Select the two user-specified points **P1** and **P2**. {A **Construction Line** will be created and you will remain in the Command as shown below.}

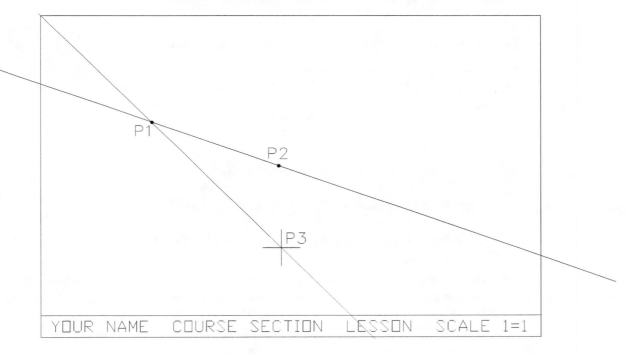

YOUR NAME   COURSE SECTION   LESSON   SCALE 1=1

   - Select a third user-specified point **P3** to create a second **Construction Line**. Then *[ENTER]*.

2. When finished, **Erase** the screen.

<u>Revcloud</u>

At times you'll need to markup Drawings for revisions. AutoCAD has a special Command named **Revcloud**, which makes this process quick and easy.

1. **Revcloud** your Drawing by doing the following:

    - Create a **Circle**, **Rectangle**, and an **Arc** at a User Specified location as shown below.

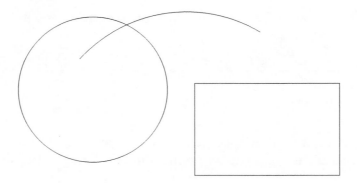

    - In the **Draw** toolbar, click on the **Revcloud** button.

    - Type *A* (for **Arc length**), then *[ENTER]*.

    - Type *0.25* for **minimum Arc length**, then *[ENTER]*.

    - Type *0.5* for **maximum Arc length**, then *[ENTER]*.

    - Pick a user-specified **Start point** near the **Arc**, then move the pointing device around the **Arc** where you want the **Revcloud** to appear. { As you move the pointing device around the **Arc,** a Revision Cloud will be created. Cloud will close automatically as you go back to the start point.}

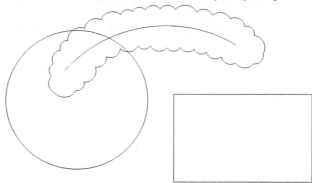

- Select on the **Revcloud** Tool again.

- Type *O* (for **Object**), then *[ENTER]*.

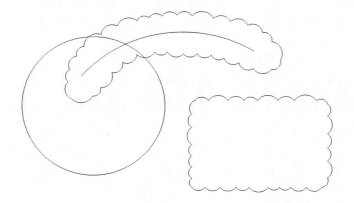

- Select the **Rectangle**. {**Rectangle** converts to **Revcloud**.}

- When the system prompt reads **Reverse Direction**, type *N,* then *[ENTER]*.

Note: As demonstrated above, closed **Polylines** can be converted to **Revclouds**.

2. **Exit** AutoCAD without saving your Drawing.

Aliases and Hot Keys

ARC ....A

BLIP MODE .... BLIPMODE

CIRCLE C

CONSTRUCTION LINE..XLINE or XL

ELLIPSE..EL

POINT.. PO

POLYGON ....POL

POLYLINE... PLINE or PL

RECTANGLE...REC

REGENERATE DRAWING ....REGEN or RE

SPLINE..SPL

Assignment 5

Objective:

1. To practice all previously learned Commands.
2. To practice **Circle**, **Rectangle**, **Polygon**, **Ellipse**, and **Arc** Commands.

Instructions:

1. Launch AutoCAD and use your **My Template** to begin a **New** Drawing.
2. **Save As** the Drawing file to your folder. Name it **"ASSIGN05_ _ _.dwg"** where the 3 blanks are your initials.
3. Make sure that **Grid**, **Snap**, **Ortho,** and **Dyn** are set to *Off*.
4. Draw the four Circles below using the given information:

   - **Center** of **C1** is located at *1.00, 4.00* with **R=0.54** .
   - **Center** of **C2** is located at *1.85,5.12* with **R=0.77** .
   - **C3** is drawn **Tangent** to **C1** and **C2** with **R=0.70** .
   - **C4** passed through the **Centers** of **C1**, **C2**, and **C3** .

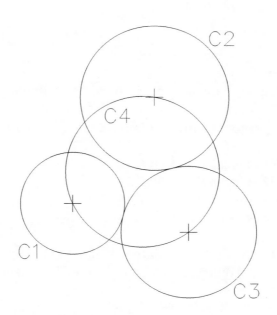

5. Construct the shapes below using the following information:

- The Horizontally positioned **Rectangle** goes through **P1** and **P2** where **P1** is located at *0.70,1.20* and **P2** is located at *2.79,2.08*.

- **Circle C1** goes through **P1** and **P2**.

- **Ellipse El1** is horizontally positioned and is **Inscribed** by the **Rectangle**.

- The **Octagon** (8 sided **Polygon**) has the same center as **C1** and the 12 o'clock corner is located at the midpoint of **L1**.

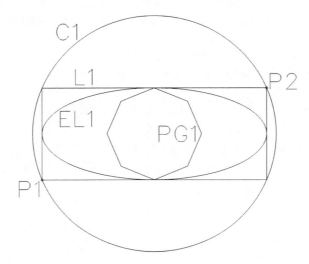

6. Construct the shapes on the next page, using the following information:

- The **Endpoints** of **Lines L1** and **L2** are given by **P1-P4**.

  P1 is located at *6.00,0.71* .
  P2 is located at *6.00,2.21* .
  P3 is located at *3.75,1.46* .
  P4 is located at *8.25,1.46* .

- **Arcs A1** and **A2** have **Centers** located along **L2** while their **Endpoints** are positioned on **P1**, **P2** and the point of **Intersection** of **L1** and **L2**.

- **Arc A3** has its **Start point** and **Endpoint** located at **P3** and **P4** and passes through the **Center** (not **Midpoint**) of **A1**.

- **Arc A4** has its **Start point** and **Endpoint** located at **P3** and **P4** and passes through the **Center** (not **Midpoint**) of **A2**.

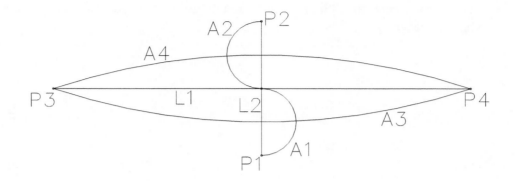

7. Construct the square **S1** (a four-sided **Polygon**) with **Center** located at **5.00,4.75** and **Circumscribed** about a circle with **0.1** radius.

8. Construct square **S2** (a four-sided **Polygon**) below **S1** such that its **Edge** is shared with the lower **Edge** of **S1**.

9. Construct square **S3** (to the right of **S1** and **S2**) such that its **Edge** is shared with the right **Edges** of **S1** and **S2** as shown below.

10. Continue this geometric progression to create square **S4, S5, S6** and **S7** as shown below.

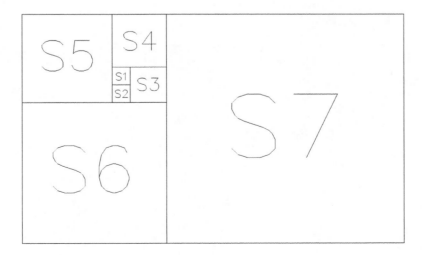

11. Start from the core, and use the **Arc 3P** option followed by the **Arc Continue** option to create the "Snail Shell" shape going through the square corners as shown below.

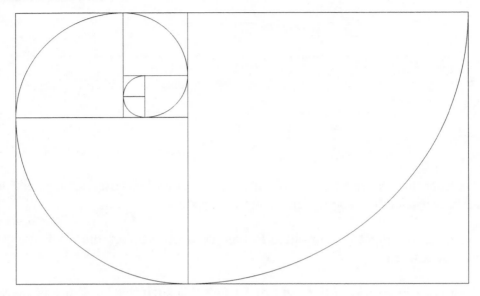

12. Check your Drawing to match that of the next page.

13. Place lesson number and **Save** the Drawing.

14. Preview and Plot Drawing using the following settings:

- Paper size: Letter (8.50x11.00 **inches**)
- Plot area: Limits
- Plot offset: Centered
- Plot scale: 1=1

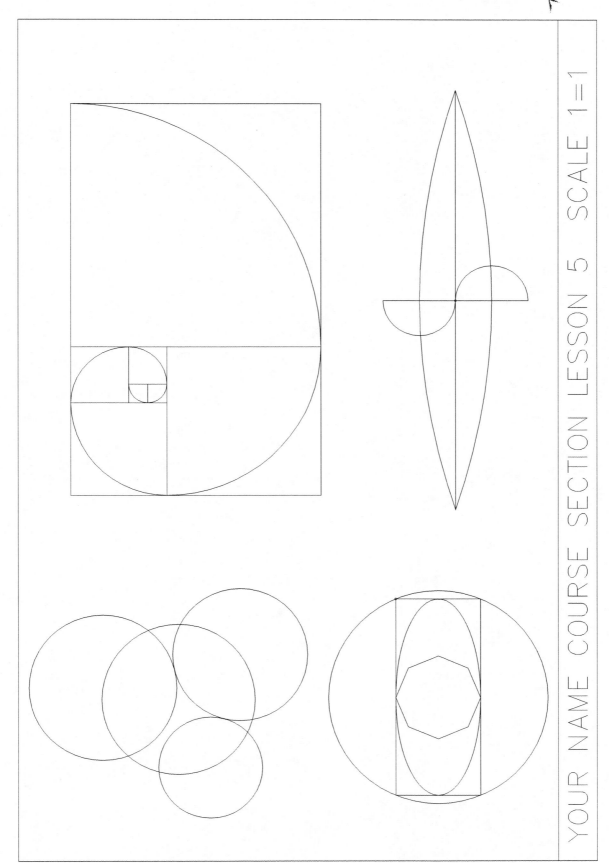

YOUR NAME COURSE SECTION LESSON 5 SCALE 1=1

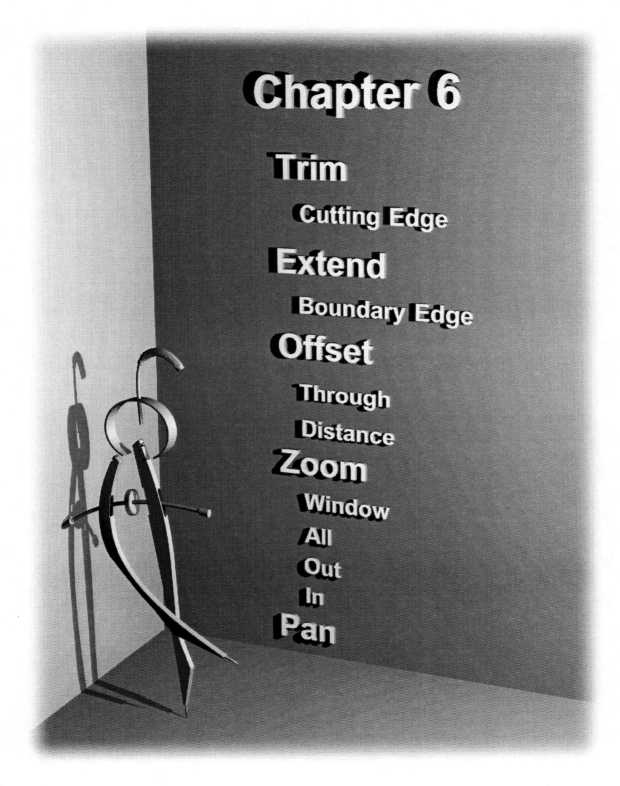

Chapter 6

Trim
Cutting Edge
Extend
Boundary Edge
Offset
Through
Distance
Zoom
Window
All
Out
In
Pan

232

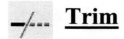 ## Trim

1. Launch AutoCAD and use your **My Template** to begin a new Drawing.

2. From the **Status Bar,** make sure that **Snap**, **Grid**, **Ortho**, **Polar**, **OSnap**, **OTrack, Ducs** and **Dyn** are set to *Off.*

3. **Trim** entities to an edge by doing the following:

   - Create Lines **L1 – L4** and Arc **A1** at user-specified locations as shown below.

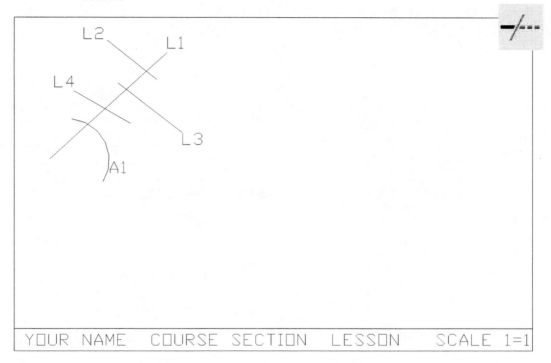

   - In the **Modify** toolbar, click on the **Trim** button.

   - As you are prompted to select Objects for cutting edges, Pick Line **L1,** then *[ENTER].*

   - As you are prompted for Object to trim, Pick the shorter segments of Lines **L2, L3, L4** and Arc **A1,** then *[ENTER].* {Objects are trimmed to that shown on the next page.}

234

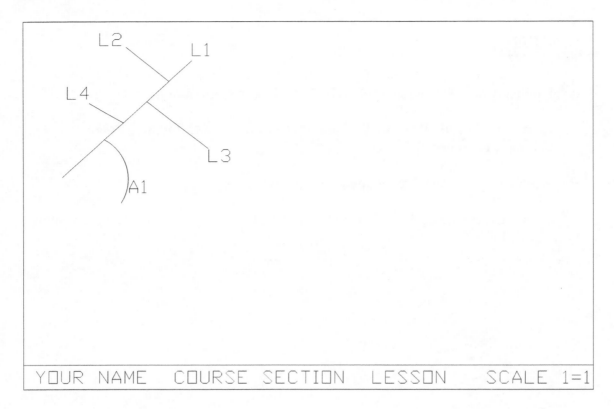

YOUR NAME   COURSE SECTION   LESSON   SCALE 1=1

- Draw Line **L5** and Circle **C1** at a User Specified location.

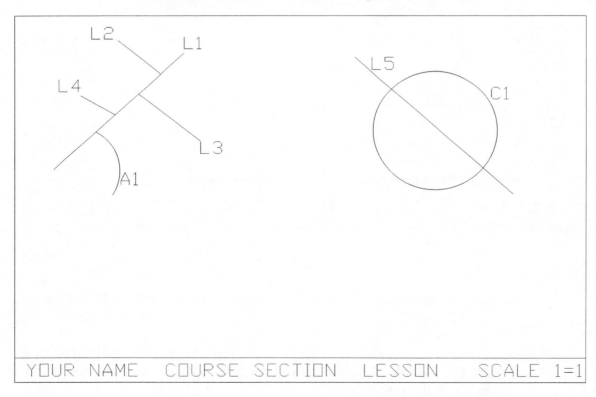

YOUR NAME   COURSE SECTION   LESSON   SCALE 1=1

- Select the **Trim** Tool.

- Pick Circle **C1** as the first Object, then *[ENTER]*.

- Pick the middle portion of Line **L5** as the Object to trim, then *[ENTER]*.

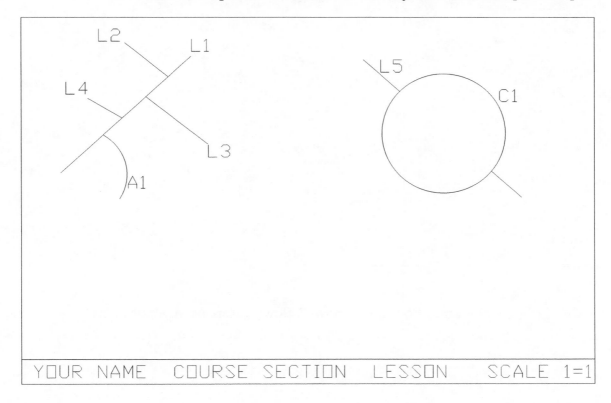

- Type *U* to **Undo** the last Command, then *[ENTER]*.

- Select **Trim** again.

- Pick Line **L5** as the cutting edge, then *[ENTER]*.

- Pick the lower half of Circle **C1,** then *[ENTER]*.

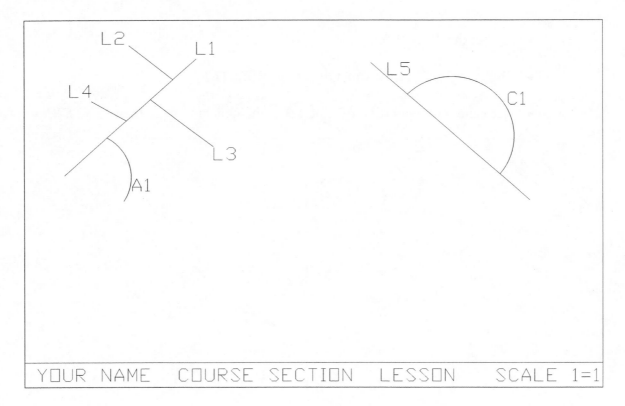

- Draw Lines **L6** – **L9** as shown below at user-specified locations.

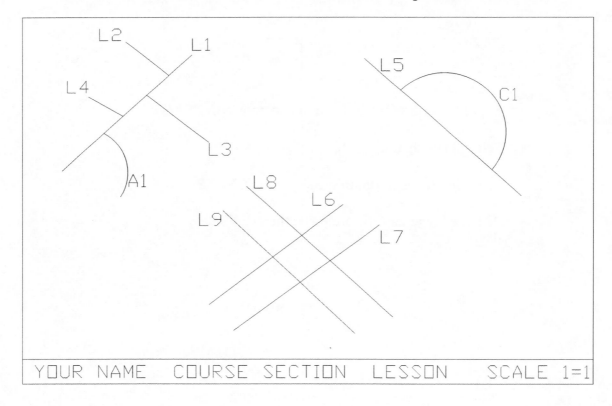

- Command: type **Try** (for **Trim**) and then *[Enter]*.

- Use the **Crossing** selection method (right to left) to Pick Lines **L6 – L9,** then *[ENTER]*.

- Pick the segments necessary to modify the shape as shown, then *[ENTER]*.

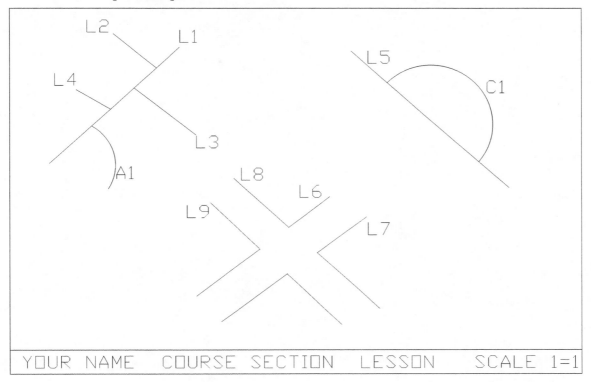

- When finished, **Erase** all geometry.

Note: When using the **Trim/Extend** Command, you can use the **Fence** and **Crossing** selection options to select your Objects. This is particularly useful when many Objects are to be trimmed or extended.

238

 Extend

1. **Extend** entities to a boundary edge by doing the following:

   - Draw Lines **L1 – L4** and Arc **A1** at user-specified locations.

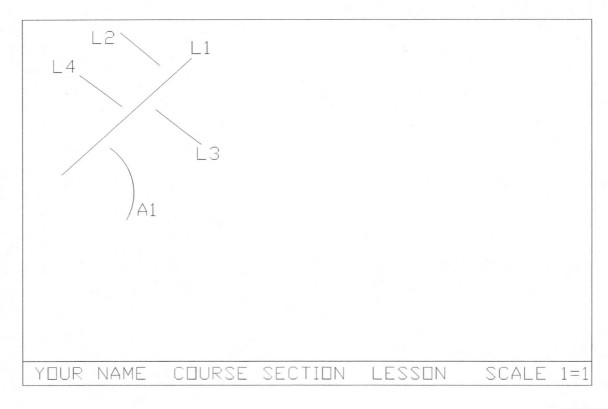

   - In the **Modify** toolbar, click on the **Extend** button.

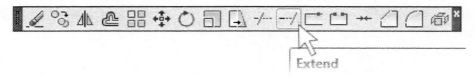

   - As you are prompted for boundary edges, Pick Line **L1,** then **ENTER.**

   - As you are prompted for Objects to extend, Pick Lines **L2 – L4** and Arc **A1** each at the end closer to **L1,** then **[ENTER].** {All Objects are extended to L1.}

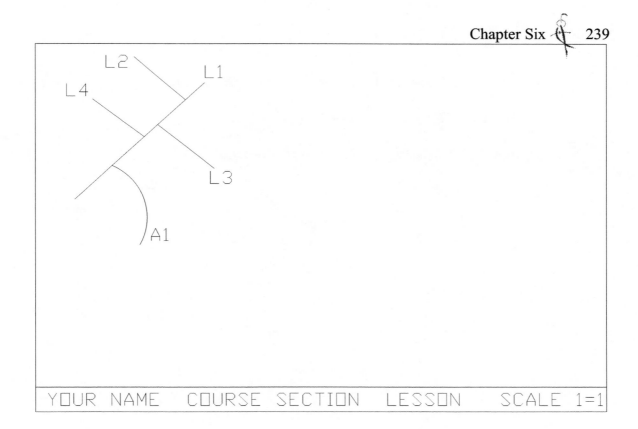

YOUR NAME   COURSE SECTION   LESSON   SCALE 1=1

- Create Line **L5** and Circle **C1** at a user-specified location.

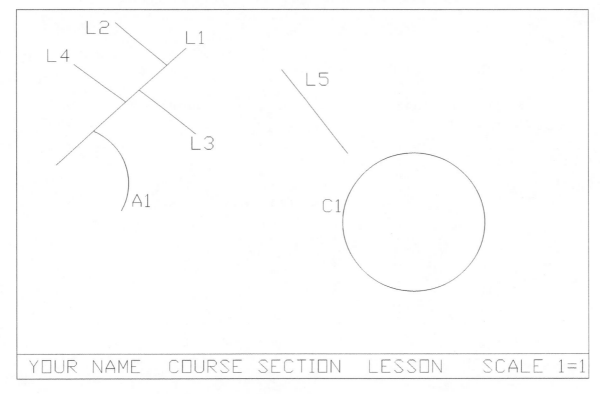

YOUR NAME   COURSE SECTION   LESSON   SCALE 1=1

240

- Command: Type **Ex** (for **Extend**) and then *[ENTER]*.

- Pick Circle **C1,** then *[ENTER]*.

- Pick Line **L5** near Circle **C1,** then *[ENTER]*.

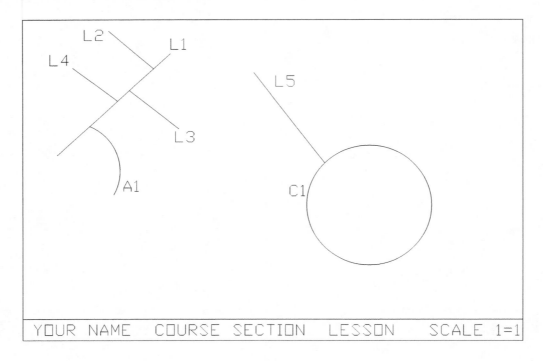

- When finished, **Erase** the geometry.

- Draw the **Lines** as shown below keeping the geometry as similar as possible.

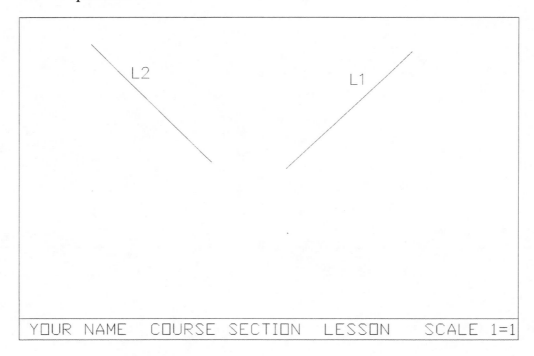

2. **Extend** Objects to one another by doing the following:

- Create a **Line L3** as shown below at a user-specified location.   Keep geometry similar.

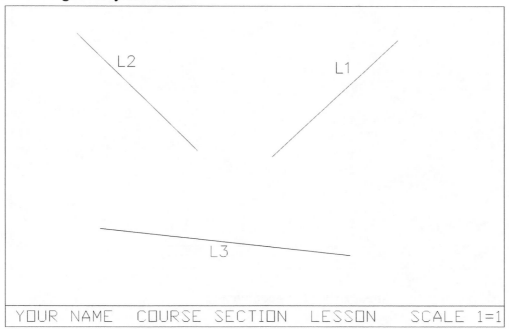

- Select the **Extend** Tool.

- Pick Line **L3**, then *[ENTER]*.

- Pick Lines **L1** and **L2** each near their lower end, then *[ENTER]*.

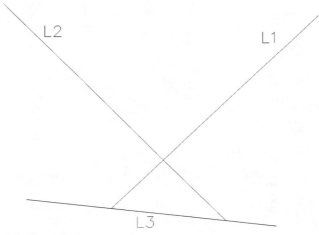

- **Erase** Line **L3**.

242

- **Trim L1** and **L2** as shown below.

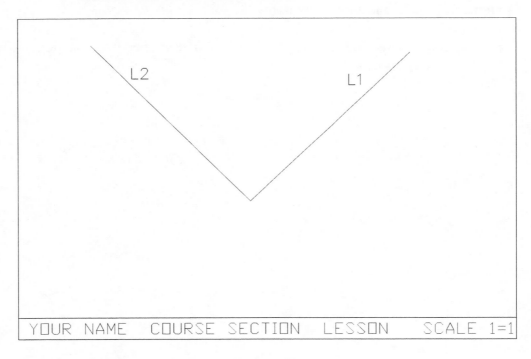

YOUR NAME   COURSE SECTION   LESSON   SCALE 1=1

- When finished, **Erase** the geometry.

Note: In chapter 8 you will be exposed to more efficient techniques for **Trimming** and **Extending** Objects to one another.

Offset

1. **Offset** entities by doing the following:

   - Create Line **L1**, Circle **C1**, and Arc **A1** at user-specified locations.

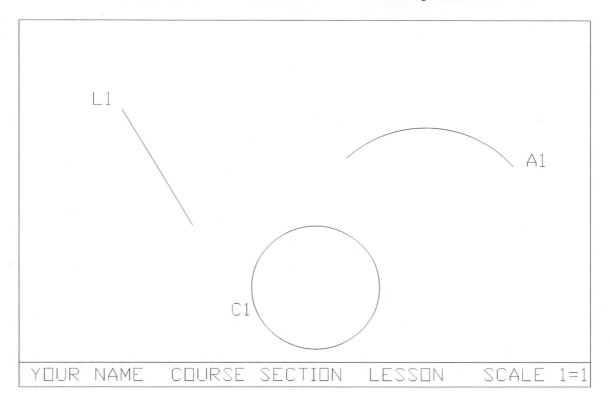

   - In the **Modify** toolbar, click on the **Offset** button.

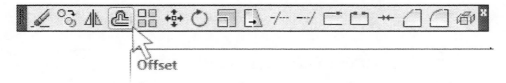

   - Enter **Offset Distance** of *0.37* then *[ENTER]*.

   - Pick Line **L1** then Click above Line **L1**.

   - Pick Line **L1** again, then Click below Line **L1**.

   - Pick Arc **A1**, then Click above Arc **A1**.

- Pick Arc **A1** again, then Click below Arc **A1**.

- Pick Circle **C1**, then Click outside Circle **C1**.

- Pick Circle **C1** again, then Click inside Circle **C1**.

- *[ENTER]*. {**Offset** is cancelled.}

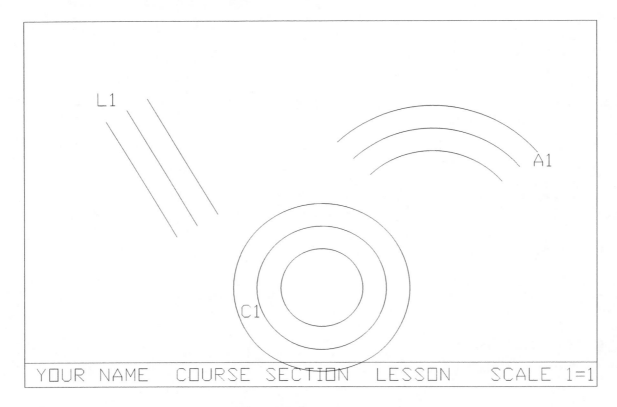

YOUR NAME   COURSE SECTION   LESSON   SCALE 1=1

- Command: *U,* then *[ENTER]*. {All offset Objects are removed.}

2. **Offset Through** Points by doing the following:

- Select the **Offset** Tool.

- Type *T* (for **Through),** then *[ENTER]*.

- Pick Line **L1**.

- **OSnap** to the **Center** Point of Circle **C1**.

- Pick Arc **A1**.

- **OSnap** to the **Midpoint** of Line **L1**.

- Pick Circle **C1**.

- **OSnap** to the End Point of Line **L1** as shown.

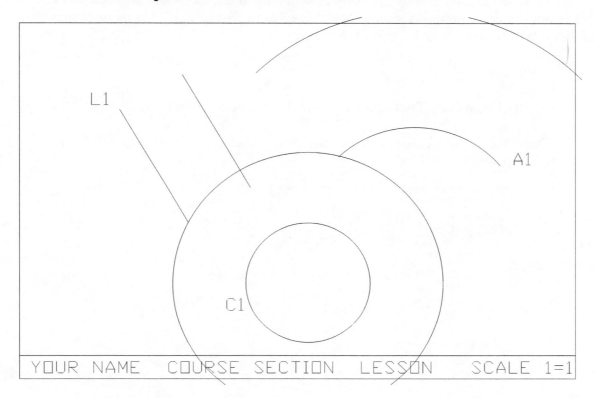

- *[ENTER]* to exit the **Offset** Command.

- When finished, **Erase** the screen.

246

 # Zoom

In the following exercise, it is assumed that you have a mouse wheel; however, if that is not the case, you may simply select the **Zoom** and/or **Pan** buttons to accomplish the same task in that particular part of the exercise.

1. Turn **Grid On**.

2. Right-click on any **Tool** to load and dock the **Zoom** toolbar.

3. Draw the entities below at about the given locations. Exact size and location is user-specified.

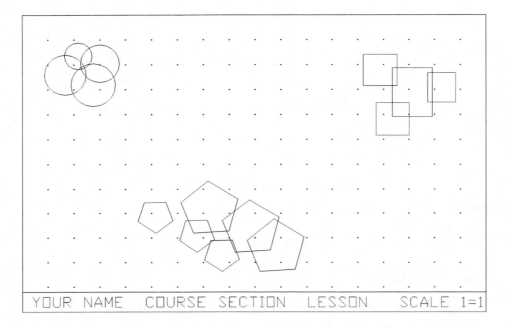

4. **Zoom Window** on the circles by doing the following:

   - In the **Zoom** toolbar, click on the **Zoom Window** button.

Note: When Zooming In/Out at times you will notice that curved entities appear to be jagged. At any point in time, you may fix this by entering **Regen** and then **[ENTER]** at the **Command Line**.

- Pick your first and then the opposite corner of the window to create the **Zoom** Window as shown below. {You **Zoom** into the selected area.}

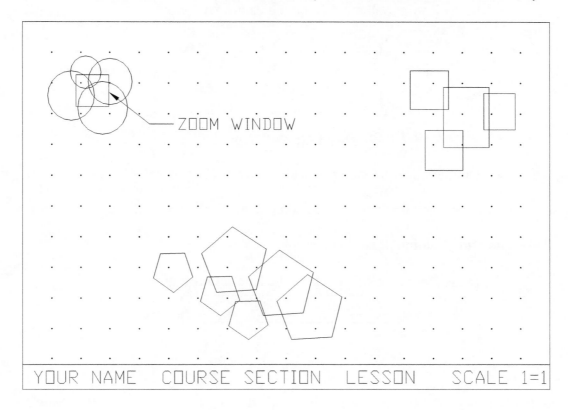

YOUR NAME   COURSE SECTION   LESSON   SCALE 1=1

5. Create Circles **C1** and **C2** by doing the following:

- Set **Grid** to *0.1* and make sure that **adaptive Grid** option is set to **No.**

- Set **Snap** to *0.05*.

- Use the mouse to create the **.05** Radius Circles **C1** and **C2** at any user-specified locations.

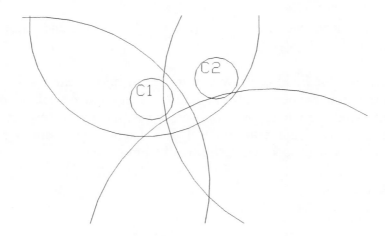

248

6. **Zoom All** by doing the following:

- In the **Zoom** toolbar, click on the **Zoom All** button.

- Type *U* (to **Undo** the **Zoom** Command), then *[ENTER]*.

- Double-click the mouse wheel. {Screen **Zooms All**.}

Note: Here it is assumed that your mouse wheel double-click is configured to **Zoom All**.

7. **Zoom Out** by doing the following:

- In the **Zoom** toolbar, click on the **Zoom Out** button.

Note: If you have a mouse wheel, you can scroll "down" on the wheel and the Drawing will **Zoom** out.}

8. **Zoom In** by doing the following:

- In the **Zoom** toolbar, click on the **Zoom In** button.

Note: If you have a mouse wheel, you can scroll up on the wheel and you will **Zoom** in to the Drawing area.}

Note: The **Zoom In/Out** buttons allow you to **Zoom** in/out using a zoom factor of 2. However, using the mouse wheel is more continuous and convenient. Especially that as you **Zoom** in/out using the wheel, the **Zooming** takes place with respect to the cursor's current position. So you have exact control on what you are zooming into. Lastly, double clicking on the wheel acts as the **Zoom All** Command.

- **Zoom All.**

Pan

1. **Pan** by doing the following:

   - In the **Standard** toolbar, click on the **Pan Real-time** button.

   - As the cursor switches to the hand symbol, Click and hold the left mouse button to **Pan**.

   - Move the mouse to **Pan** in any direction, then release the mouse button.

   - Right-click in the Drawing are and use the **Shortcut Menu** to **Exit**. {You exit the **Pan** Command.}

   - Click and hold the mouse wheel to **Pan**. {Pan icon appears.}

   - Move the mouse and when finished panning, release the mouse wheel.

Note: The **Pan** button is most useful when you are zoomed into one area and need to pan over to another area without zooming out. Also note that the **Zoom** and **Pan** functions are **Transparent** Commands, meaning that you can use them while other Commands are running.

2. Use **Pan** while constructing geometry by doing the following:

   - Select the **Zoom Window** tool to **Zoom** into the Rectangles.

   - Start a **Line** at a user-specified location..

   - While in the **Line** Command, use the **Pan** Tool to pan over to the Pentagons and if still in **Pan**, then **Exit Pan**. {AutoCAD remains in the Line Command.}

   - Specify the second point of the Line at a user-specified Location and then *[ENTER]*.

   - When finished, **Close** the Drawing without Saving changes to the Drawing.

Practical Example

As a general rule, when drawing in AutoCAD, it is standard practice to model geometry in actual size. It is however important to determine a scale factor when leaving the AutoCAD domain for an external device such as a Plotter, a CNC cutting machine, etc. You are about to create an Architectural drawing in actual size.

1. From the Menu Bar, select **File**, then **New** and use the **acad.dwt** Template file to begin a blank Drawing.

2. Set **Units** to **Architectural**, **Precision** 1/2".

3. Set **Limits** with lower left corner at *0',0'* and the upper right corner at *72', 48'*.

Note: 72' = Seventy Two Feet, 1/2" = One Half Inch, etc. If you do not enter the units (' or "), AutoCAD will assume inches.

4. Select **Zoom All** button.

5. Create a border by constructing a **Rectangle** at the boundary of your **Limits**.

6. Set **Grid** to *1'*. Make sure to set the **Grid adaptive** behavior to **No**.

7. Set **Snap** to *6"*.

8. Draw a **Line** from *0', 2'* to *72', 2'*.

    - Create **Text** using a start point having coordinates *2', 6"*, a height of *1'* and a rotation angle of *0*.

    - Enter Text as shown on the following page and *[ENTER]* twice. Your font may appear to be different that what is shown on the next page.

NAME   COURSE   SECTION   LESSON #   SCALE 1/8" = 1'

9. Create the 60' by 34' floor plan by following these instructions:

- Create the two horizontal and vertical lines so that they cross each other at coordinates 6', 6' as shown below. Keep the length of each line to about what is shown below.

NAME   COURSE   SECTION   LESSON #   SCALE 1/8" = 1'

- **Offset** the vertical Line by *24'* and then again by *60'* as shown below.

- **Offset** the horizontal Line by *14'* and then again by *34'* as shown below.

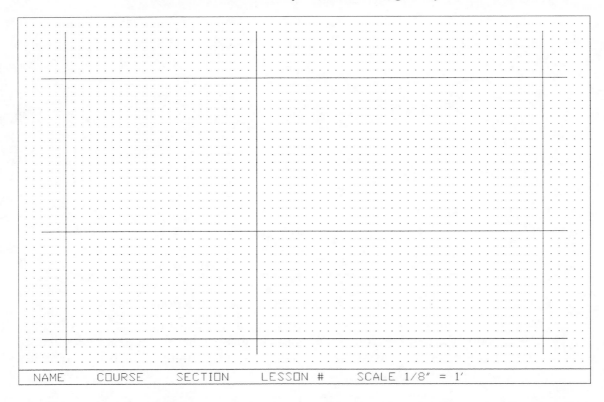

NAME   COURSE   SECTION   LESSON #   SCALE 1/8" = 1'

- Select **Trim** and use **Crossing** (right to left) to select the 6 lines, then *[ENTER]*.

- **Trim** and **Erase** as necessary to result in the diagram shown on the next page.

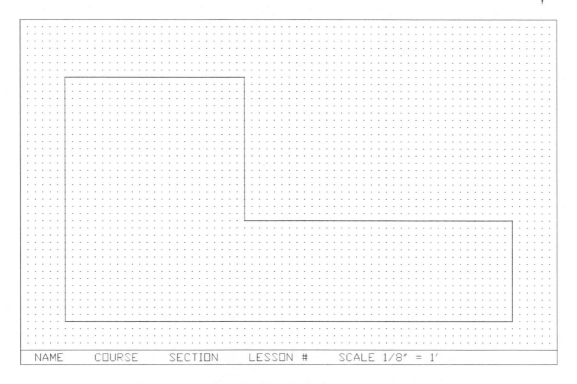

NAME   COURSE   SECTION   LESSON #   SCALE 1/8" = 1'

- To create the walls, **Offset** the lines by *6″* to the inside.

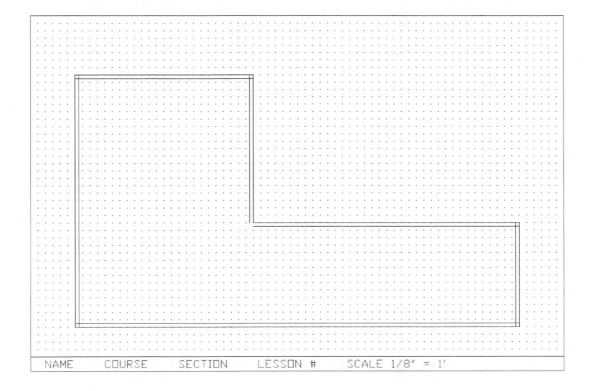

NAME   COURSE   SECTION   LESSON #   SCALE 1/8" = 1'

- Set **Snap** to *Off*.

254

- Use the **Trim** Tool (in combination with **Zoom** and **Pan**) to trim the excess geometry as shown below.

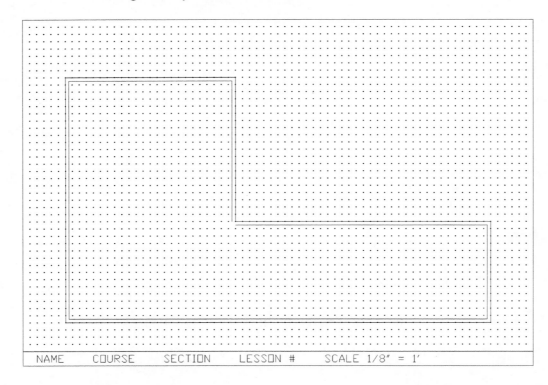

NAME   COURSE   SECTION   LESSON #   SCALE 1/8″ = 1′

- **Extend** the lines to each other so to complete the geometry of the corner as shown below. This will require constructing a line to serve as a boundary as discussed before.

- **Extend, Trim** and **Erase** as necessary to result in the geometry below.

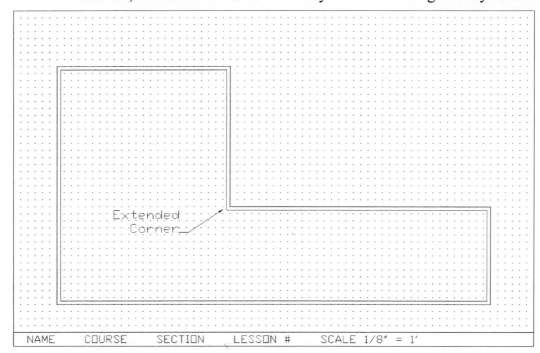

Extended Corner

NAME   COURSE   SECTION   LESSON #   SCALE 1/8″ = 1′

- Create the partition/wall as shown below using **Offset** and **Trim**.

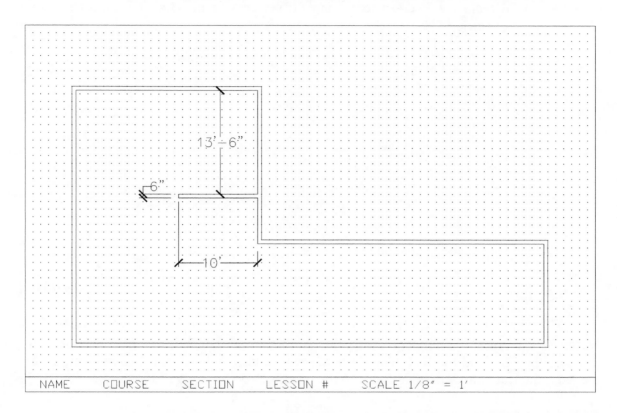

NAME   COURSE   SECTION   LESSON #   SCALE 1/8" = 1'

- **Zoom** in and then change **Snap** and **Grid** settings as needed to create the toilet as shown below. Exact size and location is your choice.

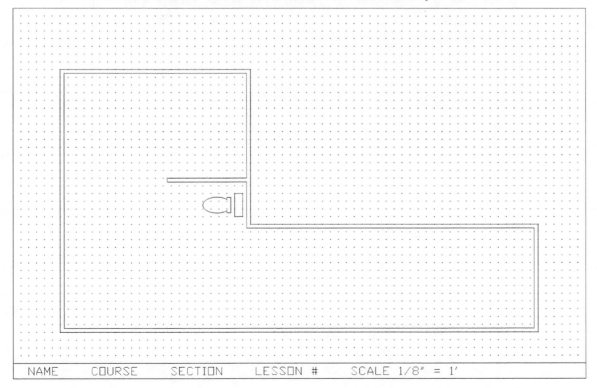

NAME   COURSE   SECTION   LESSON #   SCALE 1/8" = 1'

256

- Create the 3' doorways using **Offset** and **Trim**. Exact location is user-specified.

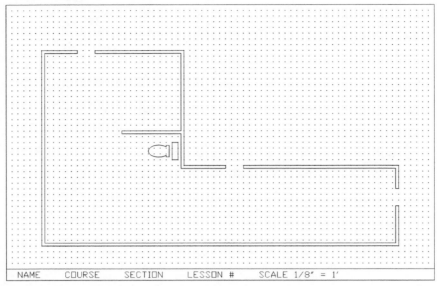

Note: When entering numbers using the Architectural Units, it is not necessary to separate the Foot and the Inch by a dash whereas a dash is required when separating the inch and the fraction of an inch. Refer to the examples below for valid notation.

5'4", 5'4, 5'4-1/4,

- Use your knowledge of **Zoom, Trim** and **Offset** Commands and the dimensions given below to construct the Kitchen counter. Do not dimension the Drawing.

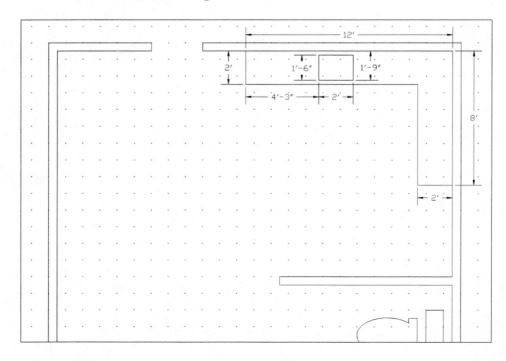

Views

In the past set of steps, you learned to **Zoom** in and out and even **Pan** as necessary to have a suitable working view. To make this process more efficient, AutoCAD also allows you to save a specific **View** so that you can restore it by name when needed.

1. Create a new **View** by doing the following:

   - Command: **View** and then *[ENTER]*

   - As the **View Manager** dialog box appears, Select **New** as shown below.

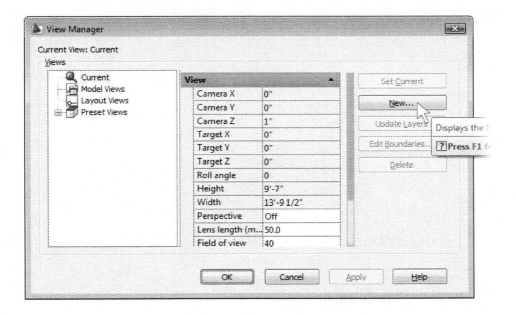

258

- As the **New View** dialog box appears, enter the View name *Kitchen*.

- In the **Boundary** area, select the **Define view window** button as shown below.

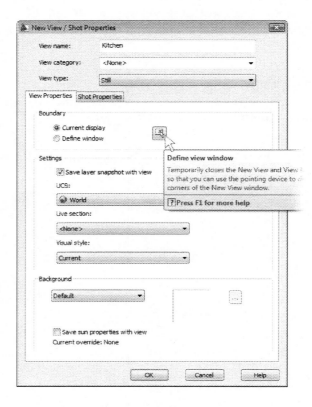

- When prompted to **Specify first corner**, **Zoom** and **Pan** as necessary and then click at about point **P1.**

- To **Specify opposite corner**, click at about point **P2**.

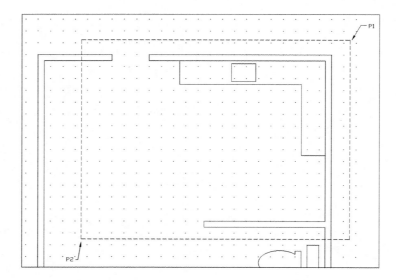

- *[ENTER]* to return to the **New View** dialog box.

- Toggle the **Save layer snapshot with view** to *Off*.

- Select **OK.**

- As the **View Manager** appears, notice that the view name **Kitchen** is listed under **Model Views**.

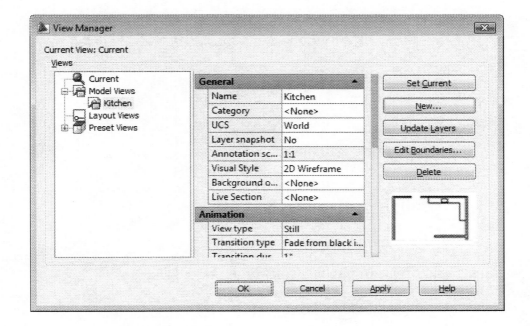

- While in the **View Manager** window, again, select the **New** button.

- As the **New View** dialog box appears, Name this view **Bathroom**.

- Select the **Define View Window** button again.

- When prompted to **Specify first corner**, **Zoom** and **Pan** as necessary and then pick at about point **P1** as shown below.

- To **Specify other corner**, pick at about point **P2.**

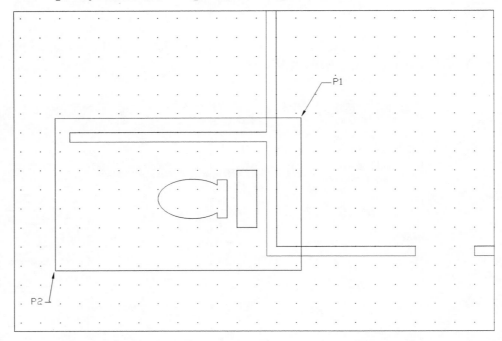

- *[ENTER]* to return to the **New View** dialog box.

- Toggle the **Save layer snapshot with view** to *Off.*

- Select **OK.**

- As the **View Manager** appears, notice that the **Bathroom** View is also listed in the **Model Views** area.

- Select the **OK** button. {**View Manager** dialog box is closed.}

- Command: **Zoom** and then *[ENTER].*

- Type **All** and then *[ENTER]*.

2. Set a **View** to **Current** by doing the following

    - Command: **View** and then *[ENTER]* { **View Manager** dialog box appears}

    - In the list of available **Model Views**, select **Kitchen** as shown below.

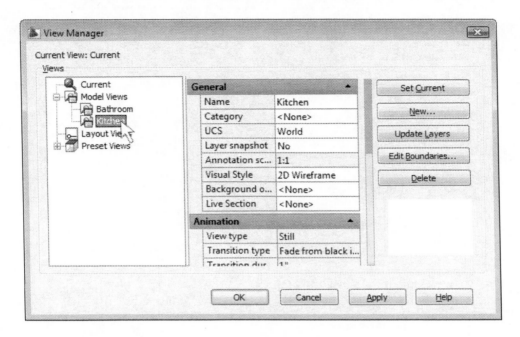

    - Select the **Set Current** button.

    - Select **OK**. {The **Kitchen** View is displayed.}

    - Command: **Zoom** and then *ENTER*

    - Type **All** and then *[ENTER]*

    - Command: **-V** and then *[ENTER]*.

    - Type **R** for **restore** and then *[ENTER]*.

    - Type in the **View** name **Bathroom** (no spaces) and then *[ENTER]*. {The **Bathroom** View is displayed.}

3. **Exit** AutoCAD without **Saving** changes to the **Drawing**.

262

Aliases

Assignment 6

Objective:

1. To practice setting **Architectural Units** and **Precision**.

2. To practice setting larger **Limits**.

3. To practice setting suitable **Grid** and **Snap**.

4. To practice the **Offset**, **Extent**, **Trim** and **Zoom** Commands.

5. To practice **Plotting** at a Scale other than 1=1.

Instructions:

1. Launch AutoCAD and enter a blank Drawing.

2. Set **Units** to **Architectural** with **Precision** set to ½".

3. Set **Limits** to **0',0'** and **72',48'**. {Make sure to enter the foot ' symbol.}

4. **Zoom All**.

5. Set Suitable **Snap** and **Grid**. Make sure that **aDaptive Grid** option is set to No.

6. **Save As** the Drawing file to your folder. Name it **"ASSIGN06_ _ _.dwg"** where the 3 blanks are your initials.

7. Use the **Rectangle** tool to create a border at the boundary of your **Limits**.

8. Create a Title box drawn at *2'* above the X axis.

9. Use **Text Height** of *1'* for the text in the Title. Start Text at **1',6"** and enter text as shown on the next page.

10. Exact location of the Plan view Drawing is user-specified but it should be constructed on suitable **Snap**.

11. Construct the Architectural Plan shown below using the given dimensions. A more detailed drawing of the Stove, Kitchen Sink, Lavatory, and the Toilet symbols is furnished below to help you with the needed dimensions of main drawing. This Drawing is not to be drawn.

12. For simplicity, all walls are 6". All doors are 30" and windows are 36". The exact locations are user-specified.

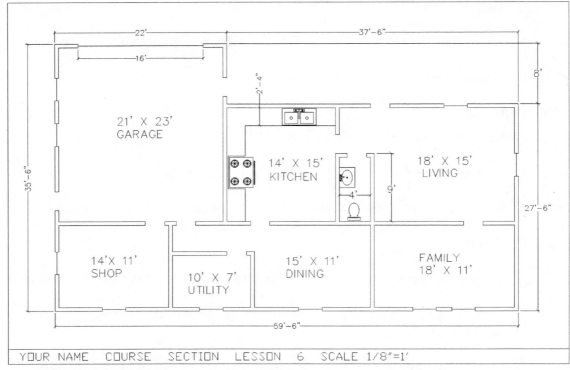

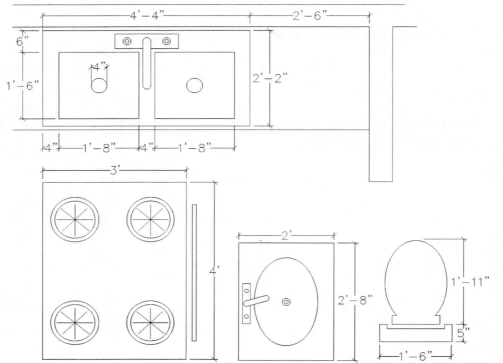

13. Your Drawing should match that on the next page.

14. **Save** the Drawing.

15. Preview and Plot the Drawing using the following settings:

- Paper size: Letter (8.50x11.00 **inches**).

- Plot area: Limits.

- Plot to be Centered.

- Plot scale: 1/8"=1' (Can be set by clicking on the **Scale** drop-down.)

16. When finished, close the **Zoom** toolbar.

17. **Exit** AutoCAD.

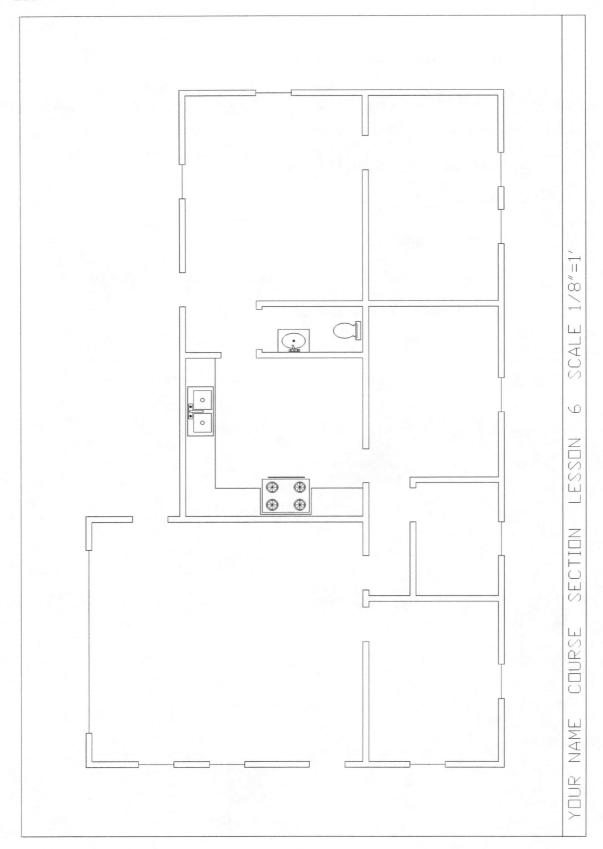

YOUR NAME COURSE SECTION LESSON 6 SCALE 1/8"=1'

Midterm Project

Objective:

1. To practice using all of the tools and Commands for Chapters 1-6.

Instructions:

1. You are about to construct the drawing as shown on page 270.

2. Launch AutoCAD to enter a blank Drawing.

   - Set **Units** to **Decimal** with **Precision** of *0.0000* (4 decimal places).
   - Set **Limits** to *0,0* and *10,7.5*
   - **Zoom All** to view the entire Limits.
   - Create a **Rectangle** at the boundary of your **Limits**.
   - Create **Layers** as necessary. You will be using **Linetypes**: **Continuous**, **Hidden** and **Center**. **Layer 0** may be used for **Continuous** lines.
   - Make sure to set a suitable **Ltscale** value.
   - Use your judgment in selecting the proper and necessary tools for accomplishing this project in an efficient, yet accurate manner.

2. **Save As** the Drawing file to your folder. Name it **"MIDPROJ_ _ _.dwg"** where the 3 blanks are your initials.

3. Although in this project, you are given the exact coordinates for your start point, in chapter 8, you will learn to **Move** objects and therefore will be able to start drawing your geometry at any random position and then simply **Move**/relocate geometry as necessary.

4. If some dimensioning appears to be missing, look for them in the other two views. After all, the three views are projections of the same 3-D Object.

5. Make frequent use of the **Offset, Trim, Extend** Tools to accomplish this project.

6. Do not **Dimension** the Drawing. You will learn to **Dimension** your geometry in chapter 11.

7. Assign **Lineweight** of *0.25mm* to **Layer 0**. All other Layers maintain the default **Lineweight**.

8. The 3-Dimensional objects shown below are to help you better visualize the orthographic projections and are not to be constructed. If you have an interest in the field of 3D Design, at the end of this book (page 551) there is more information on the path to follow.

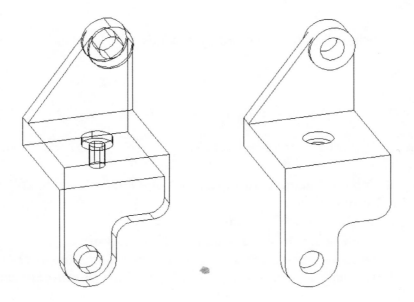

9. Title box is *0.4* units tall and Title **Text** has a **Height** of *0.2*.

10. Check your Drawing to match that on the next page and **Save**.

11. **Preview** and **Plot** using these settings:

- Paper size: Letter (8.50x11.00 **inches)**
- Plot Scale: 1=1
- Plot area: Limits
- Plot offset: Centered

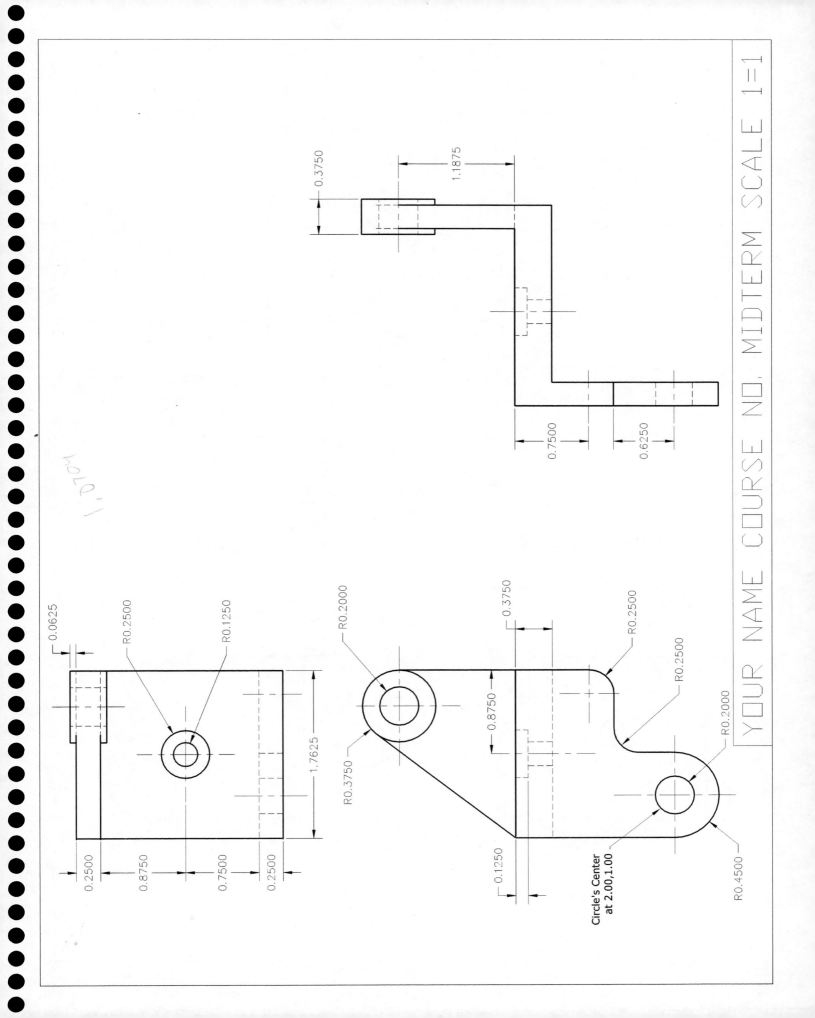

0.3750

1.1875

0.7500

0.6250

0.0625

R0.2500

R0.1250

R0.2000

0.3750

R0.2500

R0.2500

R0.2000

R0.3750

0.8750

0.1250

R0.4500

Circle's Center
at 2.00,1.00

1.7625

0.2500

0.8750

0.7500

0.2500

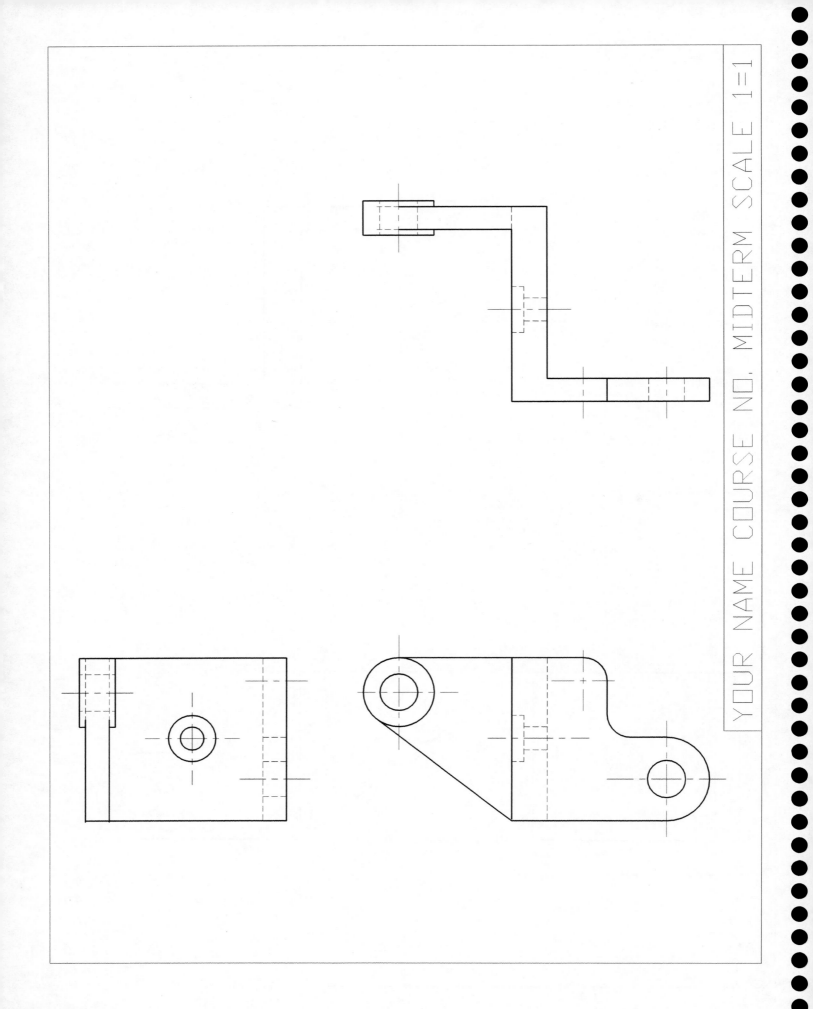

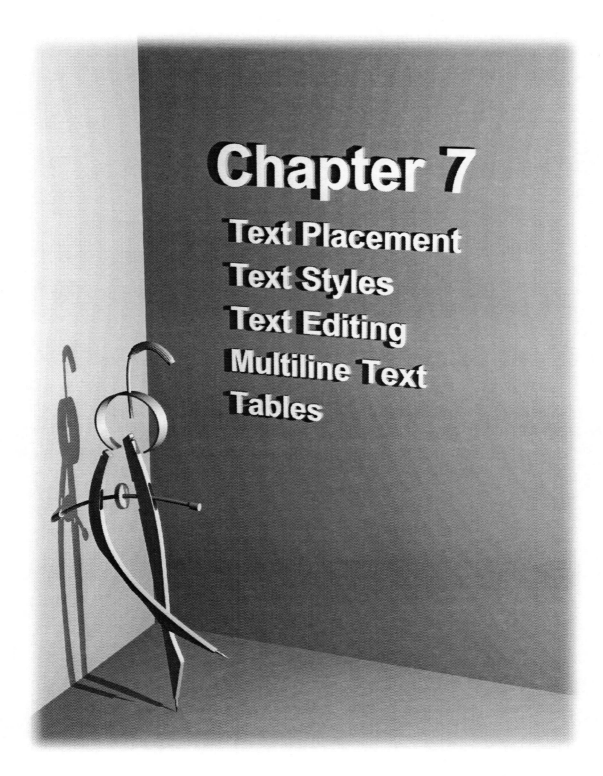

Chapter 7

Text Placement
Text Styles
Text Editing
Multiline Text
Tables

Text Placement

1. Launch AutoCAD and use your **My Template** to begin a New Drawing.

2. Set **Snap ,Grid, Ortho, Polar, OSnap, OTrack, Ducs** and **Dyn** to *Off*.

3. Set **Blipmode** to *On*. Refer to page 193 if necessary.

4. Using the **Text** Command, place Text by doing the following:

   - Press the **Caps Lock** key. {**Caps Lock** is set to **On**.}

   - Command: *Text,* then *[ENTER]*.

   - Pick start point of Text as shown by the Blip in the figure below.

   - Make sure the **Height** default value is **<0.20>,** then *[ENTER]*.

   - Make sure the Rotation Angle is *<0.0>*, then *[ENTER]*.

   - Type *"LEFT JUSTIFIED"* then *[ENTER]*. {Cursor moves to the next line.}

   - *[ENTER]* again to exit the **Text** Command. {Your **Font** may be different than that shown here. **Fonts** will be addressed later in the chapter}

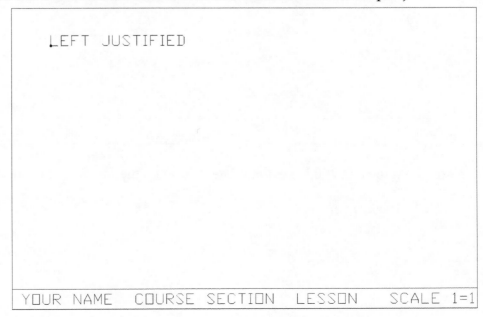

Note: **Bottom Left Justified** is the default setting in AutoCAD.

274

5. Use the **DText** Command to place **Text** by doing the following:

- Command: *DText,* then *[ENTER]*.

- Pick the start point of **Text** as shown by the dot in the figure below.

- Enter **Height** of *0.4* then *[ENTER]*.

- Enter Rotation Angle of *10* then *[ENTER]*.

- Type *"ROTATED TEXT"* then *[ENTER]* <u>twice</u> to exit the Command..

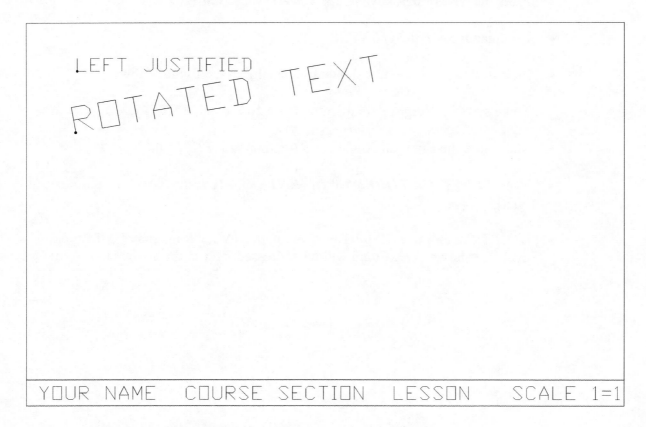

Note: In AutoCAD 2009, **Text** and **Dtext** serve as the same Command.

6. Place the **Middle Justified Text** by doing the following:

- Enter Text by using the **DText** Command.

- Type *J* (for **Justify**), then *[ENTER]*.

- Type *M* (for **Middle Justify**), then *[ENTER]*.

- Pick a start point for the **Text** MIDDLE as shown by the dot in the figure below.

- Enter **Height** of *0.4* then *[ENTER]*.

- Enter **Rotation Angle** of *0* then *[ENTER]*.

- Type *"MIDDLE",* then *[ENTER]* <u>twice</u>.

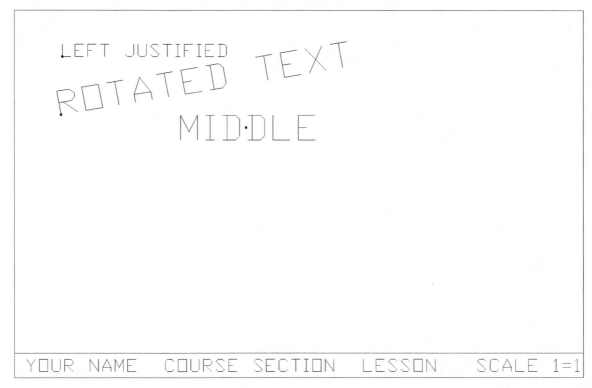

Note: Notice that the Text is justified about the geometric center.

276

7. Place the **Center Justified Text** by doing the following:

    - Command: *DText* then *[ENTER]*.

    - Type *J* (for **Justify**) and then *[ENTER]*.

    - Type **C** (for **Center**) and then *[ENTER]*.

    - Pick a start point as shown in the figure below.

    - Set **Height** of *0.4* then *[ENTER]*.

    - Set **Rotation Angle** of *0* then *[ENTER]*.

    - Type *"CENTER",* then *[ENTER]* twice.

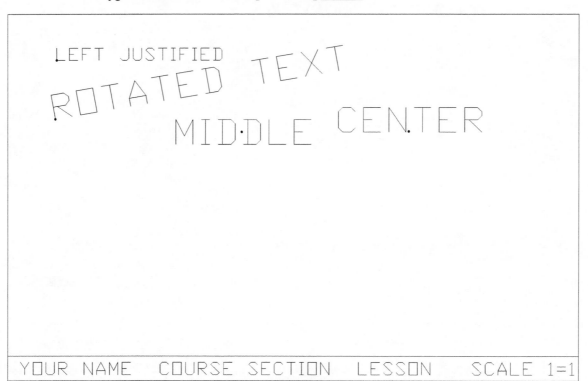

8. Place the **Right Justified Text** by doing the following:

- Command: *DTEXT* then *[ENTER]*.

- Type *J* (for **Justify**) and then *[ENTER]*.

- Type **R** (for **Right**) and then *[ENTER]*.

- Pick the starting point as shown by the dot in the figure below.

- Use **Height** of *0.4* and a **Rotation Angle** of *0*.

- Type *"RIGHT",* and then press *[ENTER]* <u>twice</u>.

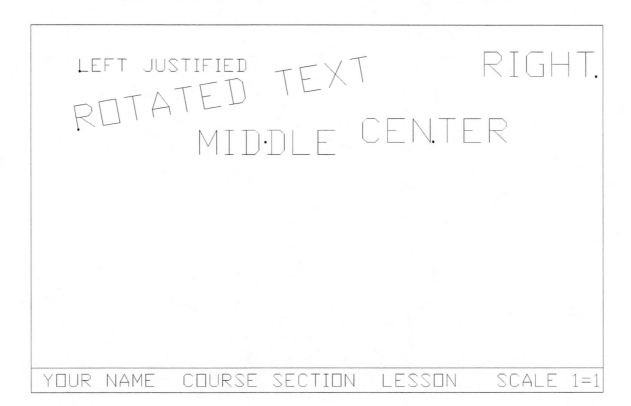

278

9. Place the **Aligned Text** by doing the following:

- Command: *DT* then *[ENTER]*.

- Type *J* (for **Justify**) and then *[ENTER]*.

- Type **A** (for **Aligned**) and then *[ENTER].*

- Follow the **Prompt** to enter the first and second points of the Text base line as shown below by Points **P1** and **P2**.

- Type *"ALIGNED TEXT"*. As you begin to enter the text characters, the text height may appear to be abnormally large. However, as you enter the characters one at a time, the text height will adjust accordingly.

- Press *[ENTER]* <u>twice</u>.

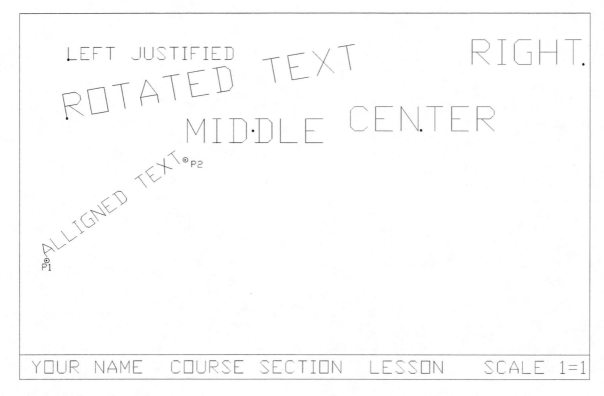

Note: In the **Aligned** option, you are not prompted for the height of the Text. The Text is automatically given a height to maintain the aspect ratio of the Text while fitting to the constraints of Points **P1** and **P2**.

10. Place the **Fit Justified Text** by doing the following:

- Command: *DT* then *[ENTER]*.

- Type *J* (for **Justify**) and then *[ENTER]*.

- Type **F** (for **Fit**) and then *[ENTER].*

- Pick two points at the Text base line as shown below by **P3** and **P4**, similar to the **Aligned Text**.

- Enter **Height** of *0.5* then *[ENTER]*.

- Type *"FIT",* then *[ENTER]* <u>twice</u>.

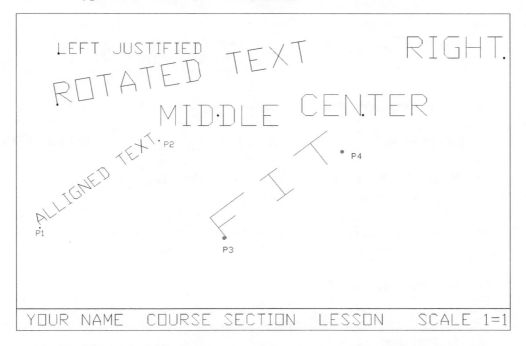

Note: Fit Justification also forces the Text to align between two points but here you have specific control of the Height.

- Erase all **Text**.

- Command: *Regen,* then *[ENTER]*. {**Blips** are removed from the screen.}

<u>Text Styles</u>

1. Create and enter a new **Text Style** by doing the following:

- Command: *Style*, then *[ENTER]*.

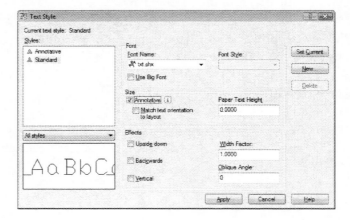

- In the **Text Style** dialog box, select the **New** button.

- In the **Style** Name text box, enter **"MYROMANCOMP"** and select **OK**.

- Select the **Font Name** drop-down, and regardless of your current **Font**, scroll and select the **romanc.shx** font.

- Make sure that in the **Size** area, **Annotative** is unchecked. You will learn about **Annotative** objects such as Text and Dimensioning in Chapter 12.

- Select **Apply** then **Close**.

- Using the default **Justification**, enter the Text with a **Height** of 0.5, **Angle** of 0° as shown below.

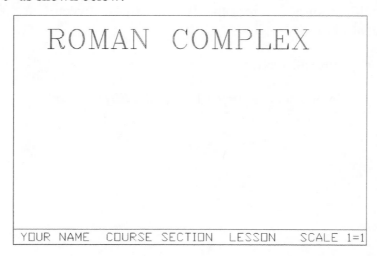

2. Create a new **Style** which is skewed "tilted" by doing the following:

- Command: *Style,* then *[ENTER]*.

- Create a **New** Style named **ROMANC-30** and click **OK**.

- Use the Current **Romanc.shx** Font.

- Enter an **Oblique Angle** of *-30°*.

- Select **Apply**, and **Close**.

- In the event that you get an alert stating the current style has been modified, select **Yes** to save changes.

- Place Text as shown below with same settings as before.

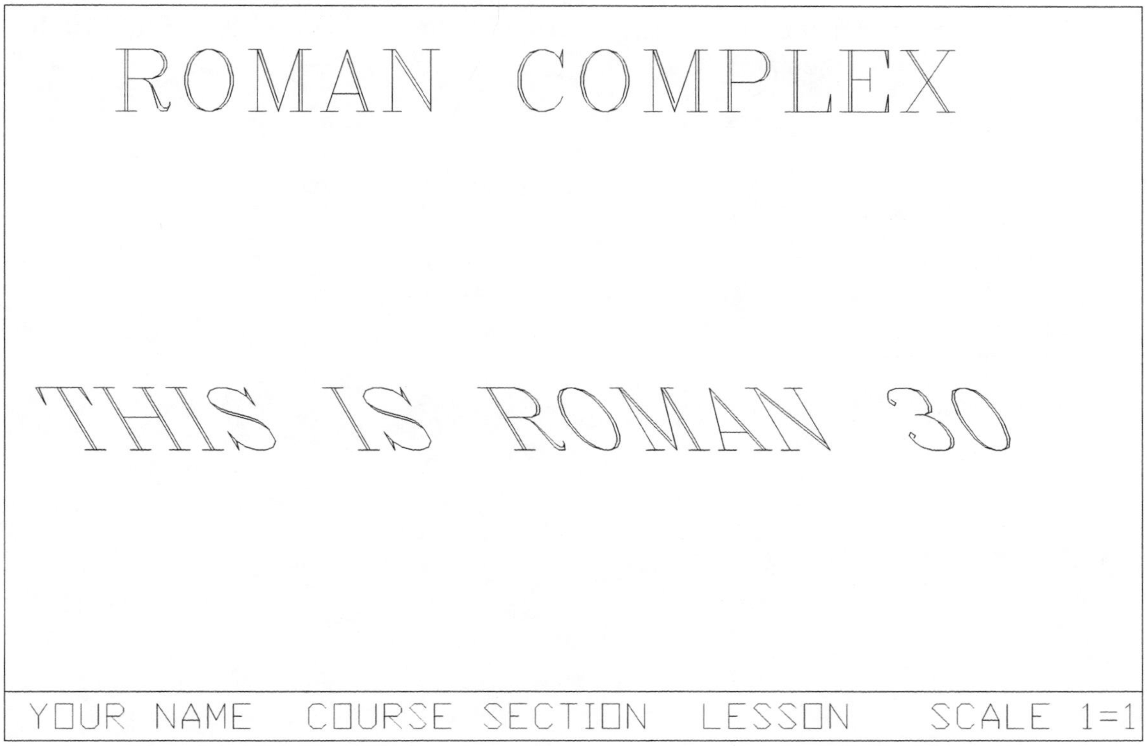

ROMAN COMPLEX

THIS IS ROMAN 30

YOUR NAME   COURSE SECTION   LESSON   SCALE 1=1

3. Create a new **Vertical** Style by doing the following:

- Command: **St** (for **Style**) and then *[ENTER]*.

- Create a **New** style name. In the event that the alert appears again, select the **Yes** button.

- Name the Style *MYROMANCOMPV*.

- Use the same font as before.

- Set the **Oblique Angle** to **0°**.

- In the **Effects** Section, Toggle **Vertical**.

- Select **Apply & Close**.

- Enter the Text as shown below with a **Height** of **.3** and the **Angle** of **270** then *[ENTER]*.

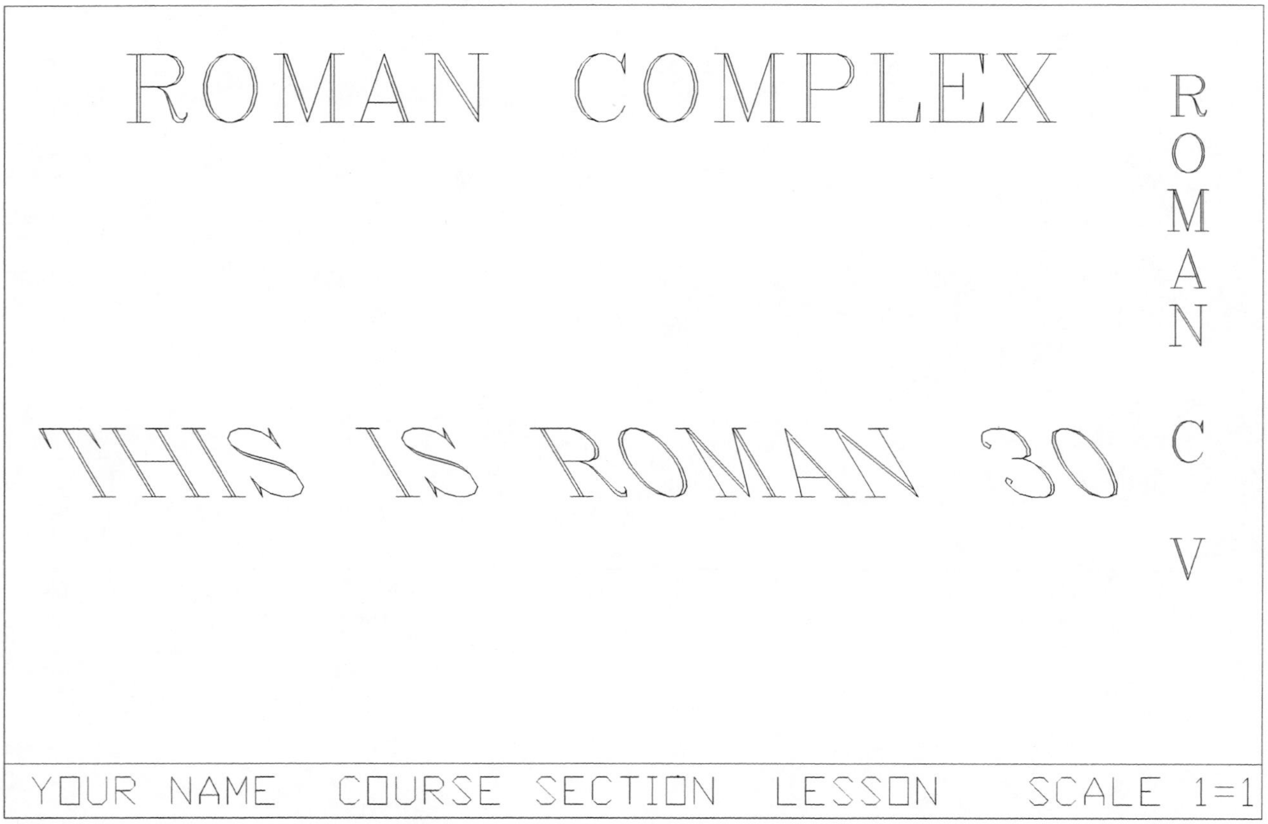

ROMAN COMPLEX

R
O
M
A
N

C

V

THIS IS ROMAN 30

YOUR NAME   COURSE SECTION   LESSON   SCALE 1=1

4. Show the **Text Bounding Boxes** by doing the following:

- Command: *QText* then *[ENTER]*.

- Type *On* then *[ENTER]*.

- Type **Regen** then *[ENTER]*.

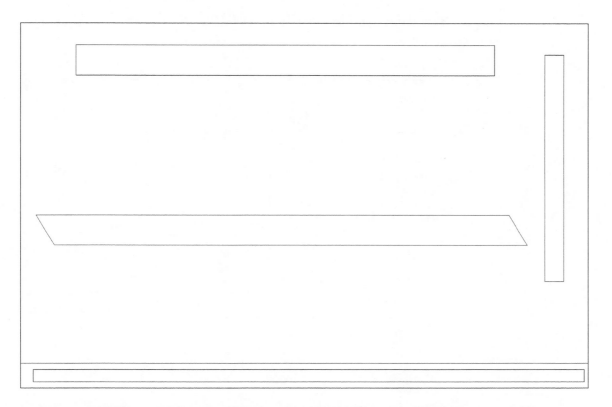

Note: Text Bounding Boxes displays the location of the Text. In a case where the Drawing has a large amount of Text, setting **QText** to *On* will allow for a shorter regeneration time. The benefit of this over **Freezing** the Text **Layer** is that you can see where the text is located in the form of a box.

- When finished, set **QText** to *Off* and **Regen**. {Text returns.}

284

Text Editing

1. **Check Spelling** by doing the following:

   - Use the **Style** command to set your **MYROMANCOMP** Text Style as the **Current** Style.

   - Use the **Text** command to place the text *CIRKLE* as shown below using a Text height of **0.5**.

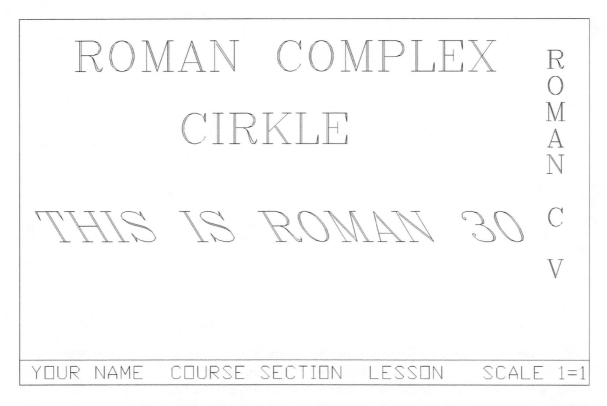

   - From the Menu Bar, select **Tools** and then **Spelling**. {The **Check Spelling** Dialog box appears as shown below.}

   - Make sure that in the **Where to check:** area, the **Entire drawing** option is selected and then select the **Start** button as shown below.

- **CIRKLE** is highlighted and in the **Check Spelling** Dialog box, **Circle** is suggested as a replacement. Select **Change** to replace the word as shown below.

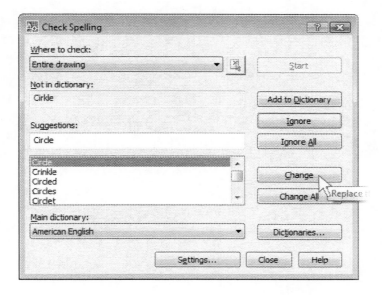

- Press **OK**.

- Select **Close.** {The **Check Spelling** Dialog box is closed.}

2. Edit the Text by doing the following:

- Command: *DDEdit* then *[ENTER]*.

- Select the Text **"CIRCLE"**.

- In the **Edit Text** Prompt, type *"POLYGON"*.

- Press *[ENTER]* twice. {The word **Circle** is changed to **Polygon** and **Edit Text** Prompt is closed.}

286

3. Edit the Text by doing the following:

- Double Click on the Text **"POLYGON"**.

- In the **Edit Text** text box type *"POLYGONAL"* then *[ENTER]* twice.

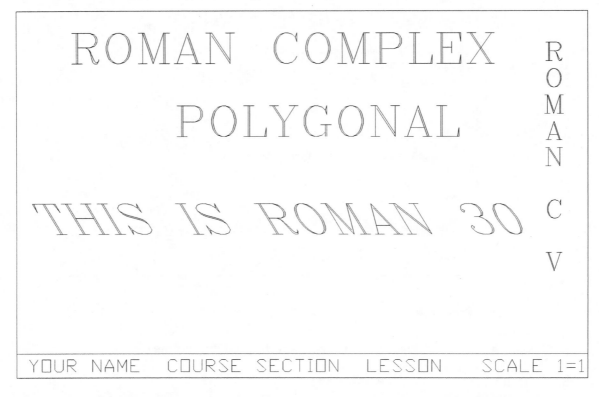

Note: You can also edit the properties of your Text (i.e. **Height** and **Style**) by first selecting the Text which will cause **Grips** (Blue Filled Squares) to display. Then by right-clicking and selecting **Properties** from the shortcut menu, the **Properties Manager** will appear. The **Properties Manager** will be discussed in detail in Chapter 9.

4. **Scale Text** by doing the following:

- Command: *Scaletext* then *[ENTER]*.

- Select all the text (excluding the title box) then *[ENTER]*.

- Type *E* (for **Existing**) then *[ENTER]*.

- Type *S* (for **Scale Factor**) then *[ENTER]*.

- Enter a **Scale Factor** of *0.5* then *[ENTER]*.

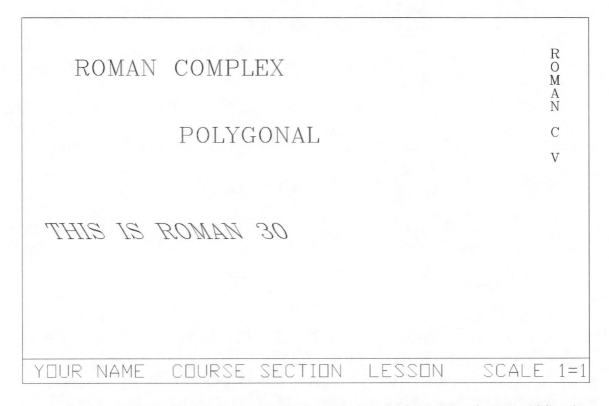

Note: Entering a Scale Factor is instructing AutoCAD to enlarge or reduce an Object by a certain factor of the original Object. A **Scale Factor** of **0.5** instructs AutoCAD to reduce the Object to one half the original size, while, conversely, a **Scale Factor** of **2** is enlarges the Object to twice the original size.

The **Scaletext** Command also allows for scaling a group of text blocks to a different justification point than the original.

288

- **Undo** the last Command. {Text reverts back to the original size.}

- Command: *Scaletext* then *[ENTER]*.

- Select all the text (excluding the title box) then *[ENTER]*.

- Type *E* for **Existing** then *[ENTER]*.

- Type *S* for **Scale Factor** then *[ENTER]*.

- Enter a **Scale Factor** of *2*.

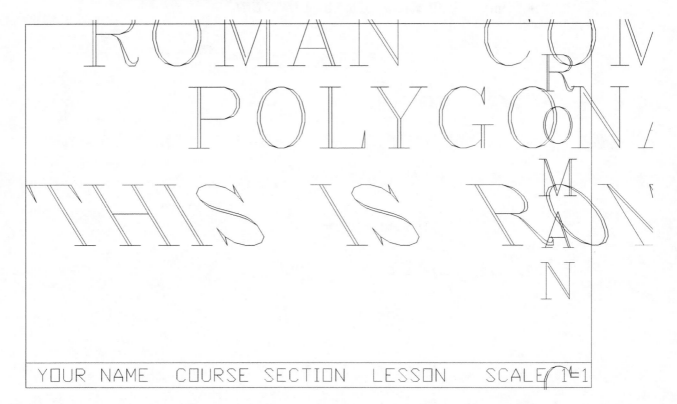

Note: As you can see, the text was again scaled according to the existing justification point. However, this time the text was scaled to twice the original size. Next, you will scale the text with respect to the **Middle** point of the text block.

- **Undo** the last Command.

- Command: *Scaletext* then *[ENTER]*.

- Select all the text (excluding the title box) then *[ENTER]*.

- Type *M* for **Middle Justified** then *[ENTER]*.

- Type *S* for **Scale Factor** then *[ENTER]*.

- Enter a **Scale Factor** of *0.5*.

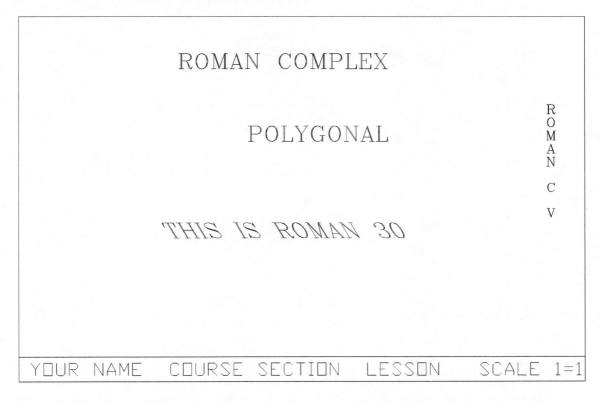

Note: When you enter a new justification point inside the **Scaletext** Command, the Text is scaled accordingly.

- When finished, **Erase** the screen.

- Set **Blipmode** to *Off*.

290

MText (Multiline Text)

1. Enter the **Multiline Text** by doing the following:

   - In the **Draw** toolbar, select the **Multiline Text** button.

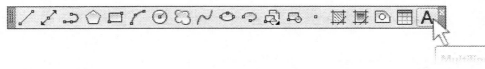

   - Click and drag the Text Window as shown below.

   - Click a second time to define the other corner.

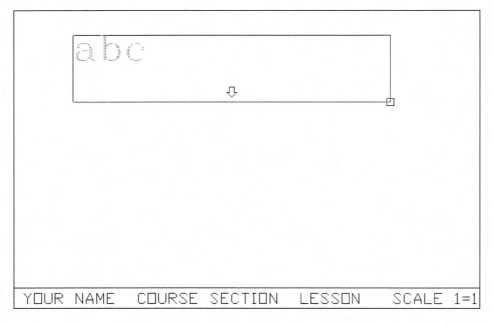

   - In the **Text Formatting** window, select the value in the **Height** text box and change to *0.25*.

   - Type *"It is convenient to create paragraphs using the Multiline Text Editor."*

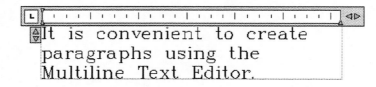

- Select **OK**. {**Text Formatting** window is **Closed**.}

- When finished, **Erase** all geometry from the screen.

When using text frequently, it is beneficial to load the **Text** Toolbar as shown below.

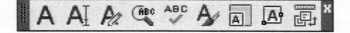

292

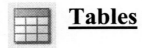 **Tables**

Note: A Table allows for entering data into cells in the form of rows and columns.

1. Set up a **Table Style** and **Insert Table** by doing the following:

   - Use the **Style** command to create a **New Text Style.**

   - Name the Style **Text Simplex** and assign the **Simplex** Font. Then **Apply** and **Close**.

   - In the **Draw** toolbar, click on the **Table** button.

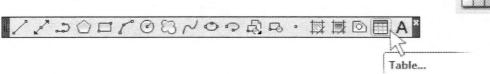

   - As the **Insert Table** dialog box appears, click on the **Launch the Table Style dialog** button as shown below.

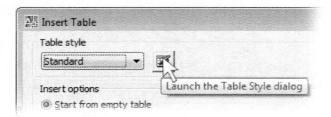

   - Notice that the **Table Style** dialog box appears as shown below and the **Standard** Table Style is the only listed Style.

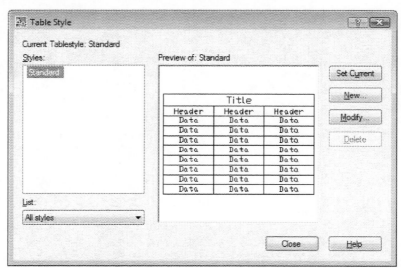

- Click **New**.

- In the **Create New Table Style** dialog box, type **Ansi Standards** for the name as shown below.

- Select **Continue**. {**New Table Style** dialog box appears.}

- In the **New Table Style** dialog box, use the **Cell styles** drop-down to select **Title** from the list as shown below.

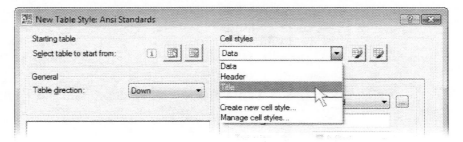

- Click on the **Text** tab and set the **Text style** to **Text Simplex** as shown below.

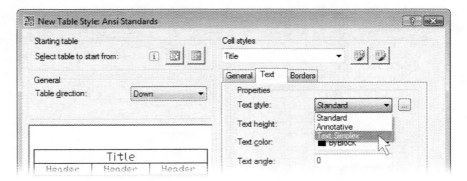

- Just as in the case of the **Title** Cell Style, assign the **Text Simplex** text style to both the **Data** and the **Header** Cell Styles.

- Click **OK** to Close the **New Table Style** dialog box.

294

- In the **Table Style** dialog box, in the **Styles** area, select the **Ansi Standards** Table Style as shown below and then click **Set Current**.

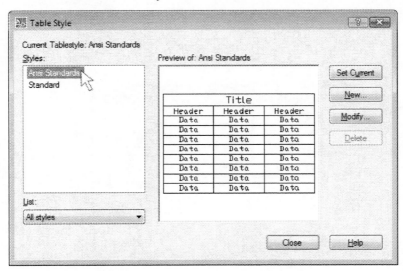

- Click **Close**. {The **Insert Table** dialog box appears.}

- In the **Insert Table** dialog box, make sure that the **Column** and **Data Row** number are set to **3** and **5** respectively. Set the **Column width** to *2.85* and the **Row height** to *1*.

- Click **OK.** {**Insert Table** dialog box is closed and the Table drags on the screen.}

- **Specify insertion point** at a user-specified location. {The **Table** is placed in the Drawing and the **Text Formatting** dialog box appears as shown below.}

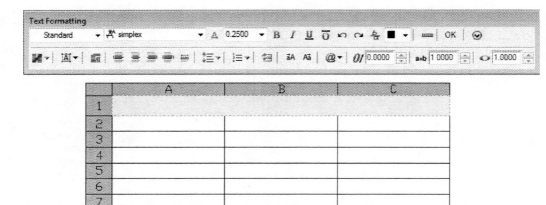

- As a blinking cursor appears in the **Title** area, type *ANSI Standard Sheet Sizes*, then press the [**TAB**] *key* on your keyboard.

Note: The [**TAB**] key advances you to the next **Cell**. If you make a mistake, you can come back at the end and double-click on the text as you have done previously in this chapter to make corrections. You may also press [**SHIFT**] +[**TAB**] to move back one **Cell** at a time.

- Complete the **Table** as shown below.

ANSI Standard Sheet Sizes		
Metric (mm)	U.S. Standard	Architectural
A4 210 X 297	A Size 8.5" X 11"	9" X 12"
A3 297 X 412	B Size 11" X 17"	12" X 18"
A2 420 X 524	C Size 17" X 22"	18" X 24"
A1 594 X 841	D Size 22" X 34"	24" X 36"
A0 841 X 1189	E Size 34" X 44"	36" X 48"

- As you type in the last **Cell**, select **OK** within the **Text Formatting** window.

- **Save As** the file to your folder naming it *Ansi Standard Sheet Sizes.dwg*

- **Exit** AutoCAD.

Note: You can extract the Data of an AutoCAD **Table** to a Microsoft Excel® file. **Database Connectivity** is covered extensively in Volume II.

<u>Aliases</u>

DYNAMIC TEXT ....DTEXT or DT

EDIT TEXT ....DDEDIT or ED

MULTILINE TEXT.. MTEXT or MT

TEXT STYLES..STYLE

STYLE ....ST

Assignment 7

Objective:

1. To practice **Placing** and **Editing Text**.
2. To practice using different **Text Styles** and **Fonts**.

Instructions:

1. Launch AutoCAD and use your **My Template** to begin a **New** Drawing.
2. From the **Status Line,** make sure that **Snap**, **Grid**, **Ortho**, **Polar**, **OSnap**, and **OTrack** are set to *Off*.
3. **Save As** the Drawing file to your folder. Name it **"ASSIGN07_ _ _.dwg"** where the 3 blanks are your initials.
4. Create a **6-sided Inscribed Polygon** (Hexagon) with center located at *3.30,3.25* and **Radius** point located *@2.5<90* as shown below.

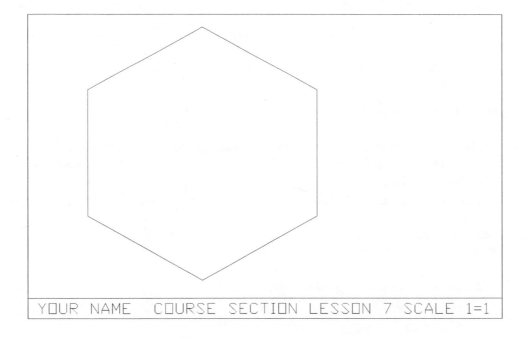

YOUR NAME   COURSE SECTION LESSON 7 SCALE 1=1

5. Create **COMP Style** with **Complex font** to place shown **Text** at the geometric center of the **Hexagon**. Use **Middle Justify** as shown below. **Text height** is *0.20*. If a Font is not available on your system, use any Font you wish.
6. Create **ARIAL Style** with **Arial font** to fit the shown **Text** using **P1** and **P2** as the two **Endpoints** of the **Text** baseline as shown below. **Text height** is *0.20*.
7. Create **SIMP30 Style** with **Simplex font** and an oblique angle of -30 to **Center Justify** the **Text** to point **P3** (**Midpoint** of hex's edge). **Text height** is *0.20* and **Rotation** is set to match the edge.

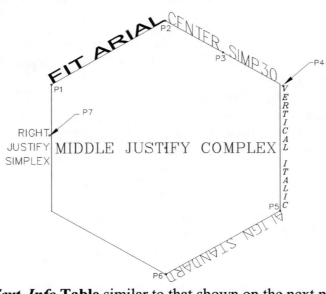

8. Create **VERT Style** with **effect** set to vertical, **Italic font,** and an oblique angle of **0** to place shown **Text** at about **P4** positioned slightly to the right of Hex corner. **Text height** is *0.11*.

9. Use **STANDARD Style** to **Align** given **Text** using **P5** and **P6** as the two points for Text baseline. Your standard style may have **txt** or **simplex** font.

10. Create **SIMP Style** using simplex **Font**. **Right Justify** shown **Text** at about **P7** (slightly to the left of Edge). **Text height** is **0.14**.

11. Create the *Text Info* **Table** similar to that shown on the next page knowing that:

    The upper left corner of the table is located at coordinates **5.75, 5.45 .**
    Table uses **SIMP Style**.
    Column with is 1.0 .
    Text height is user-specified.

12. **Save** the Drawing.

13. **Preview** and **Plot** Drawing using these settings:

    • Paper size: Letter (8.50x11.00 **inches**)
    • Plot Scale: 1=1
    • Plot area: Limits
    • Plot offset: Centered

14. Check your Drawing to match that of the next page.

15. In the event that you used the screen menu, make sure it is toggled *Off* before **Exiting** AutoCAD.

298

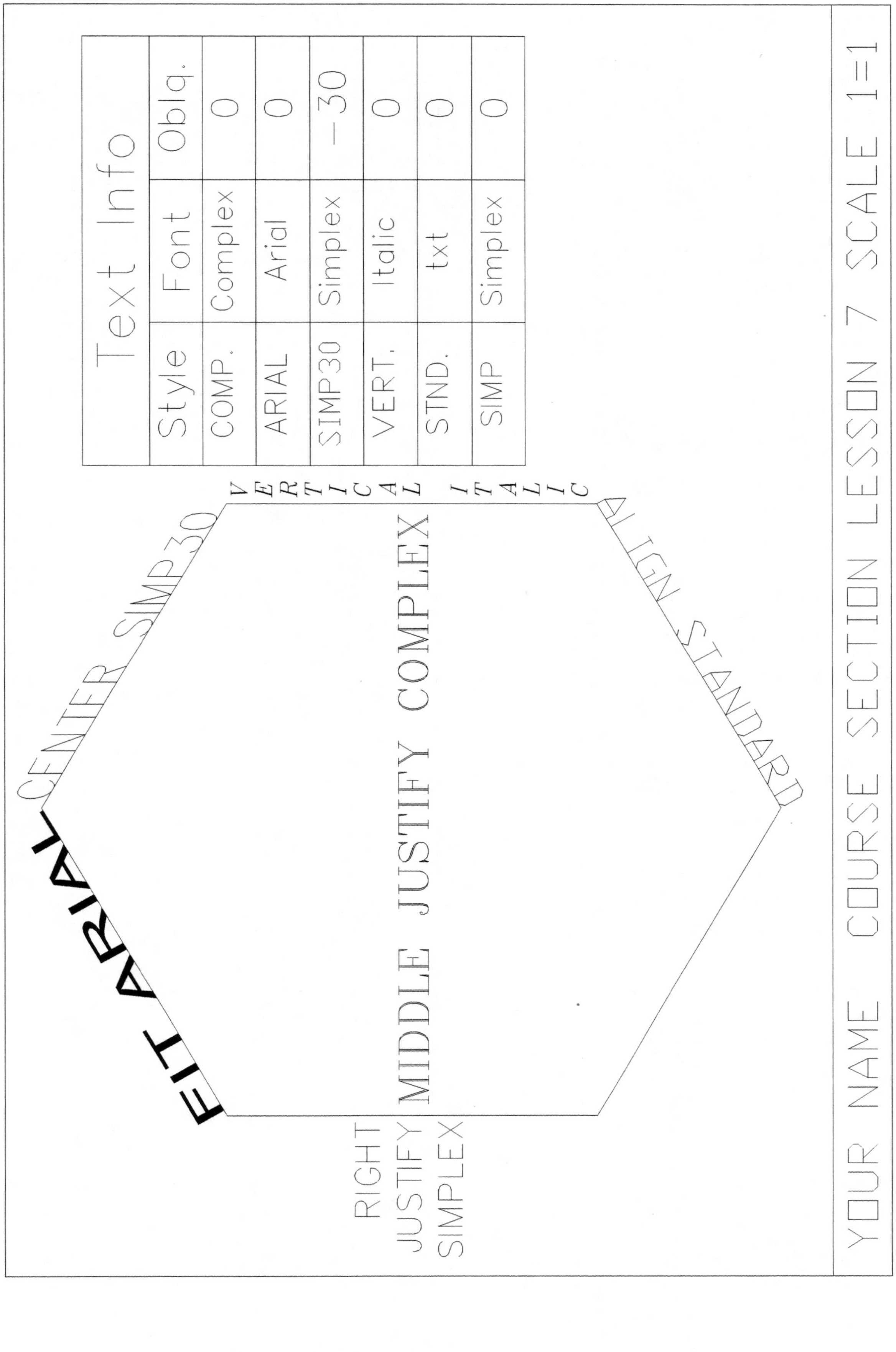

Text Info

Style	Font	Oblq.
COMP.	Complex	0
ARIAL	Arial	0
SIMP30	Simplex	−30
VERT.	Italic	0
STND.	txt	0
SIMP	Simplex	0

CENTER SIMP30

VERTICAL

FIT ARIAL

ITALIC

MIDDLE JUSTIFY COMPLEX

ALIGN STANDARD

RIGHT JUSTIFY SIMPLEX

YOUR NAME   COURSE SECTION LESSON 7 SCALE 1=1

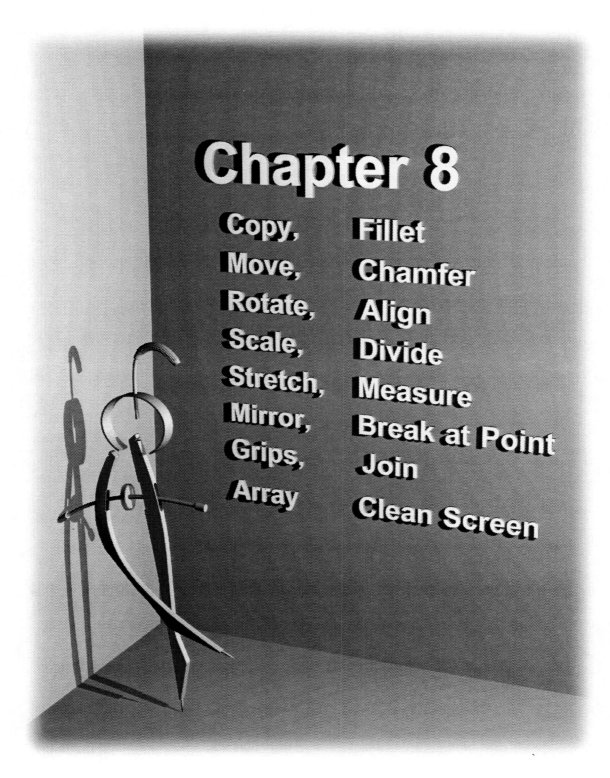

Chapter 8

Copy,

Move,

Rotate,

Scale,

Stretch,

Mirror,

Grips,

Array

Fillet

Chamfer

Align

Divide

Measure

Break at Point

Join

Clean Screen

302

 **Copy**

1. Launch AutoCAD and use your **My Template** to begin a Drawing.

2. From the **Status Bar** set **Snap** and **Grid** to *On* and then set the **Snap** value to *0.25*.

3. Set **Ortho, Polar, OSnap, OTrack, Ducs** and **Dyn** to *Off.*

4. Create the symbol as shown below in the lower left corner of the screen. The 1" square and the four circles (with the radii of 0.5") can be created using the current **0.25 Snap** setting.

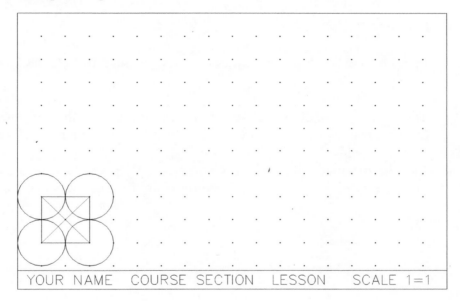

YOUR NAME   COURSE SECTION   LESSON   SCALE 1=1

- Set **Snap** to *Off* and then **Trim** the geometry to that of the symbol shown below.

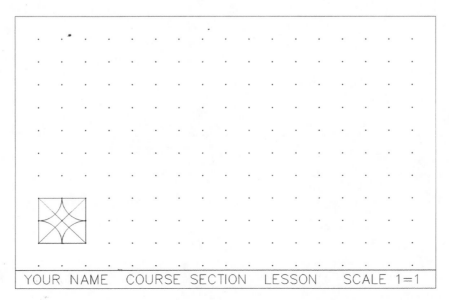

YOUR NAME   COURSE SECTION   LESSON   SCALE 1=1

304

5. **Copy** the symbol by doing the following:

- In the **Modify** toolbar, select the **Copy** Tool.

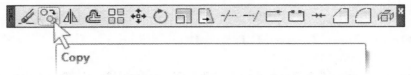

- Use **Crossing** to select the entire symbol and then *[ENTER]*.

- Set **Snap** to *On*.

- Pick the center of your symbol as the **Base Point**.{Object Drags on screen.}

- Toggle the **Coordinate Display Button** located in the left side of the Status Bar until your coordinates are displayed in **Polar** form.

- Use the distance value of the **Coordinate Display Button** to accurately Drag the symbol by 4.5 units to the right and Pick as shown below.

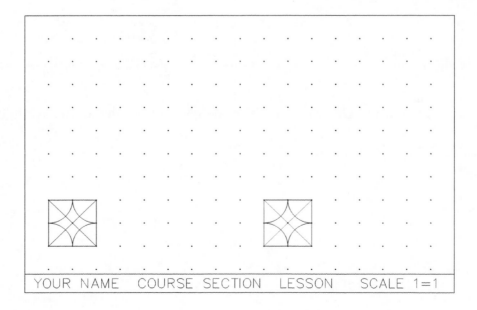

6. **Copy** the symbol by doing the following:

- Command: *Copy* then *[ENTER]*.

- Use **Crossing** to select the original symbol and *[ENTER]*.

- Select the lower left corner of the Object as the **Base Point**.

- Type the coordinates *7.0,4.5* then *[ENTER]*. {Lower left corner of the recently copied symbol is placed at coordinates **7.0,4.5** as shown below}

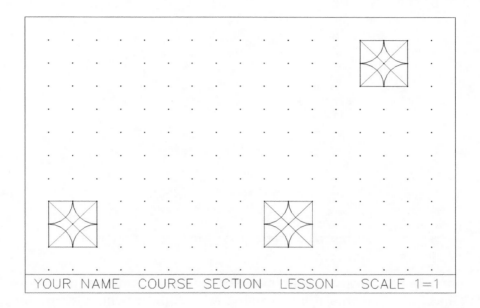

7. Command: **CP** then *[Enter]*

- Use **Crossing** to select the original symbol and then *[Enter].*

- Type **D**(for Displacement) and then *[Enter].*

- When prompted to specify displacement, type in **1.5,2.0** .

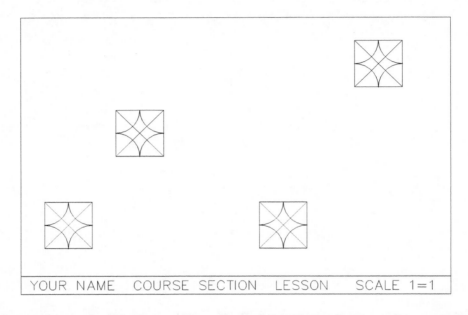

Note: You may use the Displacement option of the **Copy** Command to copy an Object. When the Object is being copied horizontally, a **Y** Displacement value of **0.0** must be used; if the Object is being copied vertically, an **X** Displacement value of **0.0** must be used. As an example, if an Object is being copied horizontally and to the right by 2 units, the displacement values would be **2.0, 0.0** .

8. **Copy** using **OSnap** by doing the following:

- Create a 3point **Arc** such that its 3 points are located at the corners of the 3 symbols as shown below.

- Set **Snap** to *Off.*

- Select the **Copy** Tool and use **Crossing** to select your original symbol, then *[ENTER]*.

- For the **Base Point**, use **OSnap** to select the geometric center of your symbol as displayed by the intersection of the two diagonals.

- For the **Second Point of Displacement**, **OSnap** to the **Center** of the **Large Arc.** {Symbol is copied to the center of the Arc.}

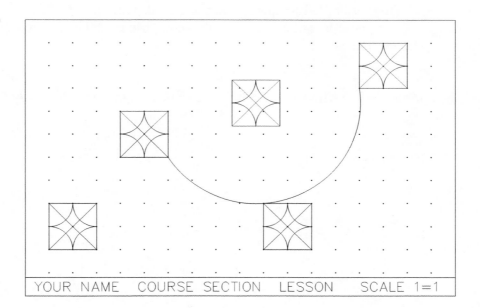

YOUR NAME   COURSE SECTION   LESSON   SCALE 1=1

308

 **Move**

1. **Move** the symbol by doing the following:

   • In the **Modify** toolbar, click on the **Move** button.

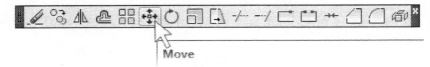

   • Use the **Window** option to select the original symbol located in the lower left corner of your screen and then *[Enter].*

   • Type **D** (for displacement) and then *[Enter].*

   • When prompted to specify displacement, type in 7.25,1.0. {Object moves to the new location such that its geometric center is located at these new coordinates.}

Note: The options for the **Move** Command are identical to those of the **Copy** Command.

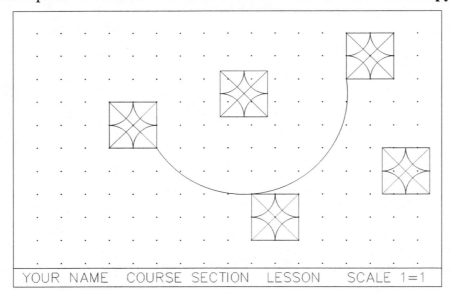

YOUR NAME   COURSE SECTION   LESSON   SCALE 1=1

Note: Make sure that you can distinguish between the **Move** and **Pan** Commands. **Moving** changes the coordinates/location of the Object while **Panning** changes your view/line of sight.

 # <u>Rotate</u>

1. **Rotate** the symbol by doing the following:

   - In the **Modify** toolbar, click on the **Rotate** button.

   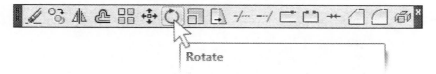

   - Use the **Window** option to select the symbol located at the center of the large arc and then *[ENTER]*.

   - Use **Object Snap** to pick the center of the large arc as your **Base Point.**

   - Type *30* for the Rotation Angle and then *[ENTER]*. {Symbol is rotated by 30 degrees.}

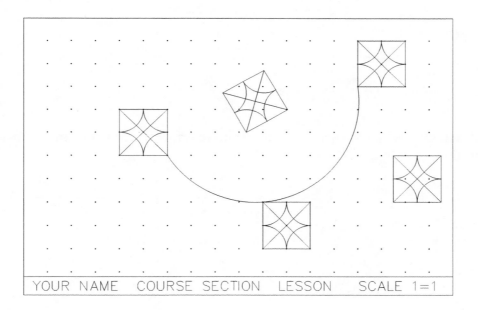

YOUR NAME   COURSE SECTION   LESSON   SCALE 1=1

310

2. Command: **Ro** (for Rotate) and then *[Enter].*

- Select the symbol located at the center of the large arc.

- For the **Base Point** select the left endpoint of the large arc.

- Type **C** (for the copy option of the **Rotate** Tool) and then *[Enter]*.

- Type **-155** for the rotation angle and *[Enter].* {The Symbol is rotated and copied in one operation.}

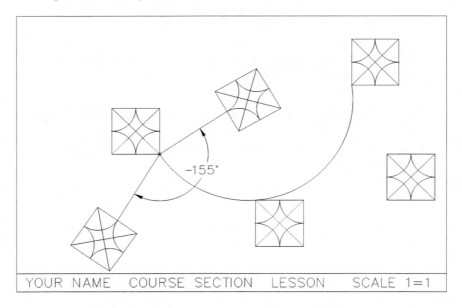

3. **Erase** all geometry except for the symbol shown below and move to the next section.

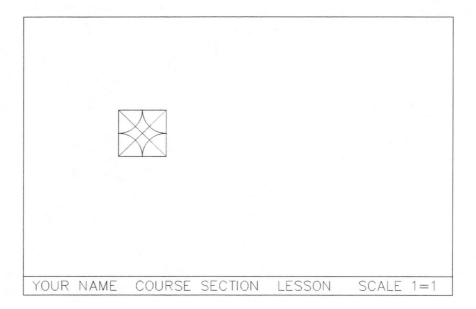

 ## <u>Scale</u>

1. **Scale** the symbol by doing the following:

   - In the **Modify** toolbar, click on the **Scale** button.

   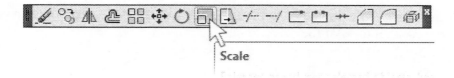

   Scale

   - Use **Crossing** to select the symbol and then *[ENTER]*.

   - Pick the geometric center of the symbol as your **Base Point**

   - For the Scale Factor, type *2.5* then *[ENTER]*. {The Symbol scales to 250% of the original size.}

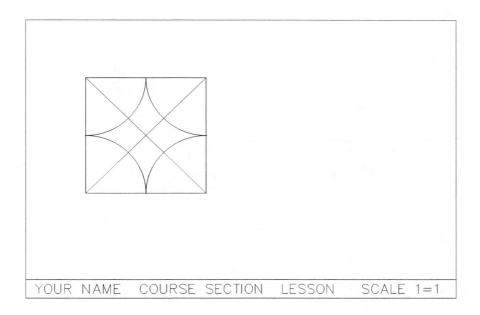

YOUR NAME   COURSE SECTION   LESSON   SCALE 1=1

312

2. Command: **Sc** (for **Scale**) and then *[ENTER]*.

- Use the **Crossing** option to select your symbol.

- Select the geometric center as your **Base Point.**

- Type **C** (for the Copy option) and then *[ENTER]*.

- For the Scale Factor, type *0.25* then *[ENTER]*. {A copy of the symbol is scaled to ¼ of the original size.}

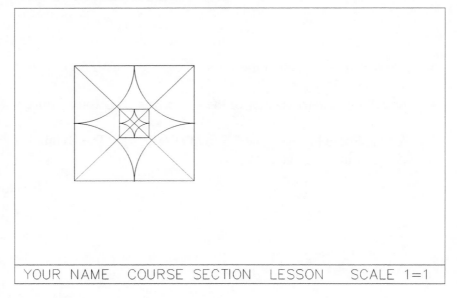

YOUR NAME   COURSE SECTION   LESSON   SCALE 1=1

- When finished, erase all geometry.

Stretch

1. Set both **Snap** and **Grid** to *0.25* .

2. Create the miniature table as shown below at a user-specified location. All dimensions are on a **0.25** unit **Grid**.

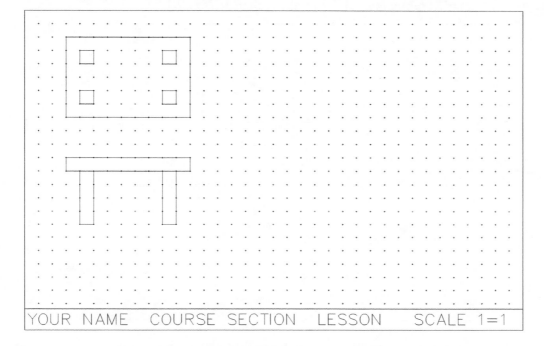

YOUR NAME   COURSE SECTION   LESSON   SCALE 1=1

3. **Copy** the Objects to the right to a user-specified location as shown below.

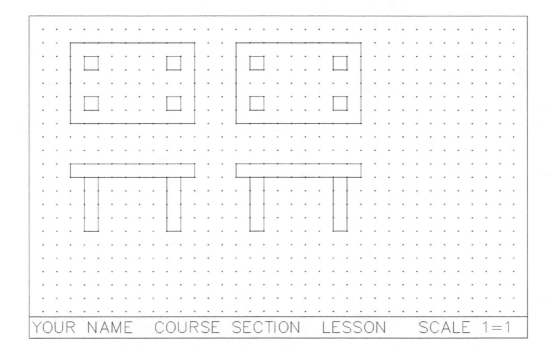

YOUR NAME   COURSE SECTION   LESSON   SCALE 1=1

314

4. **Stretch** the Object by doing the following:

- In the **Modify** toolbar, click on the **Stretch** button.

- Use **Crossing** (right to left selection) to select the right portion of the copied Objects as shown below, then *[ENTER]*.

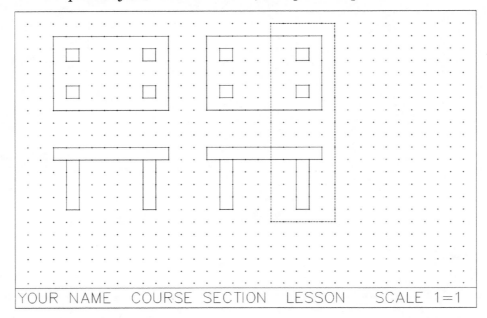

YOUR NAME   COURSE SECTION   LESSON   SCALE 1=1

- Pick any point on screen as the **Base Point** and move the mouse directly to the right by a user-specified distance and Pick. Objects stretch as shown below.

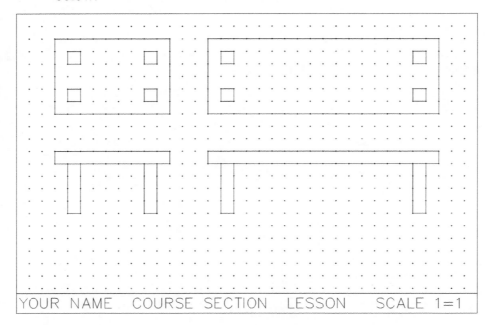

YOUR NAME   COURSE SECTION   LESSON   SCALE 1=1

- Command: **Stretch** then *[ENTER]*.

- Use **Crossing** to select the legs as shown below, then *[ENTER]*.

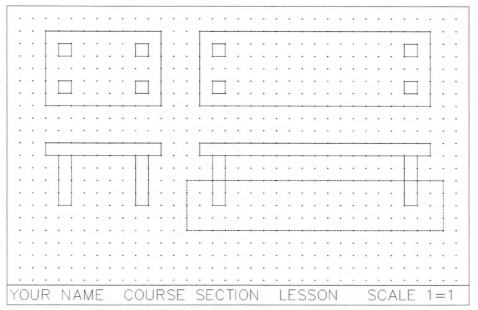

- Type **D** (for displacement) and then *[ENTER]*.

- When asked to specify displacement, type **0,-1** and then *[ENTER]* {geometry is stretched directly downwards as shown below.}

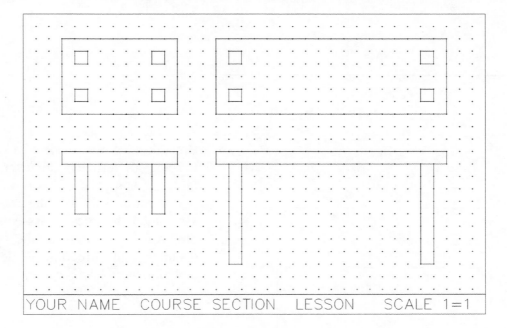

- When finished, **Erase** all geometry.

Note: When you select the Objects to stretch, you are selecting very specific vertices/ nodes. When you **Stretch** these **vertices**, they are being moved with respect to the unselected set of vertices of the same Object. An example is shown below.

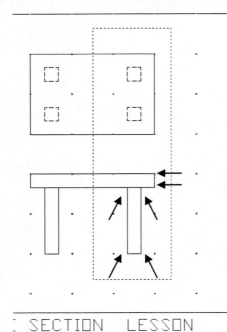

SECTION LESSON

Here all of the selected vertices for the table's front view are shown. When the selected vertices are moved to the right, the unselected vertices on the left side remain in position.

Caution: When using the **Stretch** Command, **Crossing** should be used as the Object-selection method. The **Window** selection option (left to right) will not work properly here.

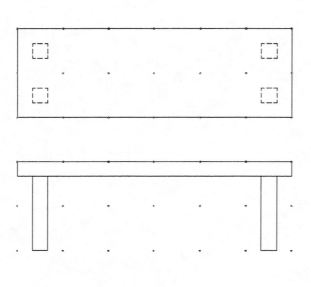

SECTION LESSON SCALE 1=

As you can see, the table top **Stretches** with respect to the unselected vertices; however, the table leg is moved. This is a result of selecting all of the entity's associated vertices. Essentially, the right leg moves the same distance and direction while the table top stretches.

 # Mirror

1. Set **Grid** to **0.5** and **Snap** to **0.25**.

2. Draw the Shape at a user-specified size and location as shown below.

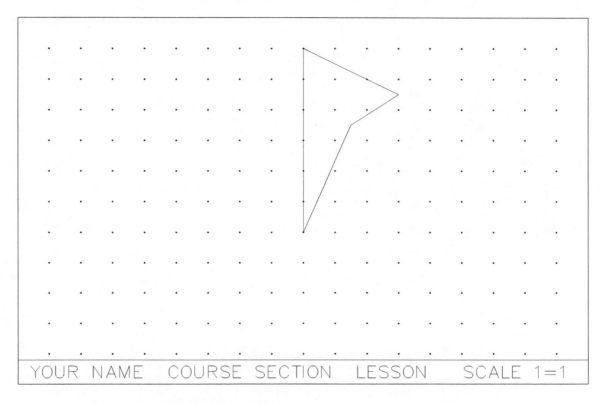

YOUR NAME   COURSE SECTION   LESSON   SCALE 1=1

3. **Mirror** Objects by doing the following:

- In the **Modify** toolbar, click on the **Mirror** button.

- Use **Crossing** to select the Object, then *[ENTER]*.

- Set **Ortho** Mode to **On**.

318

- To define the mirror line, pick about point **P1** as shown below, then move the mouse vertically downwards and pick a second about point **P2** to **Mirror** the Object as shown below.

- Press *[ENTER]* to utilize the **No** default option. {The Source Object remains on the screen.}

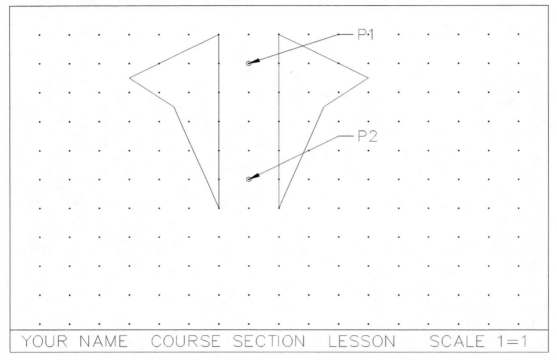

YOUR NAME   COURSE SECTION   LESSON   SCALE 1=1

- Set **Ortho** to *Off*.

- When finished, **Erase** the screen.

Grips

Grips are the filled-in squares that appear when an Object (or group of Objects) is selected. In order to activate **Grips**, you must select the object outside of any Command. These **Grips** are displayed at specific points on the geometry as shown below. For example, the **Circle** has **Grips** located at its **Center** and **Quadrants**, and the **Line** has **Grips** located at its **Midpoint** and **Endpoints**. **Grips** allow for quick editing of geometry when using the **Copy**, **Move**, **Rotate**, **Scale**, **Mirror**, and **Stretch** Commands.

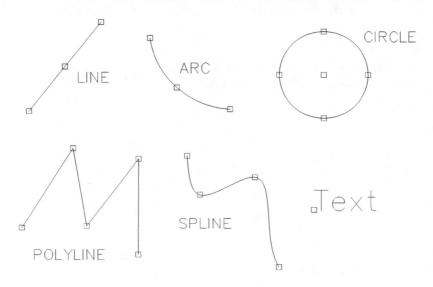

1. Set **Snap** and **Grid** to *Off*.

2. Create a **Line**, **Circle**, and **Arc** at user-specified locations as shown below.

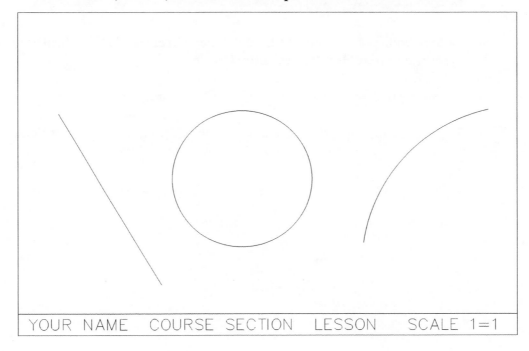

320

3. Use **Grips** to modify Objects by doing the following:

-   Before entering any Command, select the **Arc**. {**Grips** display at **Center**, **Midpoint** and **Endpoints** of the **Arc**.}

Note: In the event that Grips do not display when selecting Objects, at the Command Line type in **Grips** and then press the **Enter** key. Then change the **Grips** value from **0** to **1**. This will set the **Grips** mode to **On**.

-   Pick upper right **Endpoint Grip** of the **Arc**. {The selected **Grip** changes color.}

-   To stretch the **Endpoint** of the **Arc**, move the cursor to a user-specified location as shown below and click.

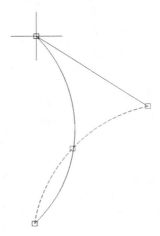

-   Press the **Esc** key to exit **Gripmode**.

-   Before entering a Command, select the **Circle**. {**Grips** display at the **Center** and four **Quadrants** of the **Circle**.}

-   Select the 6 o'clock **Quadrant**. {The **Grip** changes color.}

-   Right-click the mouse button and from the shortcut menu, select **Scale**.

- Move the mouse to see the dragging **Circle** and type *0.6* then *[ENTER]*.

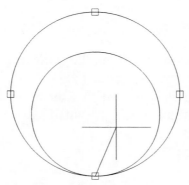

- Press the **Esc** key to exit **Grip** mode.

- Before entering a Command, select the **Line**. {Grips display at the **Midpoint** and two **Endpoints** of the **Line**.}

- Select the **Grip** located at the lower **Endpoint**. {The selected **Grip** changes color and you are currently in **Stretch** mode.}

- Move cursor to a user-specified location as shown below, but do not pick a point; however, notice that you are in the **Stretch** mode.

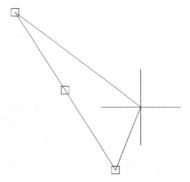

- Press the **Spacebar** once. {The system toggles to the **Move** Command with the **Basepoint** as the selected **Grip**.}

- Press the **Spacebar** again. {**Move** Command toggles to **Rotate** .}

- Press the **Spacebar** several times and move your pointing device slightly each time. {The system toggles between **Stretch**, **Move**, **Rotate**, **Scale**, and **Mirror**.}

- Press **Esc** twice. {**Grips** disappear.}

- When finished, **Erase** screen.

322

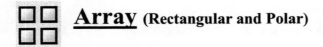 **Array** (Rectangular and Polar)

1. Set **Snap** and **Grid** to *On*.

2. Create a **Rectangular Array** by doing the following:

   - Create a 4 sided **Polygon** with **Center** located at *2,2* and **Inscribed in circle** with a **Radius** of *0.2*. {A small square is created.}

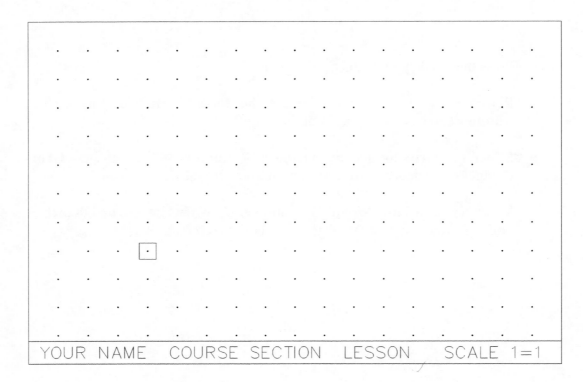

YOUR NAME   COURSE SECTION   LESSON   SCALE 1=1

   - In the **Modify** toolbar, click on the **Array** button. {The **Array** dialog box will appear.}

- In the **Array** dialog box, make sure that **Rectangular Array** option is Toggled to *On*.

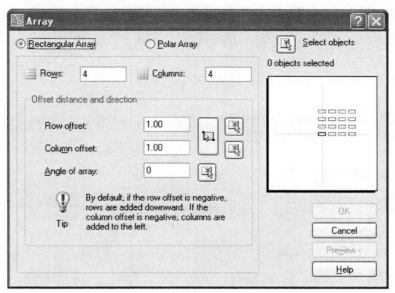

- Click on the **Select Objects** button and then select the **Polygon** (square) and then *[ENTER]*.

- Set the number of **Rows** to *3* and the number of **Columns** to *1*.

- Set the **Row** and **Column Offsets** to *1*.

- Click **Preview**; if your **Array** matches the Drawing below, right-click on the mouse button; otherwise, press **Esc** and check your data entries.

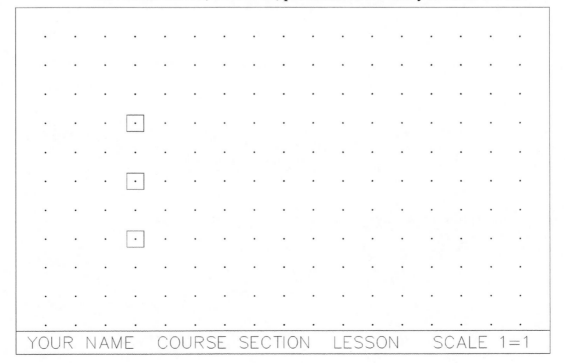

YOUR NAME   COURSE SECTION   LESSON   SCALE 1=1

324

Note: The **Preview** option allows you to see the **Array** before it is actually created.

- **Undo** the **Array**, but keep original **Polygon**.

2. **Rectangular Array** the **Polygon** by doing the following:

- Command: *Array* then *[ENTER]*.

- Click the **Select Objects** button and select the original **Polygon** as your Object then *[ENTER]*.

- Change **Rows** = *1*, **Columns** = *3*.

- Check the **Column offset** value to be *1.00*.

- Press **OK**.

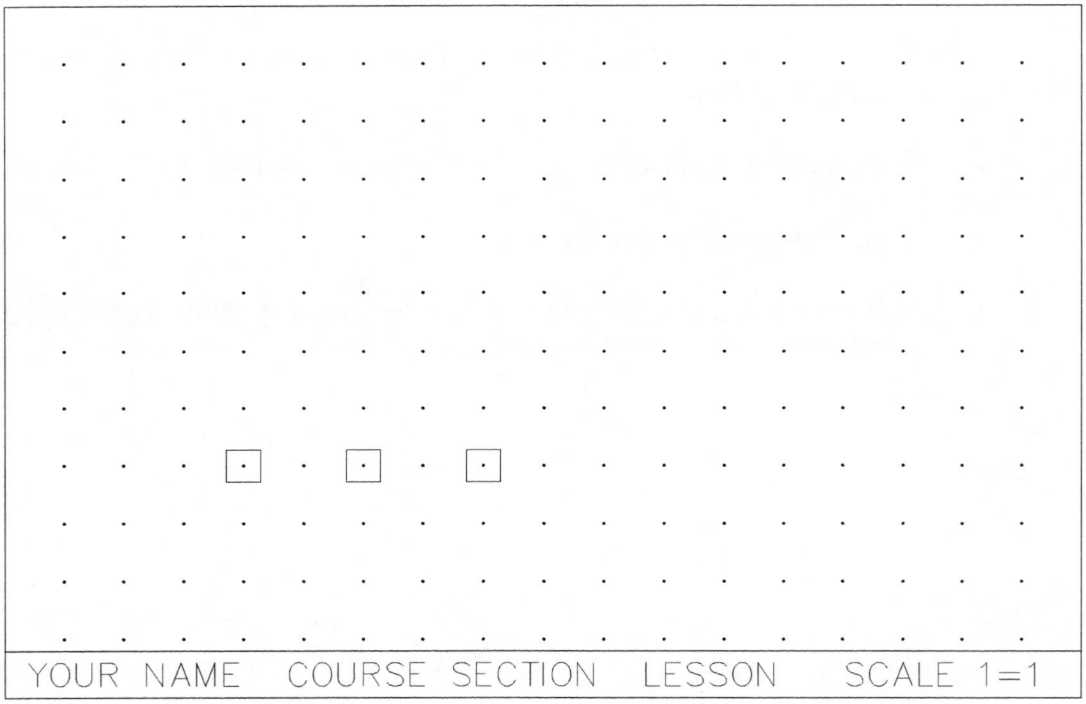

YOUR NAME   COURSE SECTION   LESSON   SCALE 1=1

- **Undo** the **Array**.

3. **Rectangular Array** the **Polygon** by doing the following:

- Select the **Array** button.

- Use the **Select Objects** button to pick the **Polygon** as your Object then *[ENTER]*.

- Change **Rows** = *6*, **Columns** = *3*.

- Set **Row offset** to *0.5*.

- Set **Column offset** to *1.0*.

- Select **Preview,** and then right-click if correct.

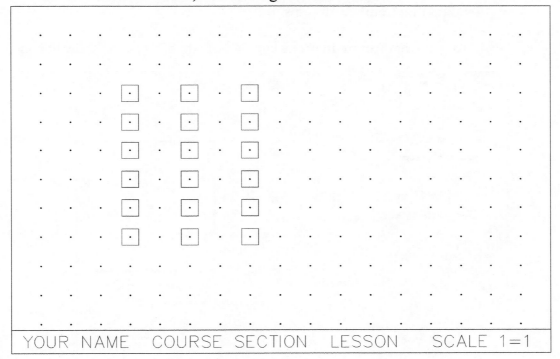

YOUR NAME   COURSE SECTION   LESSON   SCALE 1=1

4. **Undo** the **Array**.

5. **Move** the **Polygon** such that its center is located at **4.5,5.0** .

326

6. **Polar Array** by doing the following:

- Select the **Array** button.

- Toggle **Polar Array**.

- Use the **Select Objects** button to select the **Polygon** as your Object, then *[ENTER]*.

- Select the **Pick Center Point** button.

- Use **Snap** to Pick a point **1.5** units directly below the **Polygon's** center as shown by point **P1** on the next page.

- Set the **Total number of items** to *12*.

- Make sure that **Rotate items as copied** is Toggled to *On* as shown below.

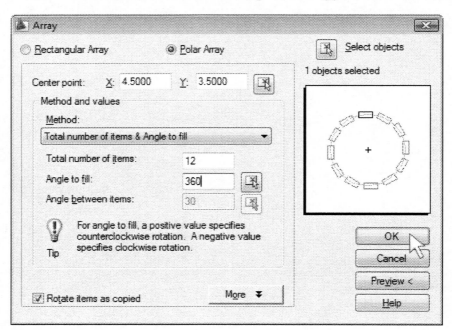

- Click **OK**. {Polar Array is generated as shown on the next page.}

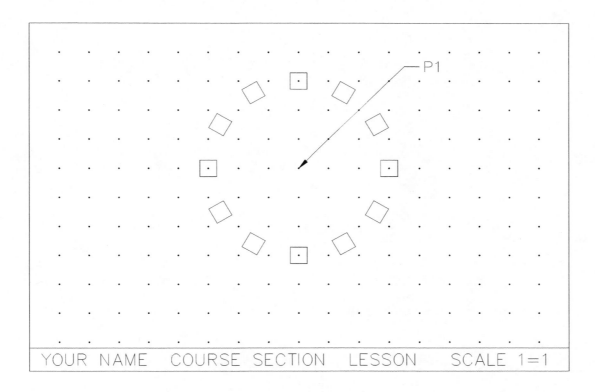

YOUR NAME   COURSE SECTION   LESSON   SCALE 1=1

- **Undo** the **Array**.

- Command: **Ar** (for **Array**) and then *[ENTER]*.

- Make sure that **Polar Array** is Toggled *On*.

- Select the four sided **Polygon** as your Object.

- Choose the same center as before.

- Set the **Total number of items** to *8*.

- Set the **Angle to fill** to *180*.

- Select **OK**. {Polar Array is generated as shown on the next page.}

328

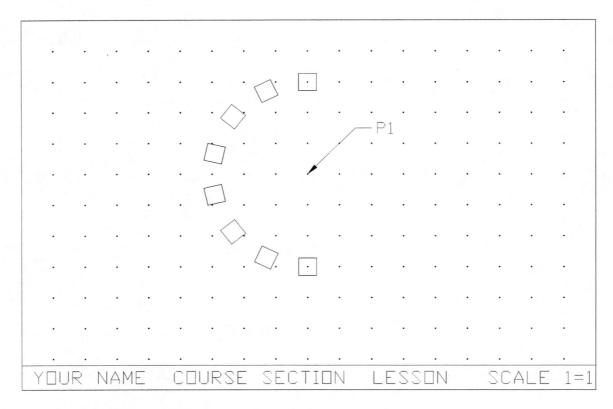

YOUR NAME   COURSE SECTION   LESSON   SCALE 1=1

7. When finished, **Erase** screen.

8. Use **Polar Array** to create a gear:

- Set **Snap** to *off*.

- Create a **Circle** with a **Radius** of **2** units with the **Center** located at **4.25,3.50**.

- **Offset** the **Circle** to the inside by *0.4*.

- Draw a **3**-unit-long horizontal **Line** starting at the **Center** of the **Circle**. For the endpoint, you can type *@3<0* to guarantee accuracy.

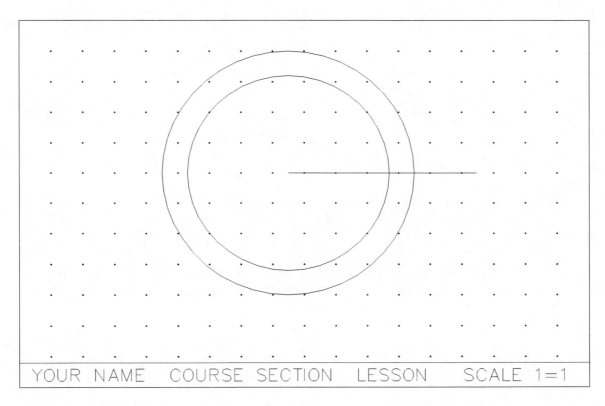

YOUR NAME   COURSE SECTION   LESSON   SCALE 1=1

Note: You are about to construct a gear having a 30-tooth configuration. To space the teeth properly, you can divide the total **360** degrees by the number of teeth **(30)** which results in a **12**-degree angle. Noting that the tooth is symmetrical, you know that ½ of a tooth covers **6** degrees.

330

- Draw a **Line** starting at the **Center** of the **Circle** with the other end point located **@3<6**.

- Construct a Circle with its Center at **5.83,2.50** and a radius of **1.125**

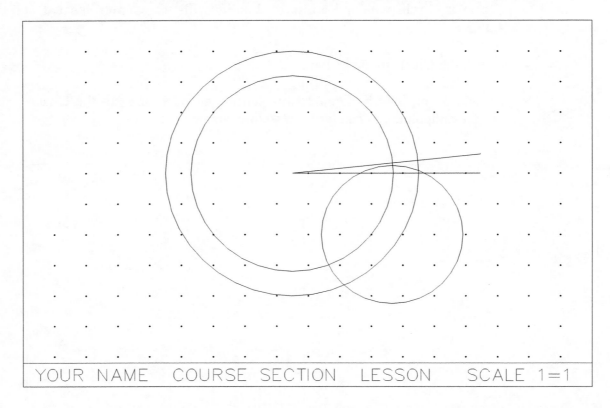

YOUR NAME   COURSE SECTION   LESSON   SCALE 1=1

- **Zoom** into the 3 o'clock area of gear and **Trim** and **Erase** the geometry as necessary to end up with the top half of a complete tooth as shown below.

- **Zoom All**.

- Command: *Mirror* then *[ENTER]*.

- Select the half-tooth as your Object, and then *[ENTER]*.

- Set **Ortho** to **On**.

- **OSnap** to the lower **End Point** of the geometry and move left and select the second mirror line endpoint along the horizontal.

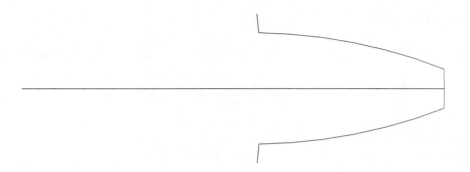

- To keep source Object, press **[ENTER]**.

- Command: *Array* then **[ENTER]**.

- In the **Array** dialog box, Toggle **Polar Array**.

- Click on the **Select Objects** button.

- Select the complete tooth geometry as your Object, then *[ENTER]*.

- Click on the **Pick Center Point** button.

- Locate the center of the gear by selecting the **OSnap** Center of the very short arc as shown below. Look for the **AutoSnap Center** Marker (shown below on the far left of the image) to assure that the larger **Arc** is not selected by error.

- From the **Array** dialog box, use the **Method and Values** pull-down menu to make sure that Method is set to **Total number of items & Angle to fill**.

- In the **Total number of items** Text box, enter *30*.

- In the **Angle to fill** Text box, enter *360*.

- Select **Preview**.

- Right-click to accept if correct. If incorrect, press **Esc** to repeat the process.

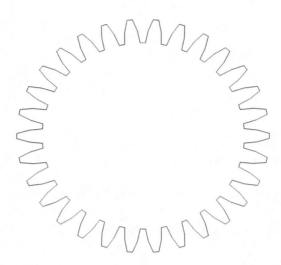

- When finished, **Erase** the screen.

Fillet

1. Create a **Fillet** between two entities by doing the following:

   - Set **Snap** and **Grid** to **On** and **Ortho, Polar, Osnap, Otrack, Ducs** and **Dyn** to *Off.*

   - Construct the geometry at a user-specified Location as shown below.

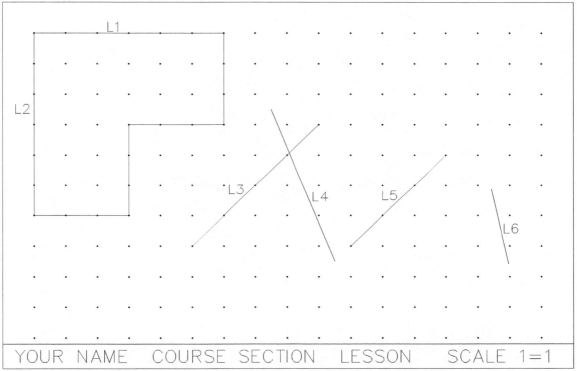

   - Set **Snap** to *Off.*

   - In the **Modify** toolbar, click on the **Fillet** button.

   - Type *R* (for **Radius**), then *[ENTER].*

   - Type *0.25* then *[ENTER].*

- As you are prompted to select first Object, select **L1**.

- As you are prompted select second Object, select **L2**.

- Use the *[ENTER]* key to start the **Fillet** Command again.

- Type *M* (for **Multiple**) and **Fillet** the remaining 5 corners of the closed shape as shown below. It is not necessary to restart the **Fillet** Command while using the **Multiple** option. *[ENTER]* when finished.

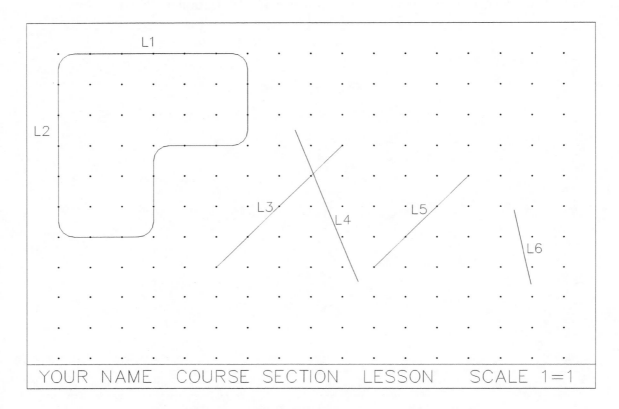

- Command: *Fillet* then *[ENTER]*.

- Pick **L3** and then **L4** below the intersection of **L3** and **L4**.{L3 and L4 are trimmed to each other as shown on the next page.}

- Command: *Fillet* then *[ENTER]*.

- Pick **L5** and then **L6**. {Lines are extended into each other as shown below.}

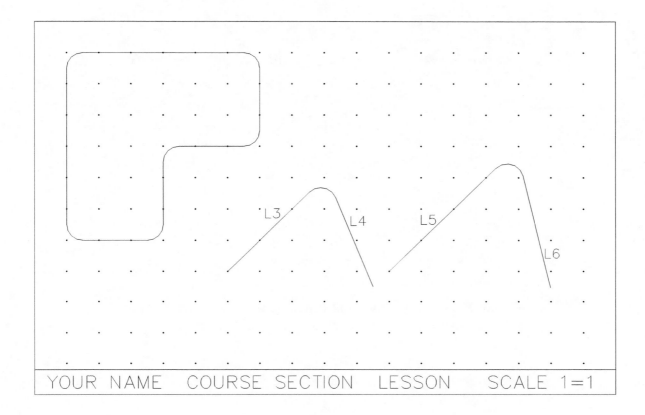

- **Undo** twice to undo the two **Fillets** placed on lines **L3-L6**.

- **Fillet L3** and **L4** with a fillet radius of **0.0**. {Lines are trimmed to each other.}

- **Fillet L5** and **L6** with a radius of **0.0**. {Lines are extended to each other.}

Note: When using the **Fillet** Tool, pressing the **Shift** key momentarily overrides the current fillet radius value. This way, you can **Trim** and/or **Extend** objects (using a fillet radius of 0) without having to constantly change the actual fillet radius value. Also note that when Zero unit **Fillet** or **Chamfer** Tools is used to **Trim** and/or **Extend** objects, in actuality, no **Fillet** or **Chamfer** is created. Objects are simply **Trimmed** and/or **Extended** to each other.

336

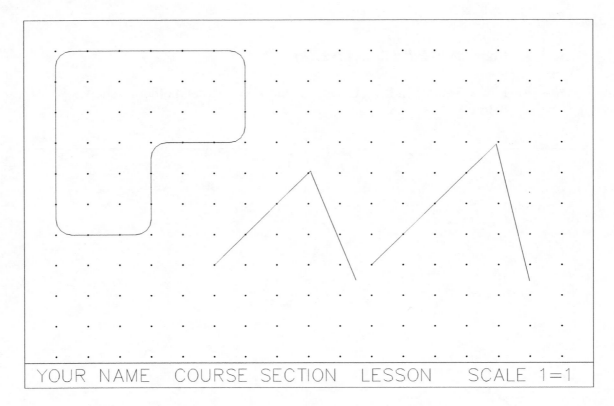

YOUR NAME   COURSE SECTION   LESSON   SCALE 1=1

- Do not **Erase** the geometry as it will be used in the next section.

Chamfer

1. **Undo** as many times as necessary to revert back to the original geometry as shown below.

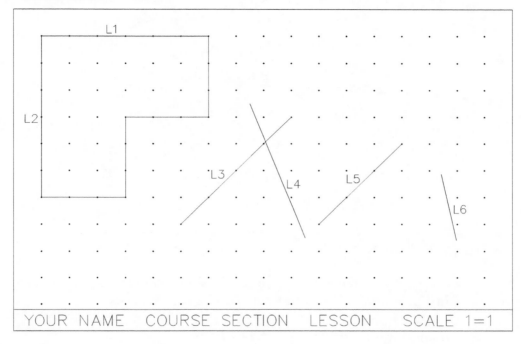

2. Create a **Chamfer** between two entities by doing the following:

- In the **Modify** toolbar, click on the **Chamfer** button.

- Type **D** (for **Distance**) then *[ENTER]*.

- Enter **First distance** of *0.25* then *[ENTER]*.

- Enter **Second distance** of *0.25* then *[ENTER]*.

- Select **L1** as your first line.

- Select **L2** as your second line.

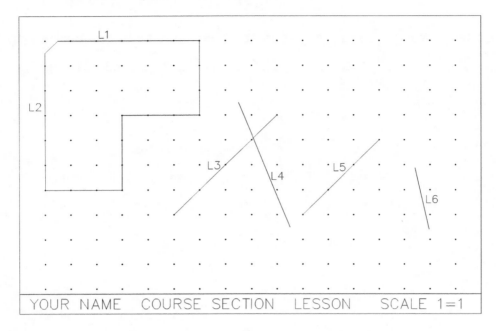

- **Chamfer** the remaining five corners of the closed shape using the **Multiple** option. When finished, *[ENTER]*.

- Command: *Chamfer* then *[ENTER]*.

- Pick line **L3** and then line **L4** (below the intersection of **L3** and **L4**).

- Command: *Chamfer* then *[ENTER]*.

- Pick **L5** and **L6** to **Chamfer** corner as shown.

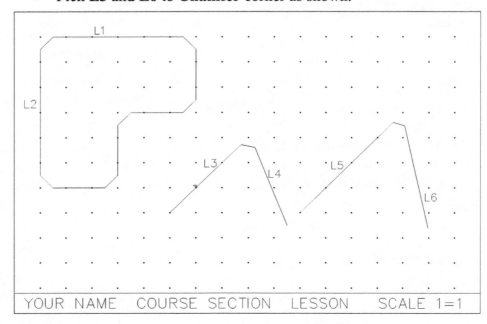

- **Undo** the last two **Chamfers** that were placed on lines **L3-L6**.

- Command: *Cha* then *[ENTER]*.

- Type **M** (for Multiple) and then *[ENTER]*.

- Hold down the **Shift** key and pick lines **L3** and **L4**. {**L3** and **L4** Trim to each other.}

- Hold down the **Shift** key and pick lines **L5** and **L6**. {**L5** and **L6** extend to each other.}

- To exit the **Chamfer** Command, press *[ENTER]*.

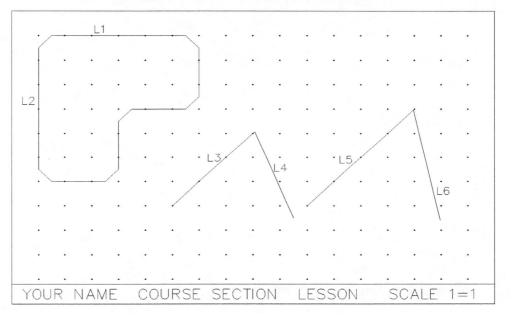

YOUR NAME   COURSE SECTION   LESSON   SCALE 1=1

Note: As in the case of the **Fillet**, the **Chamfer** Command can also be used to trim/extend two open entities into each other. Also note that you can create a zero distance **Fillet/Chamfer** by pressing the shift key.

- When finished, **Erase** all geometry.

Chamfer/Fillet Polylines

1. Make sure that **Grid** and **Snap** are set to *Off*.

2. Create the geometry shown below at user-specified Size and Location. Do not label them.

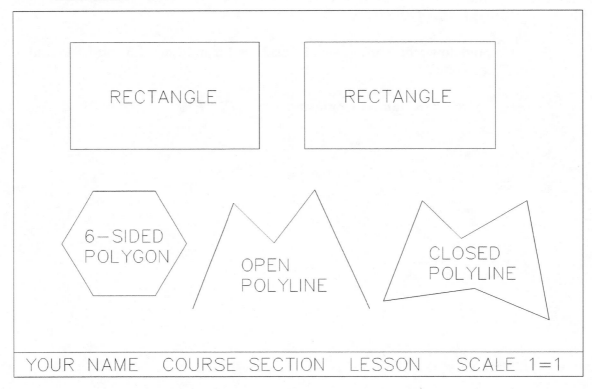

3. **Chamfer** a **Polyline** by doing the following:

   - Select the **Chamfer** button.

   - Set first and second **Chamfer Distances** to *0.25* .

   - Type *P* (for **Polyline**), then *[ENTER]*.

   - Select the upper left **Rectangle**. {All corners are **Chamfered** in one operation.}

4. **Fillet** a **Polyline** by doing the following:

- Select the **Fillet** button.

- Set the **Radius** to *0.25* .

- Type *P* (for **Polyline**) then *[ENTER]*.

- Select the upper right Rectangle. {All corners are **Filleted** in one operation.}.

- Use the polyline option of the **Fillet** Command to fillet the **Hexagon** and the open and closed Polylines as shown below.

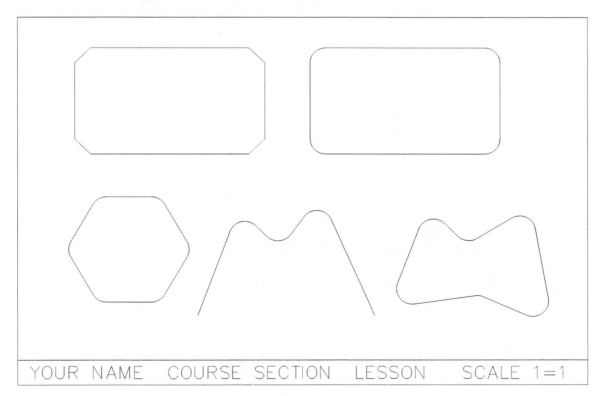

YOUR NAME   COURSE SECTION   LESSON   SCALE 1=1

- When finished, **Erase** geometry.

<u>Align</u>

1. Make sure that **Snap** and **Grid** are set to *Off*, and set **OSnap** running mode to **Endpoint**.

2. Draw a **Line** and a 6-sided **Polygon** as shown below. Exact size and location are user-specified.

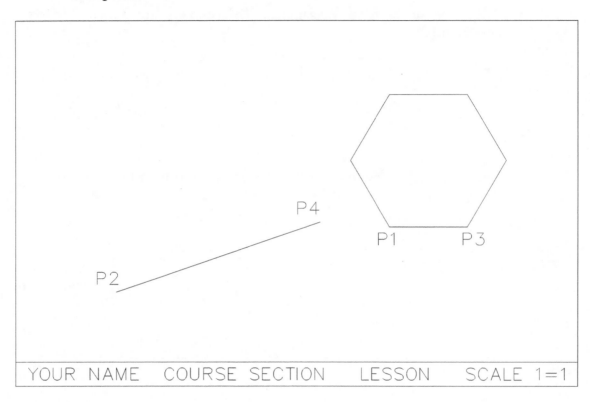

YOUR NAME   COURSE SECTION   LESSON   SCALE 1=1

3. **Align** an Object by doing the following:

    *   Command: *Align* then *[ENTER]*.

    *   Select only the **Polygon** then *[ENTER]*.

    *   Specify the **First Source Point** as **P1**.

    *   Specify the **First Destination Point** as **P2**.

    *   Specify the **Second Source Point** as **P3**.

    *   Specify the **Second Destination Point** as **P4**.

    *   When asked for the **Third Source Point,** press *[ENTER]* to **continue**.

- When asked to Scale object based on alignment point, select **No** and then *[ENTER]*. {The Polygon does not Scale.}

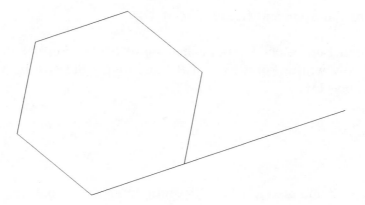

Note: The **Polygon** is **Aligned** with the **Line** as shown above. Had you entered **Yes** for the **Scale** option, the edge of **Polygon** would have also **Scaled** to the length of the **line** as shown below.

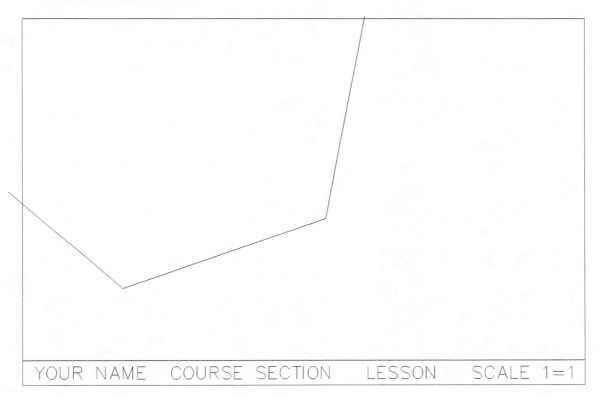

YOUR NAME   COURSE SECTION   LESSON   SCALE 1=1

4. When finished, **Erase** the screen.

344

Divide

1. Make sure that **Snap** and **Grid** are set to *Off*.

2. From Menu Bar, select **Format,** then **Point Style**. Set the **Point Style** to that shown below with a **Point Size** of *0.1* and toggle **Set size in Absolute Units** to **On** then press **OK**.

3. Draw an **Arc** and also a 3" x 2" **Rectangle** as shown below. Exact location is user-specified.

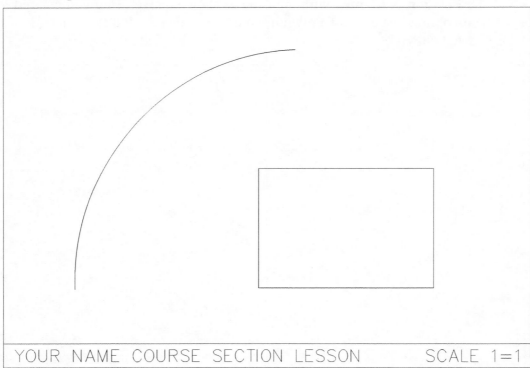

YOUR NAME COURSE SECTION LESSON   SCALE 1=1

4. **Divide** an entity into equal parts by doing the following:

- Command: *Divide* then *[ENTER]*.

- Select the **Arc**.

- Type *7* for the **Number of Segments** then *[ENTER]*.

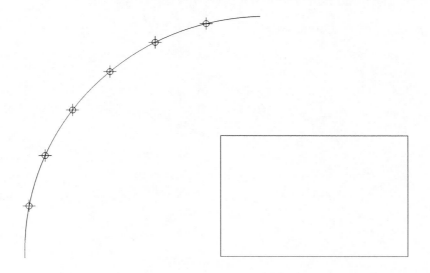

Note: A total of six **Points** have been placed on the **Arc**, **Dividing** it into seven equal parts. The **Arc** is not actually segmented, just **Divided** evenly using **Points**. **Divide** also works on a closed shape.

5. **Divide** the **Rectangle** using the same process as before with *20* segments, as shown below.

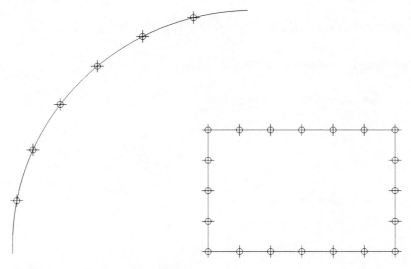

6. When finished, **Erase** the screen.

346

<u>Measure</u>

1. Set **Snap**, **Grid**, and **OSnap** to *Off*.

2. It is assumed that the **Point Style** settings are the same as in the previous exercise.

3. Draw an **Arc** as shown below at a user-specified location.

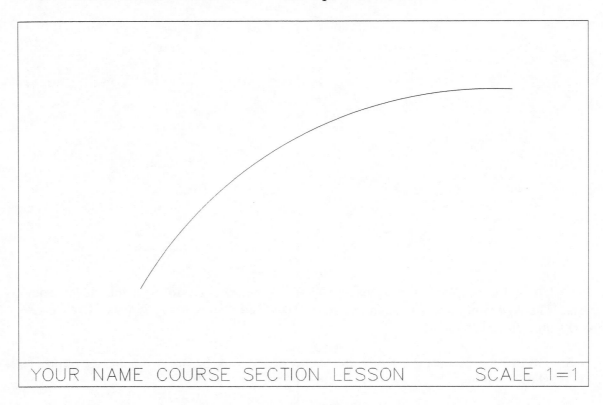

YOUR NAME COURSE SECTION LESSON   SCALE 1=1

4. **Measure** intervals along an Entity by doing the following:

   - Command: *Measure* then *[ENTER]*.

   - Select the **Arc** near the lower end.

- Type *.75* for the segment length then *[ENTER]*. {The **Arc** will appear as shown below.}

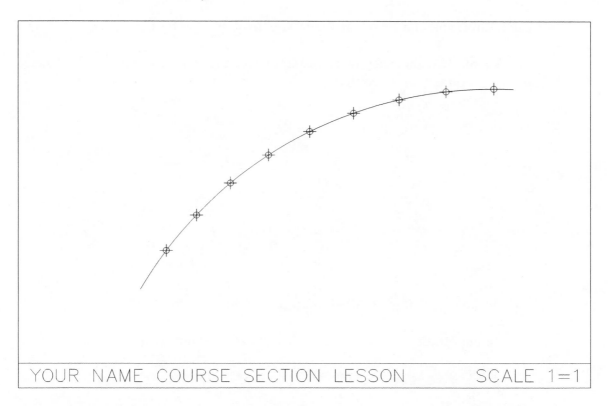

YOUR NAME COURSE SECTION LESSON   SCALE 1=1

Note: The **Measure** Command places points along the length of the selected Object, beginning at the **Endpoint** closest to the point of selection. It continues to measure at the specified interval until it reaches the end as shown by the image above. The last segment in the direction of measuring will not necessarily be the same interval as those preceding.

In contrast, the **Divide** Command places points along the Object selected to create a user-specified number of intervals of equal lengths.

5. When finished, **Erase** the screen.

Break at Point

1. Break a Line using the **Break at Point** Tool by doing the following:

- Create two intersecting **Lines** similar to those shown below. The exact location is User Specified.

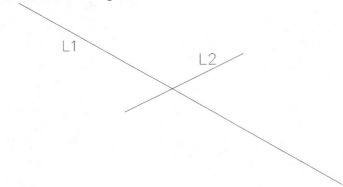

- Make sure that the **Object Snap** running mode is set to *Off*.

- In the **Modify** toolbar, click on the **Break at Point** button.

- Select Line **L1**.

- When asked to specify first break point, type **Int** (for **Osnap Intersection**) and then *[ENTER]*.

- Select the **Intersection** of the two Lines as the **First Break Point**. {AutoCAD will exit from the **Break at Point** Command and the Lines will appear unchanged; however, line **L1** is broken into two new line segments: **L1** and **L3**.}

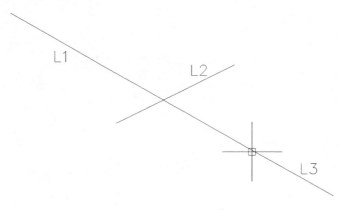

- In the **Modify** toolbar, click on the **Move** button and **Move** Line **L3** to a user-specified location as shown below.

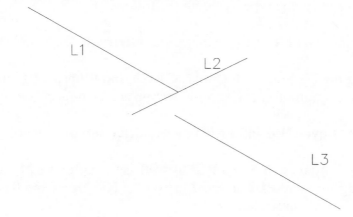

- When finished, **Erase** the screen.

Note: In order to convert a **Circle** to an **Arc** or to convert an **Ellipse** to an **Arc Ellipse**, it is more efficient to use the **Trim** Command using an edge as opposed to using the **Break** Command.

Join

1. **Join** Objects of the same type by doing the following:

   - Set **Snap**, **Grid**, **Ortho**, **Polar**, **Osnap**, **Otrack**, **Ducs** and **Dyn** to *Off*.

   - Create the Lines **L1-L4**, Circles **C1-C2**, and Ellipse **EL1** similar to the given diagram. Exact size and location are user-specified.

   - Create **Layer Hid** and assign the Hidden **linetype** to that layer.

   - Create Polylines **PL1** and **PL2** as well as the Splines **SP1** and **SP2** while making sure that **PL2** and **SP2** are on the **Hid** Layer and that they share endpoints as shown below.

   - Use the **Endpoint** option of **OSnap** to ensure that the two Polylines and the two Splines share their Endpoints respectively as shown below.

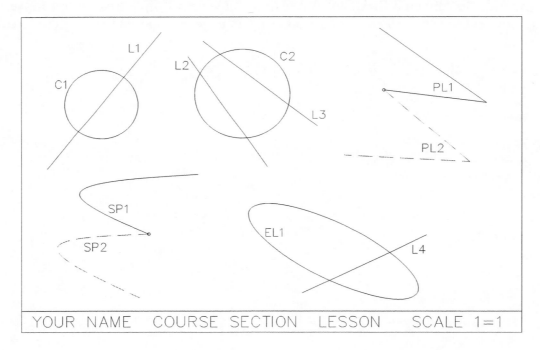

- **Trim** Line **L1** to Circle **C1** as shown below.

- **Trim** Circle **C2** to Lines **L2** and **L3** as shown below.

- **Trim EL1** to **L4** as shown below.

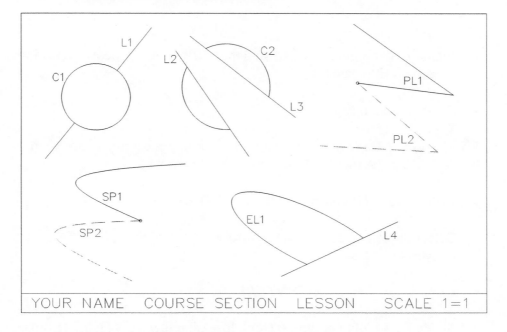

- **Erase** Circle **C1** and Lines **L2**, **L3** and **L4**.

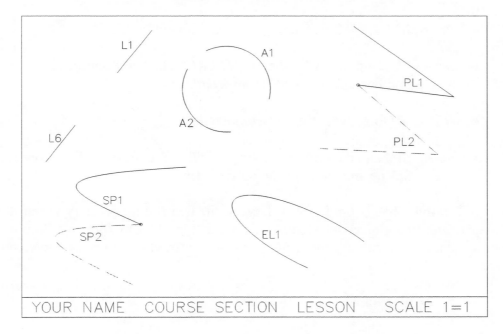

352

- Select the **Join** tool.

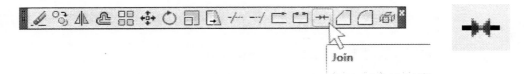

- Pick the two segments of **L1** and then *[ENTER]*. {The two lines join and become a single entity}

- Select the **Join** tool.

- Pick Arc **A1** and then Arc **A2** near their upper endpoints and then *[ENTER]*. {**A1** and **A2** join into a single arc }

- Command: **J** (for **Join**) and then *[ENTER]*.

- Select the joined arc and type *L* (for Close) and then *[ENTER]*. {Arc converts to a Circle.}

- Command: *J* and then *[ENTER]*.

- Select **EL1** and then type *L* (for Close) and then *[ENTER]*. {Ellipse Arc becomes an Ellipse.}

- Press *[ENTER]* Key to activate last Command.

- Select **PL1** and then **PL2** then *[ENTER]*. {The two Polylines Join into a single Polyline and are placed on Layer 0}

- *[ENTER]* to activate the last Command.

- Select **SP2** and then **SP1** and then *[ENTER]*. {The two Splines Join into a single **Spline** and are placed on Layer **Hid.**}

Note: When **Joining** Objects on different Layers, the end result geometry is transferred to the **Layer** of the first Object selected. Also note that in order to **Join** two Polylines or two Splines, generally speaking, they must have a shared end vertex as shown in the above example.

- **Erase** all geometry from the screen.

- Make sure that **Layer 0** is set to **Current**.

Clean Screen

At the end of each chapter, you are given a list of aliases for many useful AutoCAD Commands. Using the instructions given below, you can begin utilizing the **Clean Screen** option efficiently.

1. Create Objects using the **Clean Screen** option by doing the following:

   - Select **View** then **Clean Screen** from the Menu Bar.

   - **Zoom All** if necessary.

   - Type *L* (for **Line**) then *[ENTER]*. Create a diagonal **Line** at a user-specified location as shown below.

   - Press *[ENTER]*. {Line Command cancels.}

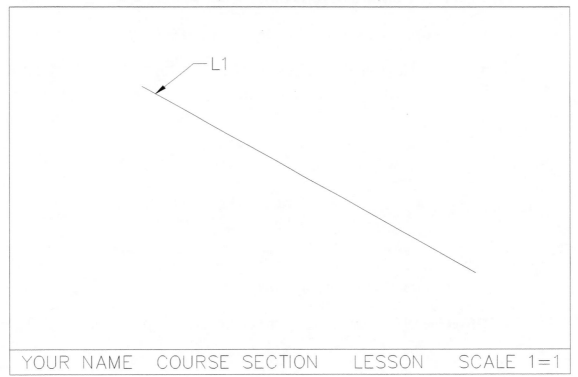

- Type *C* (for **Circle**), then *[ENTER]*. Create a **Circle C1** which overlaps the lower end of **L1** as shown below.

- Create **Line L2** such that it overlaps the upper end of **L1** as shown below.

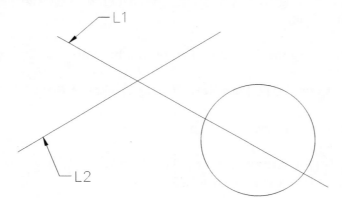

- Type *Tr* (for **Trim**) then *[ENTER]*.

- Use **Crossing** to select all of the Objects then *[ENTER]*.

- **Trim** as shown below and when finished press *[ENTER]* to exit the **Trim** Command.

- Type *O* (for **Offset**), then *[ENTER]*.

- **Offset** the Objects by **.1** units to the outside (up) as shown below.

- Press *[ENTER]* to exit the **Offset** Command.

- Type *F* (for **Fillet**) then *[ENTER]*.

- Type *R* (for **Radius**) then *[ENTER]*.

- Type *0.0* then *[ENTER]*.

- **Fillet** the geometry to that of below.

- Type *E* (for **Erase**) then *[ENTER]*. **Erase** the screen.

- From the Menu Bar, select **View** and toggle **Clean Screen** {Toolbars return.}

Note: Once you are familiar with the **Aliases** associated with common Commands and the **Clean Screen** option, you can incorporate this method into any project. If you have a need for speed, it is critical to become familiar with the use of **Aliases** and the **Clean Screen** option. This allows for a balanced act between mouse and keyboard entry. For practice, make it a point to run through the Guitar Project (assignment 8) a second time using the **Clean Screen** option.

<u>Aliases and Hot Keys</u>

ALIGN .... AL

ARRAY .... AR

BREAK AT POINT .... BR

CHAMFER .... CHA

COPY .... CO

DIVIDE .... DIV

FILLET .... F

MEASURE .... ME

MIRROR .... MI

MOVE .... M

ROTATE .... RO

SCALE .... SC

STRETCH .... S

CLEAN SCREEN .... CTRL+0

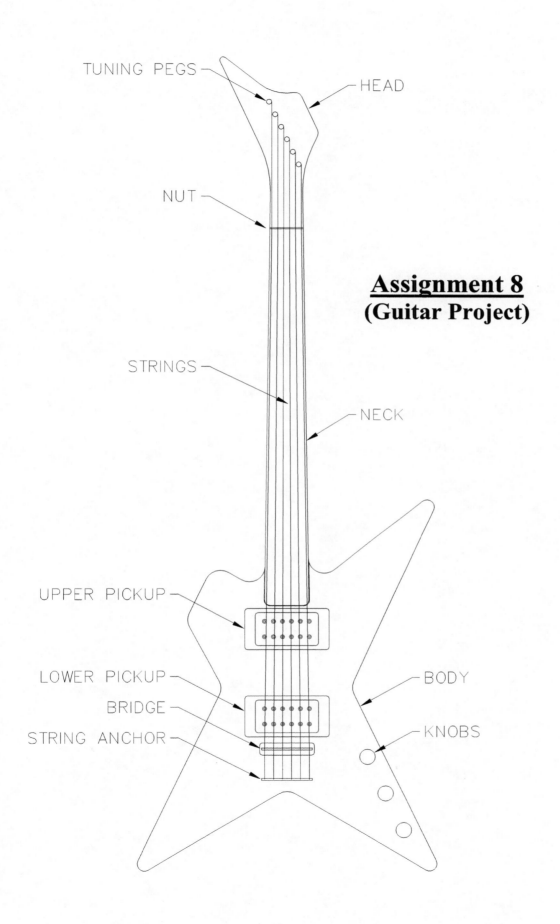

TUNING PEGS

HEAD

NUT

Assignment 8
(Guitar Project)

STRINGS

NECK

UPPER PICKUP

LOWER PICKUP

BRIDGE

STRING ANCHOR

BODY

KNOBS

1. Launch AutoCAD and enter a blank Drawing.

- Set **Units** to Decimal with a **Precision** of *0.000*.

- Set **Limits** to LL *0,0* UR *48,32*.

- Set **Grid** and **Snap** both to *0.5*. Set the **aDaptive Grid** option to **No**.

- **Zoom All**.

- Create a **Rectangle** at the boundaries of your **Limits**.

- Create new **Layers** with the names: **Body, Bridge, Construction, Head, Knobs, Neck, Nut, Pickups, Points, Strings, String Anchor**, and **Tuning Pegs** and assign a suitable color to each **Layer**.

- Set **Construction Layer** to **Current**.

- Create a horizontal **Construction Line** centered vertically.

- Create a vertical **Construction Line** located 10 units to the right of the Origin.

2. **Save** the Drawing file to your folder. Name it **"ASSIGN08_ _ _.dwg"** where the 3 blanks are your initials.

Note: In this project you will be positioning most Objects geometrically. Therefore, at times, the original position of Objects are not critical. Later you will move and position them properly. This is how most projects are actually accomplished in industry. Also remember to **Save** frequently.

3. Creating the Bridge:

- Set **Bridge Layer** to **Current**.

- Turn **Grid** and **Snap** *Off.*

- Create 2 **Rectangles** at user-specified locations with the given dimensions: **Base = 0.6 Height = 2.6** and **Base = 0.1 Height = 2.4**.

- Use **OSnap** to construct a diagonal line for each rectangle from corner to corner as shown below.

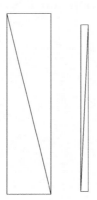

- Use the **Midpoints** of the diagonals to **Move** the smaller rectangle to the geometric center of the larger rectangle. Make sure to use **Zoom** and **Pan** as needed.

- Change **Point Type** to that shown below by selecting **Point Style** in the **Format Menu-Bar**. Set **Point Size** to *0.15* and toggle **Set Size in Absolute Units** to **On**, then select **OK**.

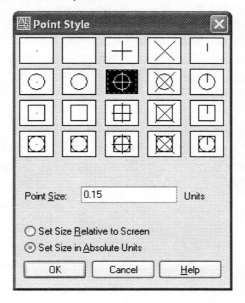

- Use the **Point** Command to create a **Point** on **Layer Points** at a user-specified location.

- **Rectangular Array** the **Point** to these settings: **Rows = 6, Columns = 1, Row offset = 0.425**.

- Draw a **Line** connecting the first and the last of the six points. Make sure to use the **OSnap Node** option.

- Use the **Midpoint** of this **Line** to geometrically center the **Points** on to the center of the Bridge.

- Geometrically Center the entire Bridge to the Intersection of the two **Construction Lines** as shown.

Horizontal **Construction Line**

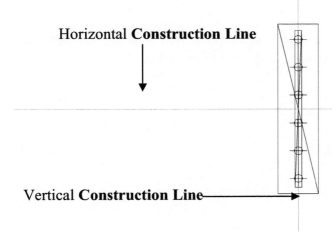

Vertical **Construction Line**

- Once the Bridge is centered, **Erase** the two diagonals.

4. Creating the **String Anchor**:

- Use the **Displacement** option of the **Copy** Command to copy the inner rectangle and the six points by **1.5** units to the left horizontally. You may refer to page 304 for a review of Copying Objects horizontally or vertically.

- Change the **Property** of the rectangular shape of **String Anchor** so that it resides on **Layer String Anchor** while keeping the **Point** Objects on **Layer Points**. If needed, refer to page 130 (item 6) for the technique to **Change** an Object's **Layer**.

5. Creating the Nut:

- Again **Copy** the inner rectangle and the six points of the Bridge to the right by *25.65*

- **Pan** over to the Nut and **Scale** it down by a factor of **0.66** using its geometric **Center** as the Base Point.

- **Change** the **Property** of the rectangular shape of **Nut** so that it resides on **Layer Nut** while leaving the **Point** Objects on **Layer Points**.

6. Creating the Strings:

- Set **Strings** as the **Current Layer**.

- Set the **OSnap Mode** to **Node** only and use the **Line** Command to connect all the **Points** first from the String Anchor to the Bridge, and then from the Bridge to the Nut respectively as shown below.

7. Creating the Lower Pickup:

- Set the **Pickups** layer **as the Current Layer**.

- **Freeze** the **Points** and **String Layers**. {The **Strings** and **Points** disappear.}

- **Offset** the vertical **Construction Line** to the right by **1.6** units.

- Create the two rectangles with dimensions: **Base = 1.6 Height = 3.0, and Base = 2.0 Height = 4.0** and use the diagonal line technique to center them to the new intersection/position as shown below.

- **Fillet** the three rectangles shown below using the **Polyline** option with a **Radius= 0.125** .

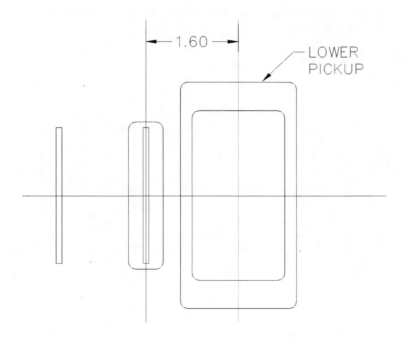

364

8. Create the Guitar's Pickup **Magnet**:

- Create a **Circle** with **R = 0.1** at a User Specified location and place an **Inscribed 6 sided Polygon R = 0.05 OSnapped** to the Circle's **Center**.

- **Array** the Pickup Magnet by: **Rows = 6, Columns = 2, Row Offset = 0.425, Column Offset = 0.75**

- Geometrically center the 12 Pickup Magnets to the Pickup as shown.

- **Erase** the right-most vertical **Construction Line**.

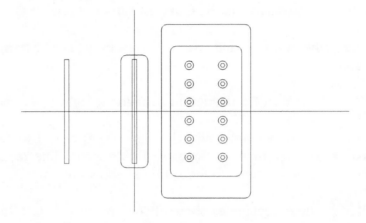

9. Creating the Lower Pickup:

- Use the **displacement** option of the **Copy** Command to copy the Upper Pickup by **4.25** units to the right.

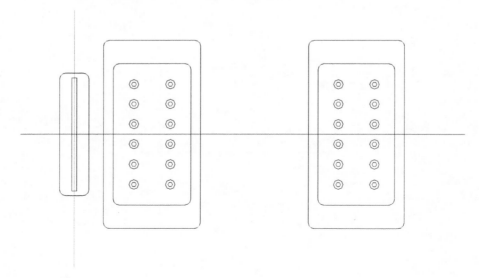

Note: Remember to **Save** your work frequently.

10. Creating the **Neck**.

- **Offset** the original vertical **Construction Line by** *7.0* units to the right and move this new **Offset Line** to **Layer Neck**.

- **Thaw Layer Strings** and **Pan** over to the Nut area.

- **Offset** the Upper String (shown below on the left by **L1**) **Through** the upper right **Endpoint** of the Nut as shown below by point **P1** . {The upper edge of Neck is constructed.}

- **Offset** the Lower String (shown below on the right by **L2**) **Through** the lower right **Endpoint** of the Nut as shown below by point **P2**. {The lower edge of Neck is constructed.}

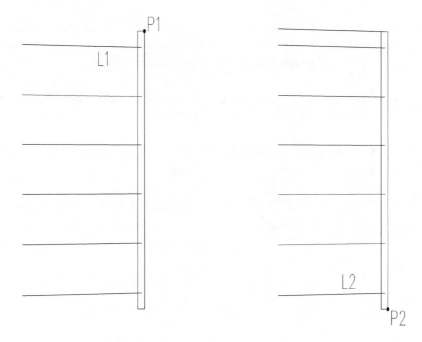

- **Change** the **Layer Property of** the two recently created Lines so that they reside on **Layer Neck**.

- **Freeze Layer Strings**.
- To achieve the neck, **Fillet** the three **Lines** to a **Radius** of *0.25* as shown below.

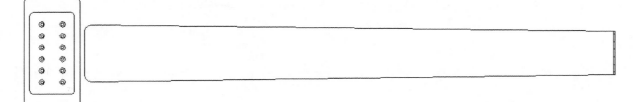

11. Creating the Body:

- **Offset** the original vertical Construction Line by **3** units to the right which defines a new intersection.

- Make **Layer Body Current**.

- Ensure that **OSnap** is set to *Off*.

- Create a Circle **R = 10.75** with the **Center** located at this new intersection.

- **Erase** the vertical construction line going through the **Center** of the large Circle.

- Use your knowledge of Relative Polar Coordinate System to create a **Line** starting at the 9 o'clock Quad of the large Circle having a length of 10 units and extending out at a 14-degree angle.

- **Mirror** the 10 unit Line (shown below in bold) about the Horizontal axis of the Guitar. Make use of **Ortho** to ensure accuracy.

- Use the **Shift** and **CTRL** techniques (discussed in Chapter 3) to select and **Lock** all **Layers** excluding **Body**.

- To create the Body, **Polar Array** the two Lines shown below in bold using a total number of **4** Items about the **Center** of the large Circle by **360** degrees.

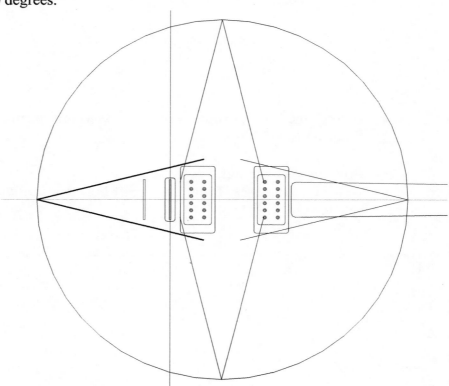

- **Rotate** the Body by 45 degrees about the **Center** of the large Circle.

- **Erase** the large Circle.

- Use **Fillet** with a **Radius=0** to trim the Body as shown.

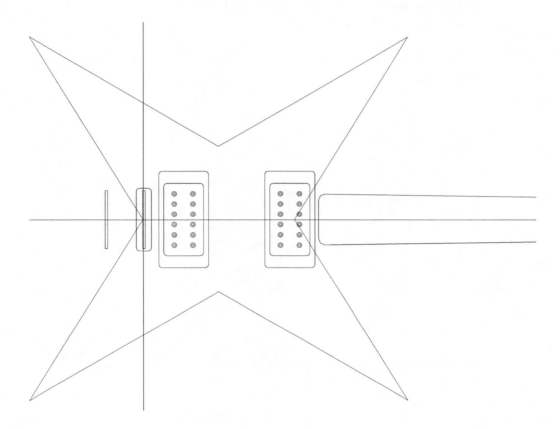

Note: You are about to use the **Stretch** Command to stretch the body of the guitar. Keep in mind that when using the **Stretch** Command, the **Crossing** selection method (Right to Left) must be used. Also note that all **Layers** other than the **Body Layer** are **Locked** and therefore cannot be selected and stretched by error.

- Set **Ortho** to **On** and Horizontally **Stretch** the right half of the Body so that corners **P1**, **P2**, and **P3** move *1.0* unit to the right. When using the **Crossing**, select window such that points **P1**, **P2**, and **P3** are selected and P4, P5, P6, P7 and P8 are outside the **Crossing** window.

- Again **Stretch** the left half of the body so that only corners **P4**, **P5**, and **P6** move *2.0* units to the left. {**P7** and **P8** will remain in their original positions.}

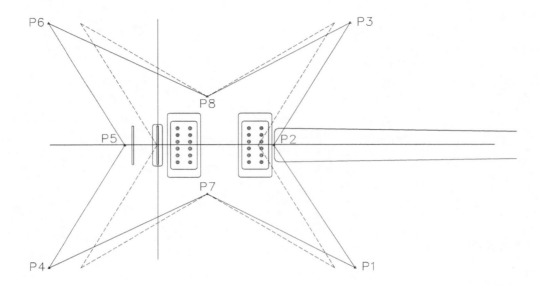

- Further **Stretch** the Lower Right Body Arm so that P1 moves *1.5* units to the right as shown below.

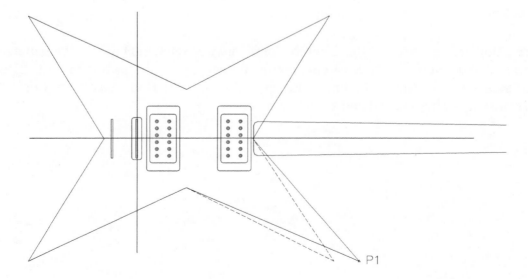

- **Fillet** the 3 corners shown with **R = 0.35** .

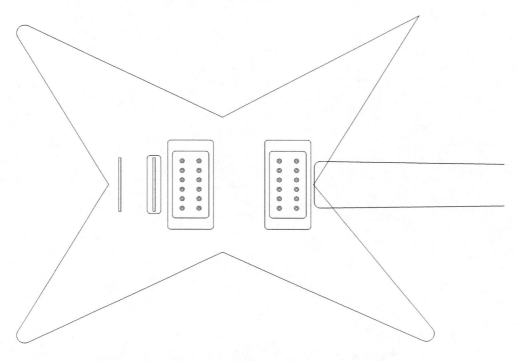

- **Offset** and then **Extend** the **Line** as shown below.

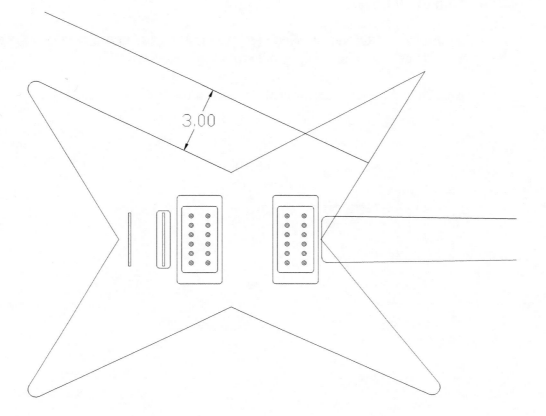

- **Fillet** the remaining 5 Body corners shown in bold with **R = 0.75** .

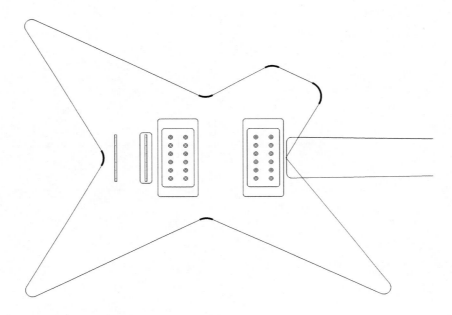

- Create **TTR Circles** with **R=0.75** tangent to both the Neck and Body on both sides and trim as shown below.

- **Unlock** all **Layers**.

- **Zoom in** and **Offset** the Neck (3 lines and 2 arcs) to the outside of Neck by *0.05* as shown in bold, then **Trim** to the two arcs.

- Move the 5 offset entities shown below to the **Body Layer**.

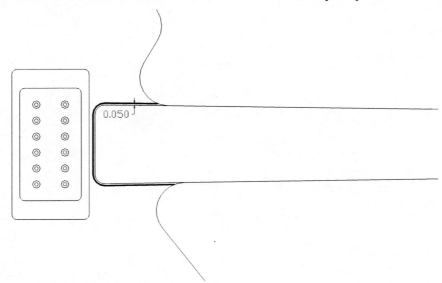

12. Creating the Head:

- **Copy** the Lower Right Body Arm (two lines shown in bold) to the right by **30.75** Units. {Objects fall outside **Limits** momentarily.}

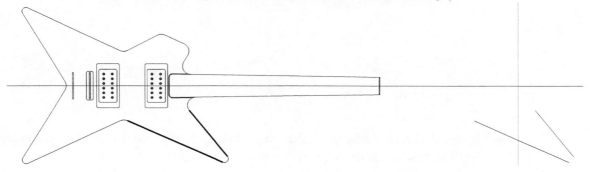

- **Extend** the two lines to the horizontal Construction Line.

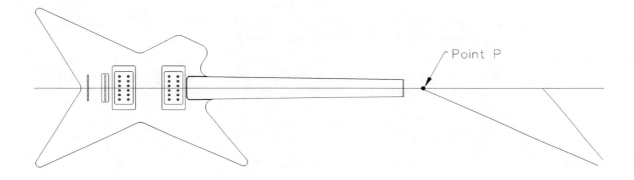

- Use point **P** as the **base point** to **Scale** the two extended lines using a scale factor of **0.45** as shown below.
- **Mirror** the Head about the horizontal axis, and **Fillet** the cleft (shown below in bold) with **R = 2.0** .

- **Offset** the Line by *2.75* as shown below.

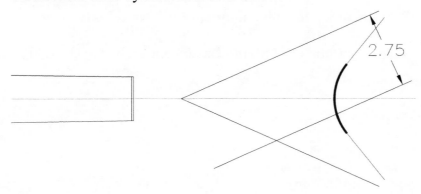

- **Fillet** the Head (3 places) with **R = 0.2** as shown and clean up.

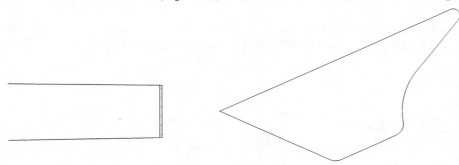

- **Extend** the two edges of the Neck to the Head and **Fillet** the geometry with **R = 5.0** as shown below.

- Use the **Break** (or the **Break at point**) tool to break Line **L1** at **P1** (the upper right corner of the Nut) as shown below.

- Use **Break** (or the **Break at point**) tool to break Line **L2** at **P2** (the lower right corner of the Nut) as shown below.

- Move all the Objects that make the head (twelve Objects shown below in bold) to **Layer** Head.

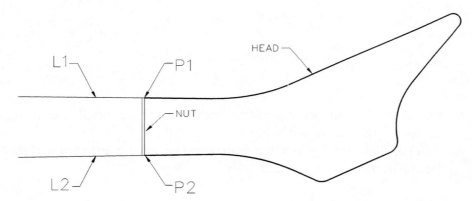

- Set **OSnap** to **On** with **Running Mode** set to **Node**.

- **Thaw** the **Points** and **String Layers** and make Layer **String Current**.

- Construct 6 Horizontal **Lines** originating from Nut **Points**, which extend past the Head. Make sure to use **Ortho**.

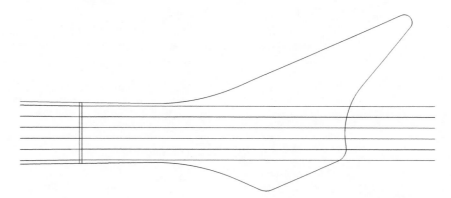

- **Freeze Points Layer**.

13. Creating the Tuning Pegs:

- **Offset** by **1.4** and **Extend** the edge of Head as shown below.

- **Trim** the six Strings to this offset **Line**.

- Make the **Tuning Pegs Layer Current**.

- Create a **Circle** with **R=0.125** at user-specified location.

- Set **OSnap Running Mode** to **Endpoint** and turn *Off* **Ortho**.

- **Copy** the Circle (a total of six times) so that the 6 o'clock **Quadrant** is located at the end of each string as shown below.

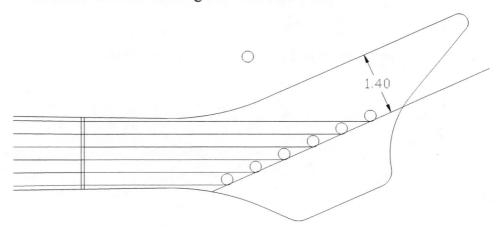

- Turn *Off* the **OSnap Running Mode**.

- **Erase** the **Offset Line** as well as the original **Circle** (Peg hole).

374

14. Make **Knobs Layer** Current and create the Knobs as shown along the *0.75* offset **Line**. Exact position is user-specified.

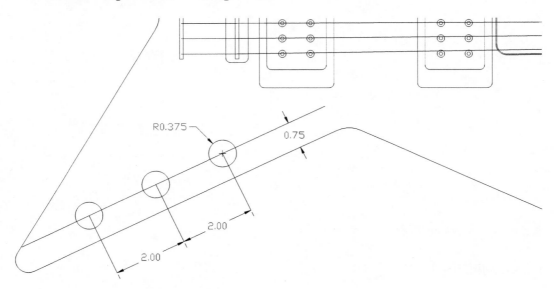

- To complete the project, **Freeze** the **Construction Layer** and **Erase** all other temporary **Offset** Lines in the Knob area.

- Add Title Block info with **Text Height** of *1.00* .

15. **Save** the Drawing.

16. Preview and Plot the Drawing using the following settings:

- Paper size: Letter (8.50x11.00 **inches**)
- Plot area: Limits
- Plot offset: Centered
- Plot scale: Scaled to Fit

Note: In Chapter 12, you will plot this Drawing again with several scale factors.

Chapter 9

Make Blocks
Insert Blocks
Modify and Update Blocks
Create a Library of Symbols
Tool Palette Blocks
Purge Blocks
Write Blocks

Make Blocks

In AutoCAD, a symbol such as a door, a window, or a hex-screw can be defined as a **Block.** Once a block is defined, it can easily be recalled by name and inserted into a Drawing. As you will also see, inserting a Block symbol in numerous locations allows for fast and easy editing and modifications.

1. Launch AutoCAD and use your **My Template** to begin a **New** Drawing.

2. From the **Status Line** set **Snap** and **Grid** to *On.* Set **Ortho, Polar, OSnap,** and **OTrack, Ducs** and **Dyn** to *Off.*

3. Set the **Snap** value to *0.25* and the **Grid** value to *0.5* .

4. Create Polygon **Pg1** using these settings: Number of sides *6,* Center located at *1.5,1.75* **Circumscribed,** Radius of *0.5.*

5. Create the Circle **C1** located at the same Center as that of **Pg1** with a Radius of *0.25*. Note that the Center of **Pg1** is on **Snap.**

6. With **Snap** set to *Off,* use **Text** to place **T** (for **Top**) and **B** (for **Bottom**) with a Text height of *.2* as shown on the given symbol as shown below.

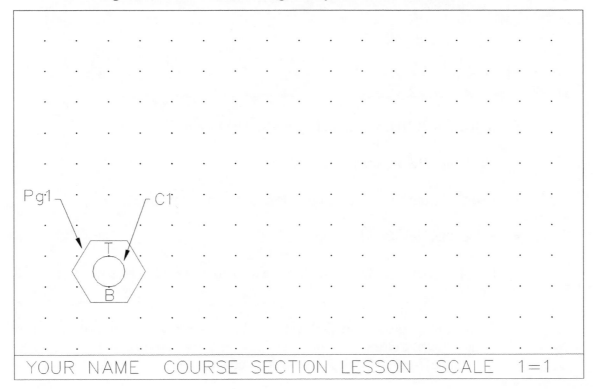

380

7. Define a Block by doing the following:

- In the **Draw Toolbar**, select the **Make Block** button.

Make Block

{The **Block Definition** dialog box will appear as shown below.}

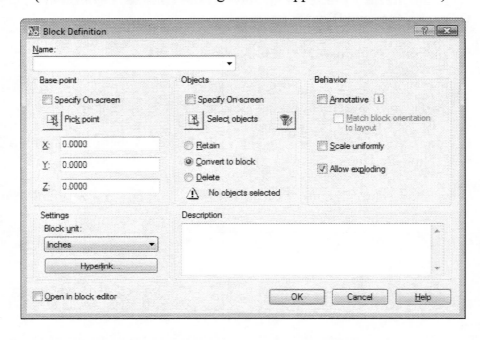

- In the **Block Definition** dialog box, enter the name *Hex*.

- Click on **Select Objects** button.

- Use **Crossing** to select the complete Hex symbol then *[ENTER]*.

- Select the **Pick Point** button.

- For the insertion **Base point**, set **Snap** to **On** and select the Center of Circle **C1**.

- In the **Block definition** dialog box, make sure that the **Retain** option is Toggled **On**. Setting **Retain** to **On** assumes that the original geometry is not converted to a Block. More on this concept later.

- Select **OK**.

Insert Blocks

In the next set of steps, you will **Insert** your **Hex Block** on the screen several times using different settings.

1. **Insert Block** by doing the following:

   - Make sure that **Snap** is set to *0.25*.

   - In the **Draw** Toolbar select the **Insert Block** button.

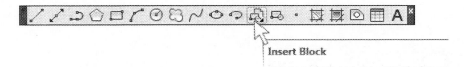

   Insert Block

   - As the **Insert Block** dialog box appears, check for the name to be pre-selected as **Hex** and that all settings do match that of diagram below.

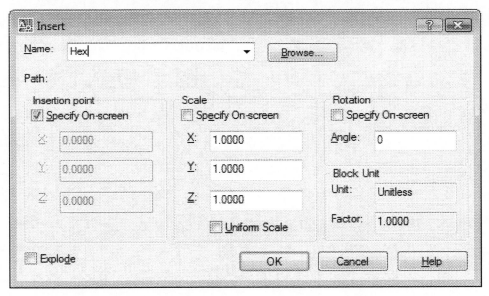

   - Select **OK**.

Note: The Hex symbol should drag within the screen area. If not, then it is possible that while making a **Block**, Objects were not selected properly, or your **Dragmode System Variable** (covered in Chapter 10) is set to *Off*. Consult with your instructor.

   - Pick a user-specified point to **Insert** the **Block** as shown in position **A** of the next page.

382

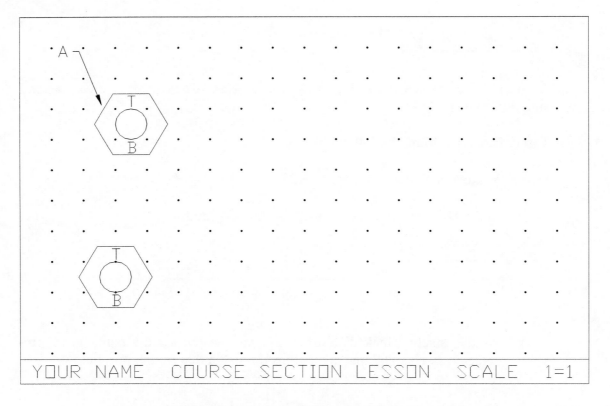

- Select **Insert Block** again. {The **Insert** dialog box appears.}

- In the **Rotation** are, set **Angle** to *10* degrees and insert this rotated Block as shown in about position **B** below.

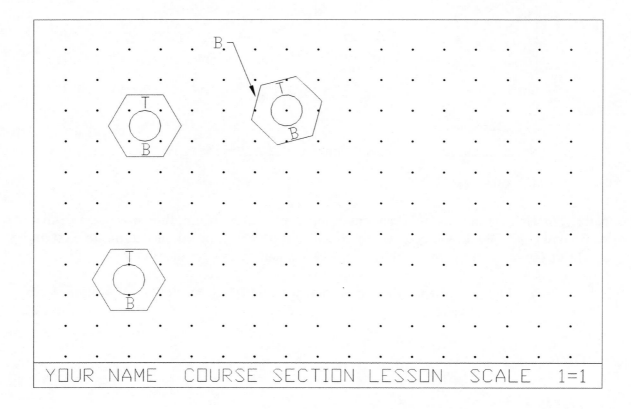

- Select the **Insert Block** tool again.

- In the **Scale** area, make sure that the **Uniform Scale** is toggled to **On** and set X=*1.5* .

- Select **OK**.

- Pick a point on the screen to insert **Hex** as shown about position **C** below.

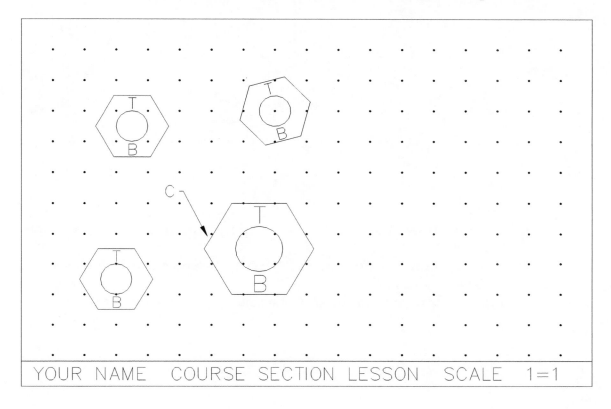

YOUR NAME   COURSE SECTION LESSON   SCALE   1=1

- Select the **Insert Block** tool.

- In the **Scale** area, toggle *Off* the **Uniform Scale** and set **X scale factor** to *–1* *(*negative).

- Select **OK**.

- Pick a user-specified point on the screen to insert **Hex** as shown about position **D** shown on the next page. {The **Block** is inverted about the Y-Axis}

384

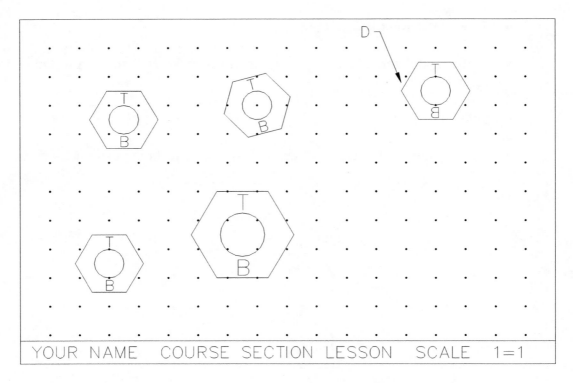

- Select the **Insert Block** tool to Insert the **Hex** Block as shown in position **E** below.
- In the **Scale** area, make sure that **Specify on-screen** and **Uniform Scale** are both toggled to *Off*
- Type in a **Y scale factor** of *−1* (for negative 1) and then select **OK**.

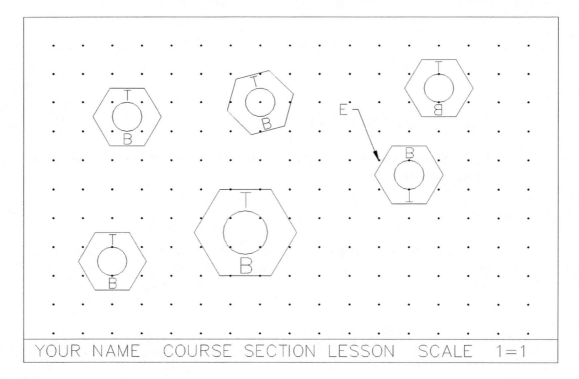

- **Insert** Hex Block again with the scale factor X=*1.5* as shown in position **F**. {The Block is Scaled about the X-Axis only.}

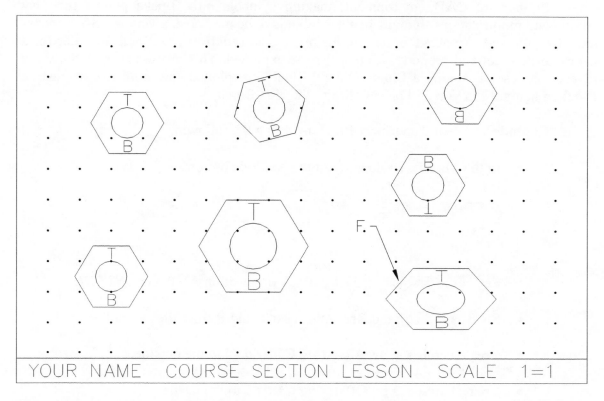

YOUR NAME   COURSE SECTION LESSON   SCALE   1=1

Note: Using negative X and Y scale factors allows for inverting (flipping) the symbol about the insertion point in the vertical and horizontal directions respectively.

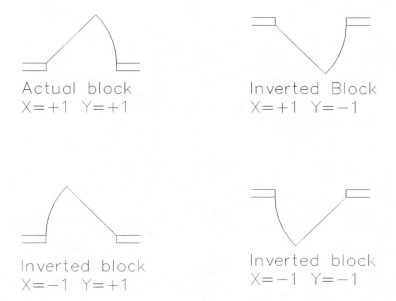

Actual block
X=+1 Y=+1

Inverted Block
X=+1 Y=−1

Inverted block
X=−1 Y=+1

Inverted block
X=−1 Y=−1

Redefine and Update Blocks

In the AutoCAD environment, making symbols into Blocks allows for easy editing and modifications. If and when a symbol is to be modified, a very specific process must be followed. AutoCAD refers to this process as **redefining** a **Block**. In order for a **Block** to be redefined properly, it must first be exploded. This process is essentially the reverse process of making a **Block**. Once a **Block** is exploded and modified, it must be **Blocked** again. Next you will be **redefining** the **Hex Block**.

1. **Explode** and then **Redefine** a **Block** by doing the following:

   - In the **Modify** Toolbar select the **Explode** button.

   - Select the first inserted Hex Block (in position A), then *[ENTER]*.

   - Set **Snap** to *Off* and **Erase** the Text **T** and **B** from the symbol.

   - Create Circle **C2** by **Offsetting C1** by *0.25* to the outside.

   - Create Circle **C3** by **Offsetting C1** *0.05* to the inside.

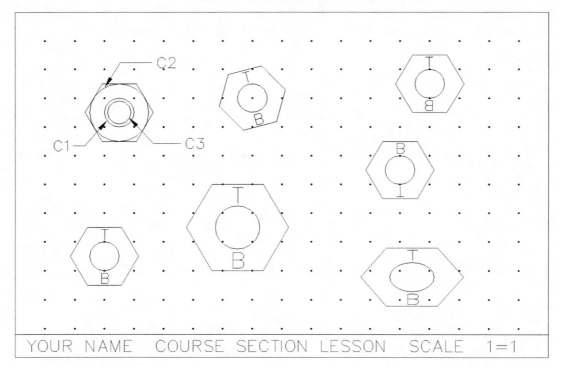

- Create **New Layers HID** and **CEN** and assign line-types **Hidden** and **Center** to those **Layers** respectively. Keep Layer **0** Current.

- Set **LTscale** to *0.25*.

- Change the **Layer Property** of Circles **C1** to the **HID Layer**. Refer to page 130 (item 6) if necessary.

- Set **Snap** back to *On* and draw the two centerlines on **Layer 0** as shown.

- Change the **Layer** property of the Center Lines to **Layer CEN**.

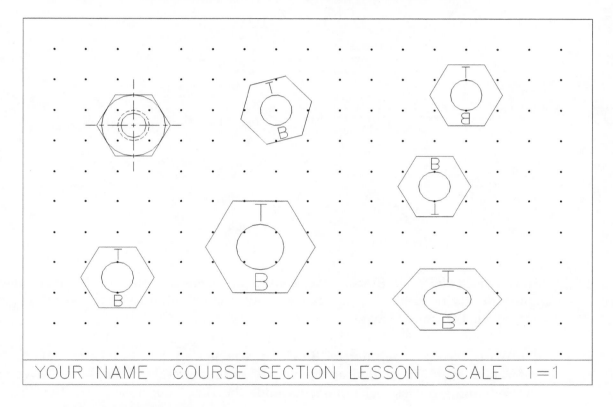

YOUR NAME   COURSE SECTION LESSON   SCALE   1=1

- Select the **Make Block** tool.

- Name the **Block** the same as before. You should not have to type in the name again. From the drop-down list, select the name **Hex**.

- Click on the **Select Object** button and then select the Object by crossing on the modified symbol and then *[ENTER]*.

- Select the **Pick Point** button to choose the Center of the symbol as your **Base point**.

- Select **OK**.

388

- When asked if you want to **Update Block Reference,** select **Yes**. {The Hex symbol updates across the screen. Keep in mind that the original Hex geometry was retained and therefore is not a Block}

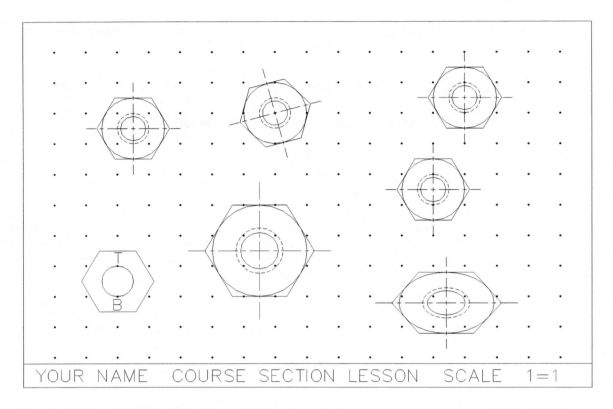

YOUR NAME   COURSE SECTION LESSON   SCALE   1=1

Note: Since the **Hex Block** is redefined, all inserted copies of the **Hex Block** are automatically updated. As you can see, this method allows you to easily update your symbols in the entire Drawing at once.

Caution: When **redefining** a **Block**, if you get an error message stating: **"Block references itself,"** it could mean that you did not successfully **Explode** the **Block** prior to the **redefining** process. Therefore, **Explode** the **Block** and repeat the **Block** definition process.

2. When finished, **Erase** the screen while remaining in the Drawing.

Note: The **Explode** Command can also be used to change Objects such as **Rectangles**, **Polygons**, and **Polylines** into less complex entities (i.e., Lines, Arcs).

Create a Library of Symbols

In this section, you will create your own library of symbols. Then by using the **Design Center**, you will have easy access to them for **Insertion** into any Drawing.

1. **Insert Hex Block** at coordinates **3,2** with **Rotation Angle** = *0* and **Scale** = *1*.

2. **Insert Hex Block** to the right of the first as shown below. Exact location is user - specified.

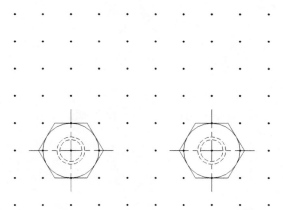

3. **Explode** the **Hex Block** on the right.

4. With **Snap** set to *Off,* **Erase** the Hexagon and Hidden Circle in the **Exploded Block** as shown below.

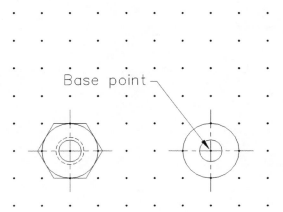

5. Set **Snap** to *On*

6. **Block** this new symbol, naming it **Washer**. Use its center as the **Basepoint** as shown above.

7. Construct the **Screw** symbol directly above the **Hex** as shown on the next page. Include **Centerline**. All Corners of shape fall on a **0.25 Snap**.

8. **Block** the symbol with the name **Screw** and select the **Basepoint** as shown below.

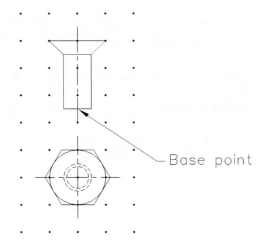

Base point

Note: Below is a summary of the **Blocks** created which will serve as your Symbols Library.

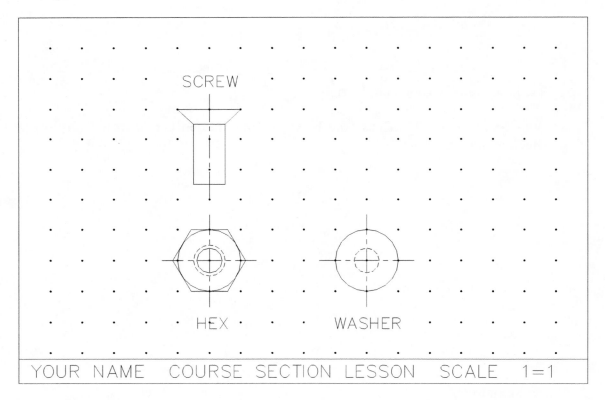

SCREW

HEX   WASHER

YOUR NAME   COURSE SECTION LESSON   SCALE   1=1

9. **Save** the Drawing as *My Mechanical Symbols* and keep the Drawing Open.

10. Begin a **New blank** Drawing by using the **acad.dwt Template File**.

11. **Insert Blocks** using the **Design Center** by doing the following:

- From the Menu Bar select **Tools, Palettes** and then **Design Center** as shown below.

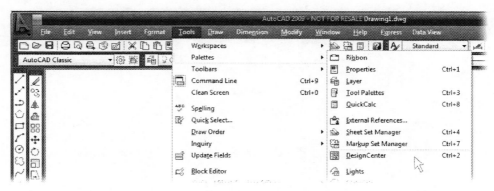

- Select the **Open Drawings** tab of the **Design Center** as shown below.

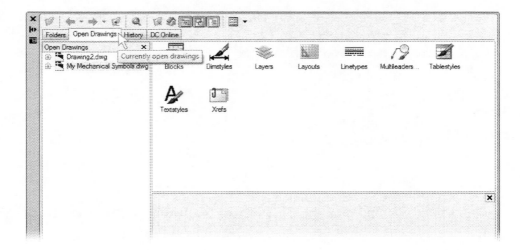

- Make sure that the **Tree View Toggle** is set to **On**. {The Open Drawings list appears on the side as shown below.}

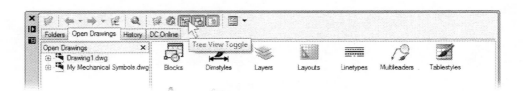

- Click on the + next to your **My Mechanical Symbols** file under **Open Drawings** as shown below. {The + will change to a – and the Drawing category will be expanded as shown.}

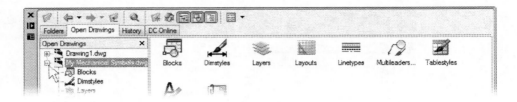

- Make sure that the **Preview** Button is Toggled to **On**.

- Select the **Blocks** category of the Drawing as shown below. {The window on the right will show thumbnails of all **Blocks** contained within the Drawing as shown below.}

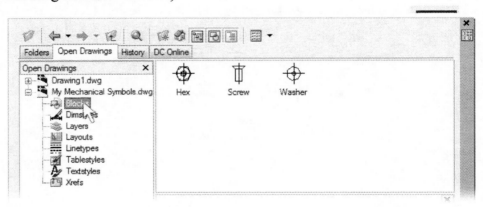

- Click and drag the Title Bar of the **Design Center** and Dock the window to one side of the screen as shown on the next page.

- Click on the **Hex Block** and drag and drop the **Block** into the **New Drawing** area as shown below.

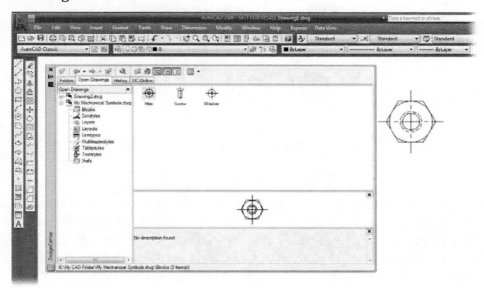

12. Use the **Design Center** to **Insert a Block** with specific **Scale** and **Rotation Angle** by doing the following:

- Double-click on the **Hex Block** in the **Design Center** window. {The **Insert** dialog box will appear.}

- For the Insertion point, Toggle the **Specify on screen** option to *On*, with the **Uniform Scale** Toggled to **On**, enter a **Scale factor** of *2.00* and a **Rotation angle** of *30.0*, and then click **OK**.

394

- Select a user-specified location to **Insert Block** in the Drawing as shown below.

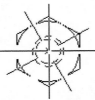

Note: As you can see, the **Design Center** gives you the option to **Insert Blocks** from the currently **Open** Drawings as well as from saved files accessible through the **Folders** tab. Furthermore, notice that in addition to **Blocks**, you can drag and drop **Dimstyles** (chapter 11), **Layers** (chapter 3), **Layouts** (chapter 12), **Line types** (chapter 3), **Text styles** (chapter 7) and **Xrefs** (covered in Volume II) into your Drawings.

DC Online tab is used to connect to other users across the Internet and exchange files and other useful information.

13. Select **[X]** to **Close** the **Design Center** Palette.

14. **Close** the two open Drawing without **Saving**.

Note: When working with multiple open files while the AutoCAD window is maximized, only one Drawing file can be viewed in the foreground at any given time with the other open Drawings hidden in the background. You can review the concept of working with multiple open Drawings on page 90.

Tool Palettes

1. Begin a **New** blank **Drawing** using the **acad.dwt Template**.

2. Set **Units** to **Architectural**.

3. **Set Limits** to **0,0** and **12',9'** and then **Zoom All**.

4. **Insert Block** using the **Tool Palette** by doing the following:

   - From the Menu Bar, select **Tools**, **Palettes** and then **Tool Palettes**.

   - Click on the **Architectural** tab in the **Tool Palettes Window** as shown below.

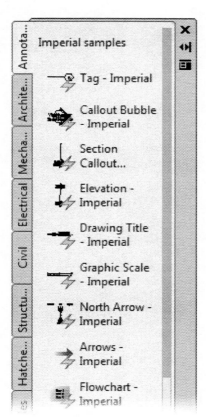

   - Click on the **Aluminum Window (Elevation) Block** on the **Architectural** tab of the **Tool Palettes Window**.

5. Drag and **Insert** the **Block** into your Drawing as shown below.

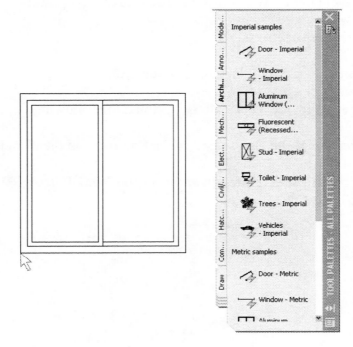

6. **Close** the **Tool Palette Window**.

7. **Close** the Drawing without saving.

Purge Blocks

When you erase a **Block** from a Drawing (including those on **Frozen** and **Off** layers), the **Block** still resides within the Drawing. In order to permanently remove a **Block** from a Drawing, it should first be **Erased** and then **Purged**. At times, **Purging** can help substantially reduce file size.

1. **Purge** a **Block** by doing the following:

   - Open your **My Mechanical Symbols** Drawing.

   - Insert another copy of **Screw** and **Washer Blocks** somewhere on the screen and **Erase Hex** so that there is no **Hex** Block on the screen.

   - Command: *Purge* then *[ENTER]*.

   - In the **Purge** Dialog box, select the + sign to the left of **Blocks** to expand that category.

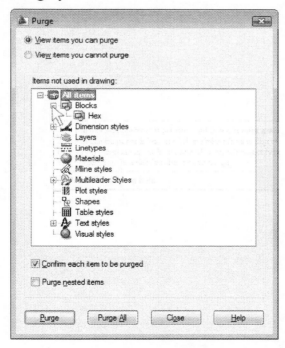

   - Select the Block **Hex** from the list and then select the **Purge** button.

   - When asked if you want to Purge Block **Hex**, select **Yes** and **Close**.

Note: Since the other two blocks are utilized, they remain unlisted as AutoCAD does not allow to Purge Blocks that are currently in use.

Note: At this point, if you attempt to insert the **HEX Block**, you will notice that it is no longer available on the list of Blocks in this Drawing.

2. **Exit** AutoCAD without saving. {This avoids the purging of the Hex Block.}

Write Blocks (Wblock)

Another method of having access to a **Block** symbol is by means of **WBlocking**. A **Block** can be written to a file using the **Wblock** Command and then inserted into other Drawings.

1. **Wblock** the **Hex** Block by doing the following:

    • Open your **My Mechanical Symbols** Drawing.

    • At the **Command Prompt**, type in *Wblock* then *[ENTER]*.

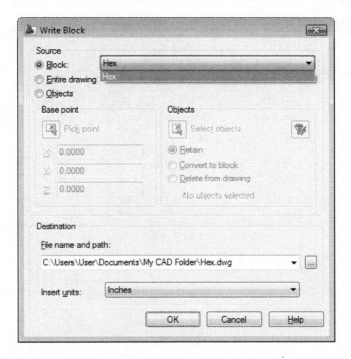

    • In the **Write Block** dialog box, in the **Source** section, Toggle **Block** as your source and use the drop-down to select **Hex** as the Block name. Your destination file name should also read **Hex.dwg**.

    • In the **Destination** section, select the small Browse button and make sure to assign the File name **Hex** and Path to your **My_CAD_Folder** as shown above.

    • Select **OK**.

    • **Close** this File without saving changes. A **Hex.dwg** Drawing is already created using the **WBlock** command.

- From the Menu Bar, select **File**, and then **New** to start a blank Drawing using the **acad.dwt Template File**.

- **Zoom All**.

- Select the **Insert Block** button.

- Select the **Browse** button.

- Use the **Look in** pull-down menu to locate your Folder.

- Select the **Hex** File.

- Select **Open** and select **OK**.

- **Insert Block** in a user-specified location.

- **Close** this **File** without Saving the Changes.

Note: When a Block is inserted into a Drawing, it creates all the necessary layers. For instance when Hex is inserted in a new Drawing, it automatically generates **Layers Hid** and **Cen**. Therefore at times, you may have far more layers in a Drawing then you created.

Aliases and Hot Keys

BLOCK ....B

INSERT BLOCK I

PURGE ....PU

WBLOCK ....W

Assignment 9

Objective:

1. To practice **Making**, **Writing**, and **Inserting Blocks**.

Instructions:

1. Launch AutoCAD and use your **Template** to begin a **New** Drawing.
2. **Save As** the Drawing file to your folder. Name it **"ASSIGN9a_ _ _.dwg"** where the 3 blanks are your initials.
3. Create and label the 6 symbols as shown below using the following information:

   - The 5 smaller symbols are in 1" squares.
   - The larger symbol is in a 2" square.
   - The symbols should fit within the square border and should look similar to the Drawing below, but the exact dimensions of each symbol are user - specified.
   - Insertion points of all six blocks are shown by the black dots. They are shown as reference points only and are not to be drawn.

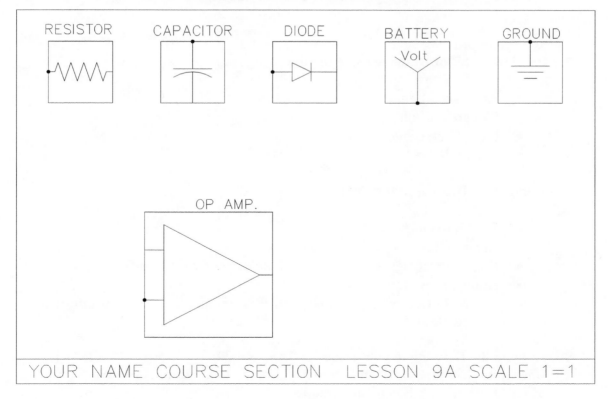

4. Make **Blocks** out of each of the 6 symbols, but exclude squares.

404

5. **Insert** each **Block** as shown below to test its validity.

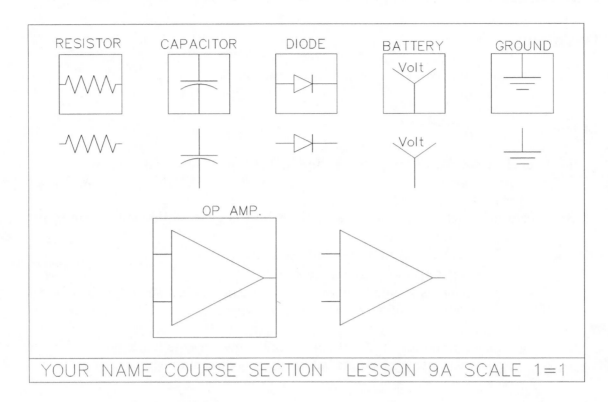

6. **Save** your Drawing again.
7. **Preview** and **Plot** Drawing using the following settings:

   - Paper size: Letter
   - Plot area: Limits
   - Plot offset: Center
   - Plot scale: 1=1

8. Start a **New Drawing** from Scratch.

   - Set **Limits** to *0,0* and *24,16*.
   - **Zoom All**.
   - Create a rectangular border at the boundary of your **Limits**.
   - Draw a **Line** from *0,1* to *24,1*.
   - Create **Title Text** with a height of *0.5*. Include the standard information with **Scale to fit**.

9. **Save As** the Drawing to your folder as **"ASSIGN9b _ _ _.dwg"**
10. Open the Design Center and from the Folder tab, locate **Assign9a_ _ _.dwg** which contains your Electrical Symbols.

11. Use the **Blocks** created in the previous Drawing to create the schematic shown in the final plot sample. Although you should keep the schematic similar to the diagram on the next page, the exact location of each symbol is user-specified.
12. **Save** your Drawing.
13. **Preview** and **Plot** Drawing using the following settings:

- Paper size: Letter (8.50x11.00 **inches**)
- Plot Scale: Fit to paper
- Plot area: Limits
- Plot offset: Centered

406

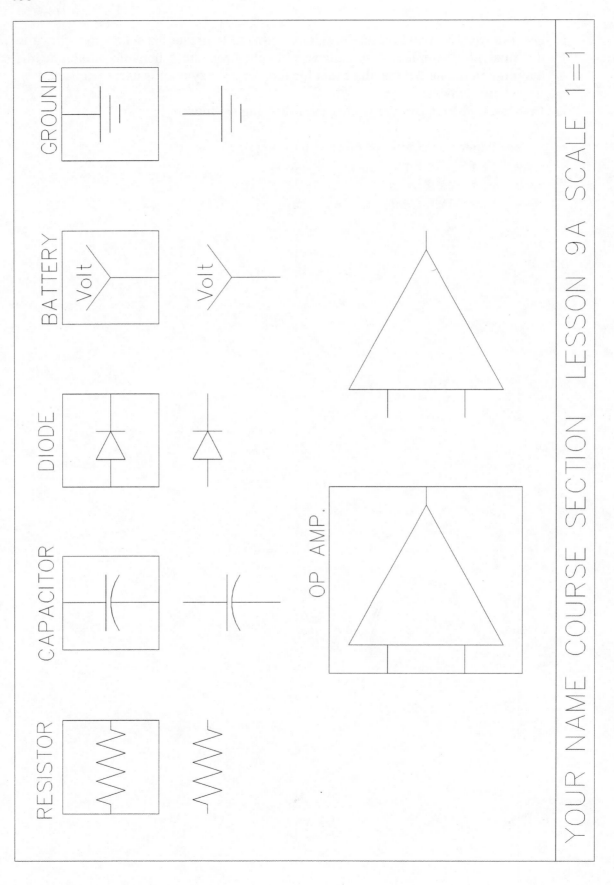

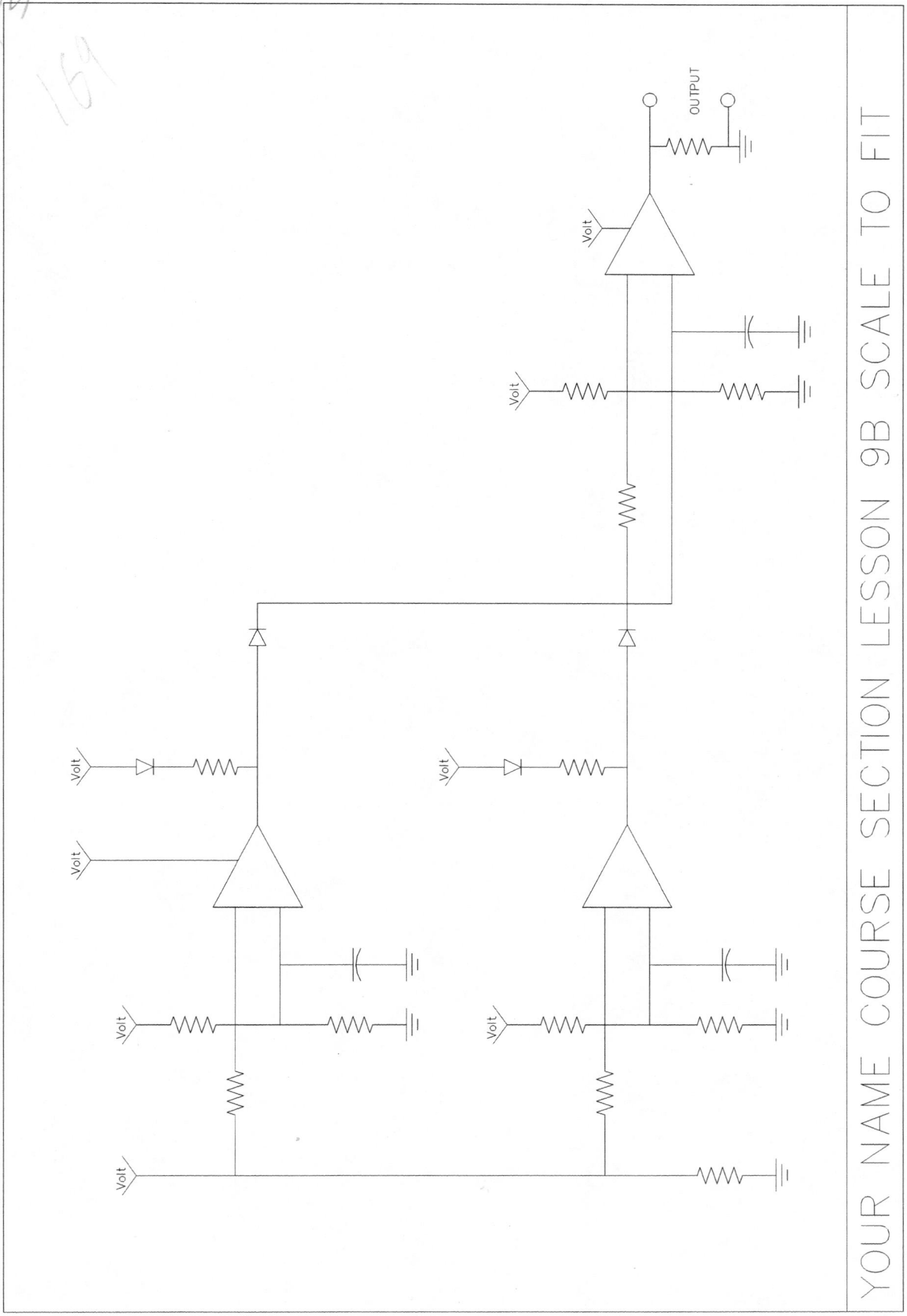

OUTPUT

Volt

Volt

Volt

Volt

Volt

Volt

Volt

Volt

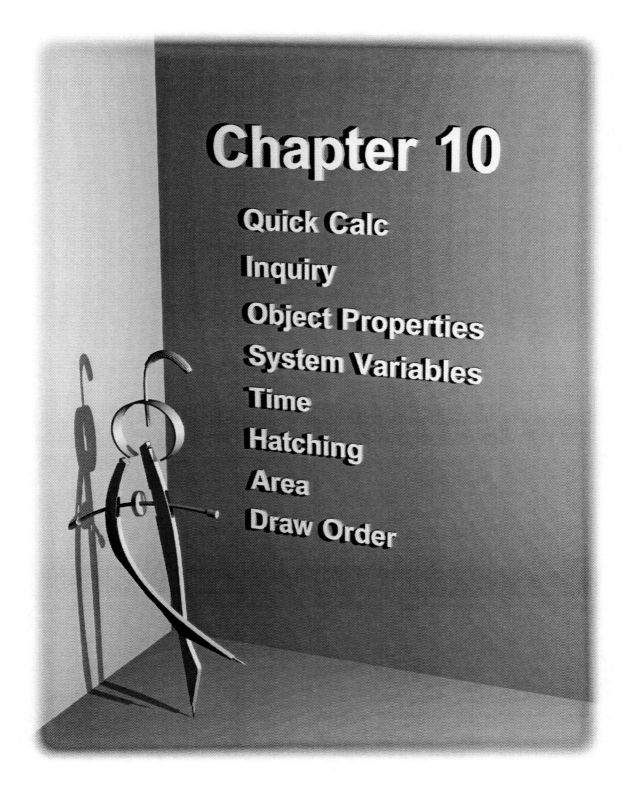

Chapter 10

Quick Calc

Inquiry

Object Properties

System Variables

Time

Hatching

Area

Draw Order

410

 ## Quickcalc

1. Start AutoCAD and use your **My Template** to begin a **New** Drawing.

2. From the **Standard** Toolbar, select the **Quickcalc** Tool as shown below.

{The Calculator appears somewhere on screen as shown below.}

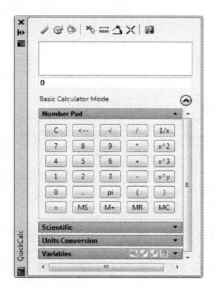

Note: You can also use the **CTRL+8** shortcut to open the **Quickcalc** Palette.

412

When using the calculator, you can use the number pad (on your keyboard) as long as you have **Num Lock** set to **On**. With the number pad you may enter numbers or perform the four basic arithmetic operations: addition (+), subtraction (-), multiplication (*), and division (/). However, for more complex operations such as the square root, exponent, etc., you should use the calculator's interface directly.

3. Press the **Num Lock** Key to ensure that the Keyboard's **Num Lock** is set to **On**.

4. Use the calculator to perform the arithmetical operations by doing the following:

- Select within the **QuickCalc** palette to make sure it is the current window.

- Type in *10*4+9* and then *[ENTER]*. {Expression is evaluated as 49.}

- From the Number Pad of the **Quickcalc** palette, select the **Square root** symbol as shown below.

- Press *[ENTER]*. {The Expression is evaluated as 7.}

- Type */2* (to divide by 2) then *[ENTER]*. {The Expression is evaluated as 3.5}

- Type - to subtract and then select *pi* as shown below and then *[ENTER]*. {**3.5 – pi** is evaluated as approximately 0.358.}

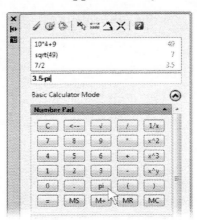

5. Dock the **Quickcalc** on the left side of the screen as shown below.

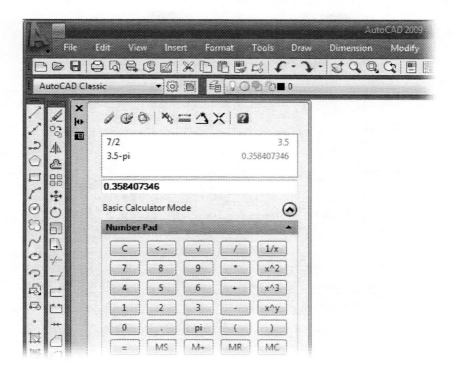

6. In the **Quickcalc** palette, select the **Clear** button as shown below. {This clears the Quickcalc display.}

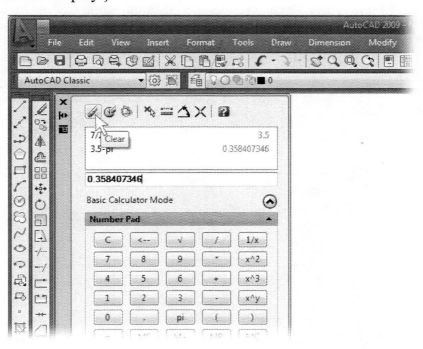

414

7. In the **Quickcalc** palette, select the **Clear history** button as shown below. {This clears the Quickcalc history display.}

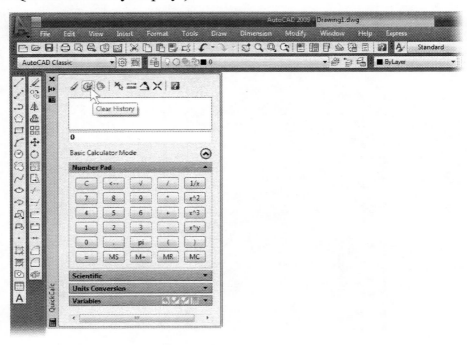

8. Use **Quickcalc** to create geometry by doing the following:

  • Create Line **L1** at a user specified location while having **2.0** units in length as shown below.

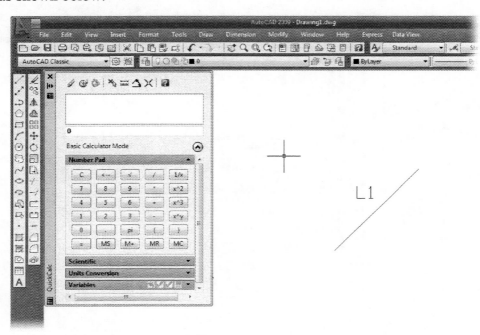

- Set the **OSnap** running **Mode** to **Endpoint** only and make sure it is set to **On.**

- In the **Quickcalc** palette, select the **Distance Between Two Points** button as shown below.

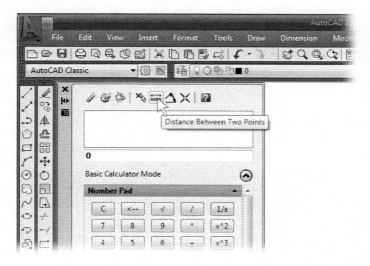

- Select the two **Endpoints** of line **L1.** {The value **2** appears in the **Quickcalc** display.}

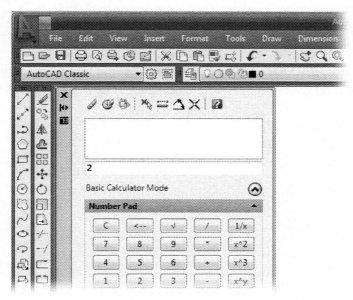

- In the **Quickcalc** display, divide the value by **3** and then **[ENTER].**

- Create a Circle with its **Center** point at the lower **Endpoint** of Line **L1.**

- For the Radius, select the **Paste value to Command line** button in the **Quickcalc** palette as shown below. {0.666 appears at the Command Line.}

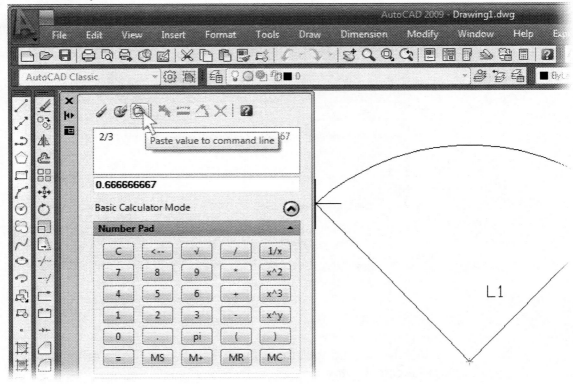

- Place the cursor at the Command line.

- Press *[ENTER]*. {The **Circle** will have a radius of the length of the line divided by 3.}

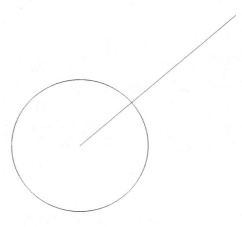

- In the **Quickcalc** palette display, multiply the previous result by **2**. {1.33 is displayed.}

- Create another Circle having its center located at the lower endpoint of **L1**.

- For the radius, from the **Quickcalc** palette, click on the **Paste value to Command line** button.

- Place the cursor at the Command line, and then press *[ENTER]*.

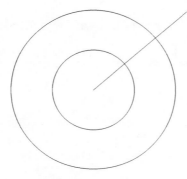

- **Close** the **Quickcalc** Palette by selecting the **X** located on the upper right corner of the **Quickcalc** interface.

- **Erase** all geometry from the screen.

418

__Inquiry__

1. From the **Status Line** make sure that **Snap**, **Grid**, **Ortho**, **Polar**, **OSnap**, and **OTrack** are set to *Off*.

Note: In this lesson you will use **AutoCAD Text Windows** several times. You can use the **F2** key to turn the **Window** *On* or *Off*. Using the **AutoCAD Text Window** enables the user to view more Text lines than are set to view at the **Command Window**.

You can change the number of lines viewed at the **Command Window** by clicking and dragging the border surrounding the **Command Window**. It is recommended to maintain at least 3 lines.

2. Draw a **Line**, **Circle**, and **Arc** as shown below. Size and Location are user-specified.

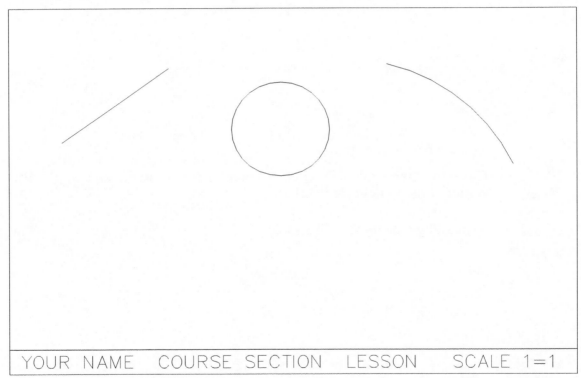

YOUR NAME   COURSE SECTION   LESSON   SCALE 1=1

3. Load and dock the **Inquiry** toolbar.

4. Get a Database listing of selected Objects by doing the following:

- In the **Inquiry** toolbar, select the **List** button.

List

- Use the **Crossing** option to select the **Circle** and the **Line** then *[ENTER]*. {The **AutoCAD Text Window** will appear with similar data as shown below.}

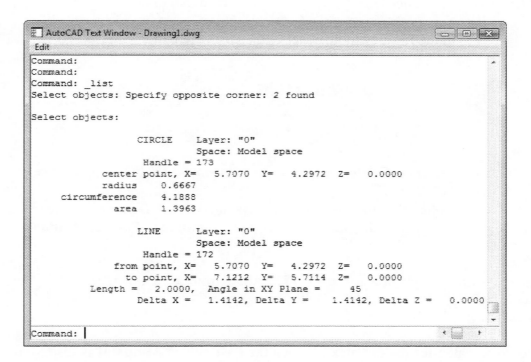

Note: Using the **List** button, useful database information is displayed, such as the radius, circumference, and the length of selected Objects. You can also view Object-related information such as the coordinates of Object Endpoints, Center points, etc.

- Press **F2** to close the **Text Window**.

- Use the **Units** Command to load the **Drawing Units** dialog box.

- Set the **Decimal Precision** to 4 decimal places (**0.0000**).

- Click **OK**.

- Command: *List* then *[ENTER]*.

- Select the **Arc** then *[ENTER]*. {Information related to the Arc now is displayed with 4 decimal place accuracy.}

- Press **F2** to close the **AutoCAD Text Window**.

- Use the **Units** Command to change **Decimal Precision** back to 2 decimal places (**0.00**).

6. Set your **OSnap Running Mode** to **Midpoint** and **Center** and make sure that **OSnap** is set to **On**.

7. Find the **Distance** between two points by doing the following:

   - In the **Inquiry** toolbar, select the **Distance** button.

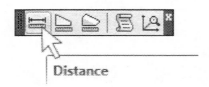

   - Select the **Center** of the **Circle** and then the **Midpoint** of the **Arc**.

   - Notice that the information pertaining to the **Distance** between the two points will be displayed in the **Command Prompt Window**. For example:

Distance = 2.63, Angle in XY Plane = 171, Angle from XY Plane = 0
Delta X = -2.60, Delta Y = 0.39,   Delta Z = 0.00
Command:

Note: The value for the distance between the **Center** and **Midpoint** is displayed. The **Command Window** must display at least three lines in order for the distance values to show. If this is not the case, press **F2** to view the **AutoCAD Text Window**, or you can carefully resize the **Command Prompt Window**.

8. Find the **Coordinates** of a point by doing the following:

- In the **Inquiry** toolbar, select the **Locate Point** button.

- Select the **Midpoint** of the **Arc**.

- The X, Y, and Z coordinates are displayed in the **Command Prompt Window**. For example:

Command: '_id Specify point: X = 7.16   Y = 4.49   Z = 0.00
Command:

- Do Not **Erase** the screen.

Note: The **Area** tool of the **Inquiry** Toolbar will be covered later in this chapter.

422

Object Properties

1. View **Object Properties** by doing the following:

   - In the **Standard** toolbar, select the **Properties** button.

   - Move the **Properties** window to the right side of the Drawing Area.

   - Click on the **Line**. {Information about the **Line** will be displayed in the **Properties** Palette similar to what is shown below.}

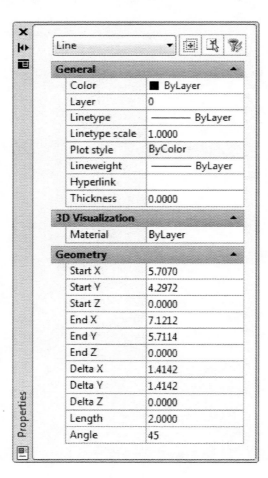

- Press the **Esc** key to deselect the **Line**.

- Select the **Circle**. {Information about the **Circle** will appear in the **Properties** Palette.}

- In the **Properties** Palette under **Geometry**, click on **Radius** as shown below. {The Radius value is highlighted and ready for editing.}

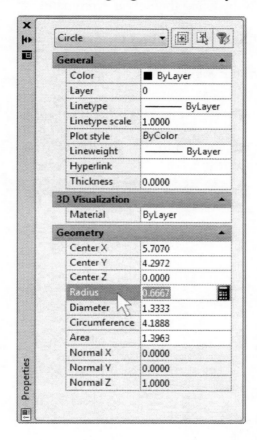

- Type *1.50* for the **Radius** of **Circle**, then *[ENTER]*. {**Radius** of **Circle** is modified.}

- Close the **Properties** window.

Note: You may also double click on an Object to view its properties or select the Object then right-click and scroll down to properties. Keep in mind that the properties (such as Layer, Geometry Coordinates, etc.) of an Object, or a group of Objects, can be changed through this Palette.

- Press **Esc** to unselect the Circle.

- Do not **Erase** the screen.

<u>System Variables</u>

AutoCAD's operating environment is affected by the values stored in the form of variables better known as **System Variables**. Some **System Variables** may be changed, but others are read only. Any writable **System Variable** can be changed at the **Command Prompt** or by using the **Setvar** Command.

1. View a list of **System Variables** by doing the following:

   - Command: *Setvar*.

   - When asked to enter variable name or [?]:, type *?* and then *[ENTER]*.

   - Enter variables(s) to list <*>: *[ENTER]*. {The **AutoCAD Text Window** will appear.}

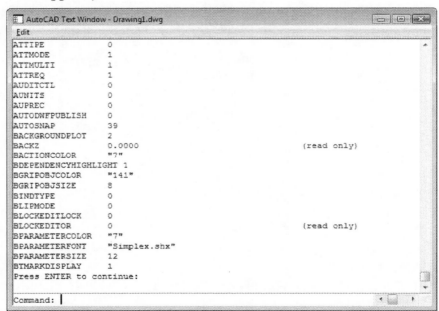

   - *[ENTER]* as many times as necessary for the **Command Prompt** to read "Command:".

Note: In this last step you used the asterisk as a wild card. The asterisk symbol is a way of selecting an entire list of variables or names. By typing just the symbol "*" you will display the entire list of variables or names, while typing in a letter prior to the asterisk will list all variables that start with that character (i.e.: **S*** will list variables such as **SaveFile, Snap**, etc). Typing an asterisk "*" is accomplished by holding down the **Shift** key while pressing the **8** key at the top of your keyboard.

   - Press **F2**. {The **Text Window** is closed.}

When using the **Setvar** Command, the **AutoCAD Text Window** will appear. AutoCAD will display only one screen of variables at a given time. To view more Commands you can press *[ENTER]* or use the scrollbar.

Writable **System Variables** most commonly appear in two forms: the first type takes only a value of 1 or 0 representing *On* or *Off*, and the other takes on various numerical values. For example, when you turn **Grid** to *On*, you are actually setting the **Gridmode System Variable** to **1**, and when you set the actual **Grid** value to **0.5**, it is set in both the horizontal and the vertical direction, **Gridunit System Variable** is set to **0.5,0.5** .If you recall our discussion on using the **Drafting Settings** dialog box, you can set the horizontal and vertical **Grid** independent from one another; therefore, AutoCAD must save each individually in the form of **System Variables**.

- Command: *Setvar* then *[ENTER]*.

Enter variable name or [?]: *?* then *[ENTER]*

- Enter variables(s) to list <*>: **grid*** then *[ENTER]*.

- A list of all system variables that start with **GRID** will appear in an **AutoCAD Text Window** similar to what is shown below:

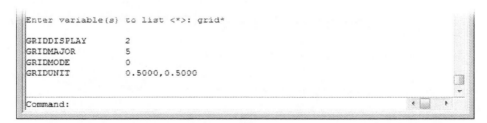

```
Enter variable(s) to list <*>: grid*

GRIDDISPLAY      2
GRIDMAJOR        5
GRIDMODE         0
GRIDUNIT         0.5000,0.5000



Command:
```

- Press **F2** to close **AutoCAD Text Window**.

2. Change **System Variables** by doing the following:

- Command: *Setvar* then *[ENTER]*.

- Enter variable name or [?]: *Gridmode* then *[ENTER]*.

- Enter new value for GRIDMODE <0>: **1** then *[ENTER]*. {This will turn **Grid** *On*.}

Note: System variables can be changed either while in the **Setvar** Command or simply just at the **Command Prompt**. Going into the **Setvar** Command can be helpful if the exact **System** Variable name is not known, or is forgotten. Therefore, the **Setvar** Command is best used for getting a listing.

- Make sure **Grid** is set to **On**.

- Command: *Gridunit* then *[ENTER]*

- Enter new value for GRIDUNIT <0.50,0.50>: *0.25,0.25* then *[ENTER]*. {**Grid** is changed to *.25* along the x and y axis.}

- Command: *Copy* then *[ENTER]*.

- Select a group of Objects to copy, then *[ENTER]*.

- Select a **Base Point** at a user-specified location.

Note: As you enter the second point of displacement, note that the Objects are dragging.

- Press the **Esc** key to get out of the **Copy** Command without pasting the Objects in a new location.

- Command: *Dragmode* then *[ENTER]*.

- Enter new value [ON/OFF/Auto] <Auto>: *Off* then *[ENTER]*.

- Command: *Copy* then *[ENTER]*.

- Select a group of Object to copy then *[ENTER]*.

- Select any base point and move the mouse onto the screen.

Note: The Objects do not drag as they did in the previous exercise. Setting **Dragmode** to *Off* is only beneficial for Drawings having large file sizes. Imagine having to **Move**, **Copy**, **Stretch**, etc. thousands of objects in one operation. At times like this, you may notice a lag in your system's performance. For the most part, it is best to have **Dragmode** set to **Auto**. The book moves forward with the **Dragmode** settings set to **Auto** as it is the default setting in AutoCAD.

- Press the **Esc** key to get out of the Command without pasting the Objects in a new location.

- Command: *Dragmode* then *[ENTER]*.

- Enter new value [ON/OFF/Auto]: **Auto** then *[ENTER]*.

- **Erase** all Objects and Make sure to close **Inquiry** toolbar.

Time

1. Keep track of the **Time** spent on editing a **Drawing** by doing the following:

   - Command: **Time** then **[ENTER]**. {The AutoCAD Text Window will appear as shown below.}

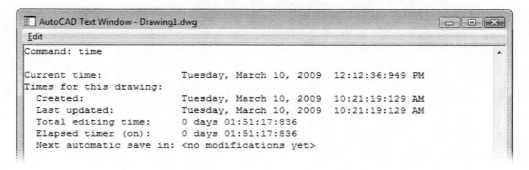

```
AutoCAD Text Window - Drawing1.dwg
Edit
Command: time

Current time:                Tuesday, March 10, 2009  12:12:36:949 PM
Times for this drawing:
  Created:                   Tuesday, March 10, 2009  10:21:19:129 AM
  Last updated:              Tuesday, March 10, 2009  10:21:19:129 AM
  Total editing time:        0 days 01:51:17:836
  Elapsed timer (on):        0 days 01:51:17:836
  Next automatic save in: <no modifications yet>
```

   - **[ENTER]**. {Exits **Time** Command.}

   - Press the **F2** key to turn off the **AutoCAD Text Window** after having taken a look at the times.

428

 <u>Hatching</u>

1. From the **Status Line** make sure that **Snap**, **Grid**, **Ortho**, **Polar**, **OSnap**, and **OTrack and Dyn** are set to *Off*.

2. Draw **Lines L1**, **L2**, and **L3** as shown below.

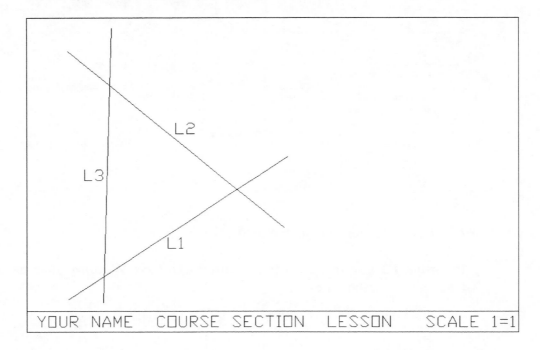

3. Use the **Copy** Command to make duplicates of **L1**, **L2**, and **L3** to the right and then **Trim** the copied Lines to each other as shown below.

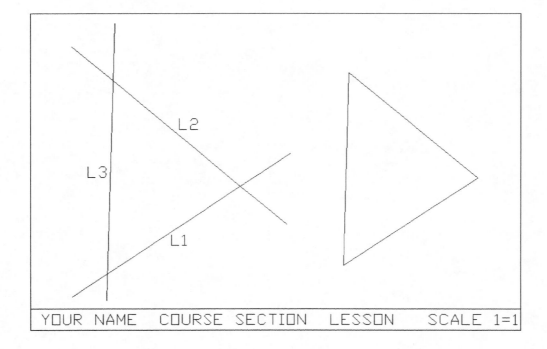

4. Hatch an Object using boundary lines by doing the following:

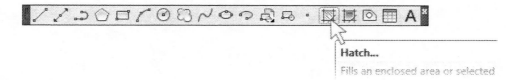

- In the **Draw** toolbar, select the **Hatch** button.

- In the **Hatch and Gradient** dialog box, select the **Hatch** tab.

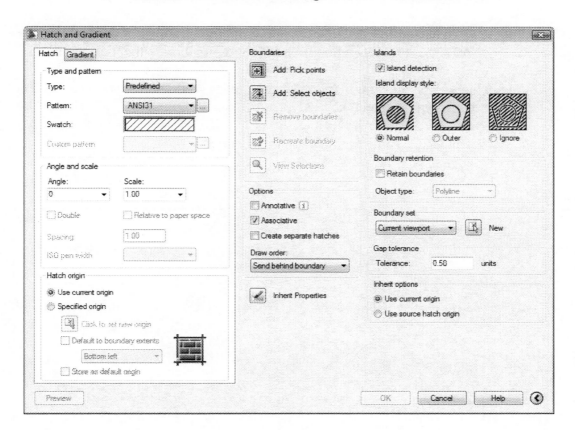

430

- Click on the **Add: Select Objects** button.

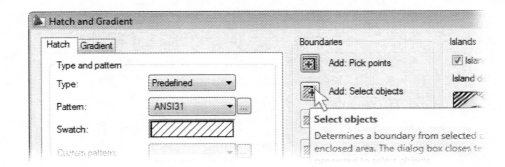

- Use **Crossing** to select all 3 sides of the triangle located on the right, then *[ENTER]*. {The **Hatch and Gradient** dialog box will appear again.}

- Check to make sure that the **Pattern** reads **ANSI31**. If not, use the drop-down menu to select **ANSI31**.

- Select **OK**. {The **Hatch** pattern is generated.}

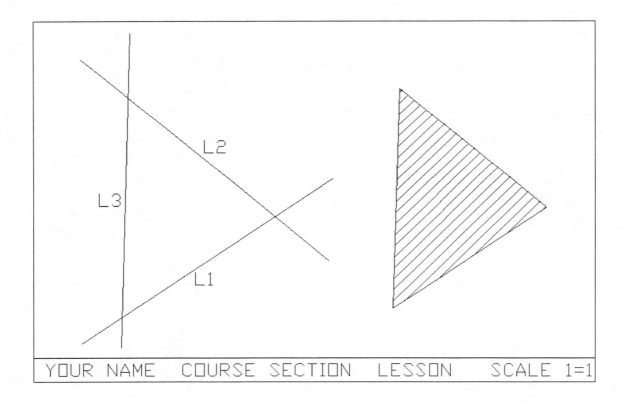

- In the **Draw** toolbar, select the **Hatch** button again.

- Select the **Add: Select Objects** button again.

- Select Lines **L1**, **L2**, and **L3** to **Hatch** the area contained by the three Lines then *[ENTER]*. {The **Hatch and Gradient** dialog box appears.}

- Click **OK**.

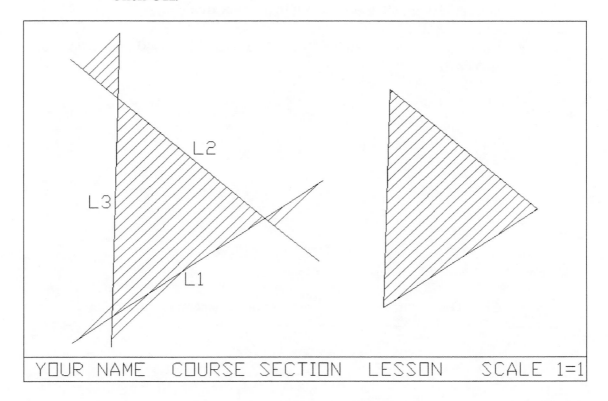

Note: The **Hatched** area on the left spreads beyond the triangle because the boundaries are not well defined; however, since the **Hatch Pattern** is grouped, with little effort, it can be **Erased**.

- Use **Erase** to select the **Hatch Pattern** on the left, and then *[ENTER]*.

Note: When selecting a **Hatch**, you must pick a point on the specific geometry as opposed to the overall **Hatch** pattern.

432

5. **Hatch** Objects using **Add: Pick points** by doing the following:

Note: The **Add: Pick points** option can be utilized to pick a point within a set of boundaries as long as the boundaries define a closed area. This tool is useful when the entities extend beyond the boundaries of the hatched area as in this example.

- In the **Draw** toolbar, click on the **Hatch** button.

- Select the **Add: Pick points** button of the **Hatch** tab.

- Click in the area contained by **L1**, **L2** and **L3** as shown below then **[ENTER]**.

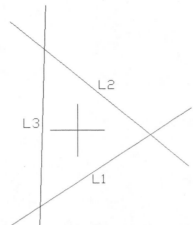

- Click **OK**. {Hatching should successfully appear as shown below}

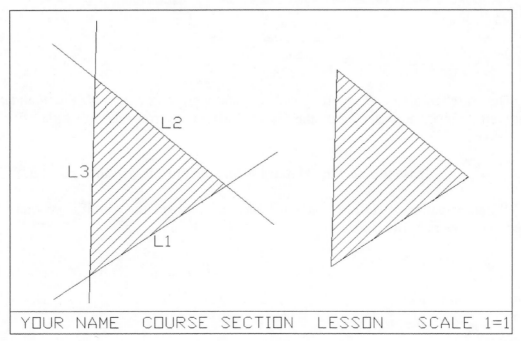

- **Erase** all the Objects and Hatching.

6. **Hatch** nested Objects by doing the following:

- Draw a **Rectangle** and a **Circle** such that the Circle is completely within the boundaries of the Rectangle as shown below.

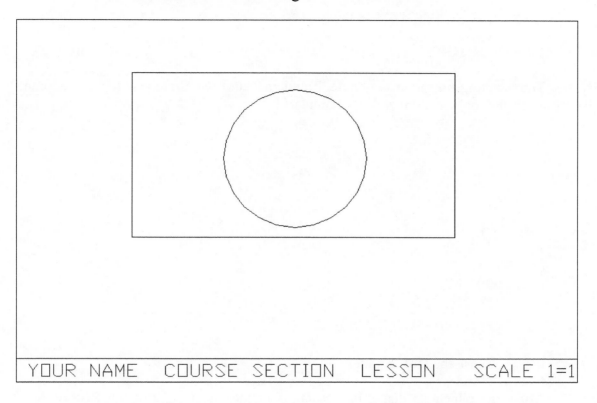

YOUR NAME   COURSE SECTION   LESSON   SCALE 1=1

- In the **Draw** toolbar, click on the **Hatch** button.

- Click on the **Add: Select Objects** button of the **Hatch** tab.

- Pick both the **Circle** and the **Rectangle** then *[ENTER]*.

- Click **OK**.

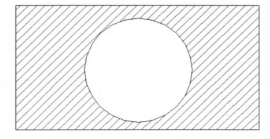

- **Erase** the **Hatch** pattern only.

434

- Command: **H** (for **Hatch**) and then *[ENTER]*.

- Click on the **Add: Select Objects** button on the **Hatch** tab.

- Pick the **Rectangle** only then *[ENTER]*.

- Click **OK**.

Note: The hatching runs over the circle. This is because the circle was not selected and therefore would not be recognized as a boundary.

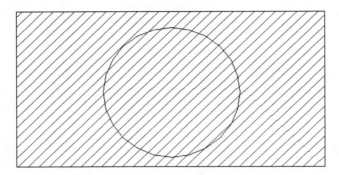

- **Erase** the **Hatch** pattern only.

7. **Move** the **Circle** so that it is crossing over the lower edge of the **Rectangle** as shown below.

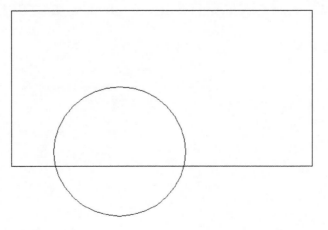

8. Use **Associative Hatching** by doing the following:

- In the **Draw** toolbar, click on the **Hatch** button.

- Use the **Add: Pick points** option and Pick within the "Shared" area as shown below, then *[ENTER]*. {The **Hatch and Gradient** dialog box appears again.}

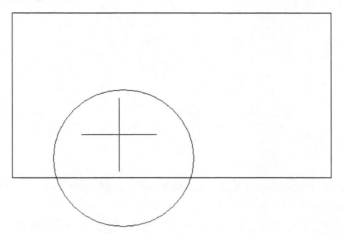

- In the **Options** section, make sure **Associative** is Toggled **On** then select **OK**.

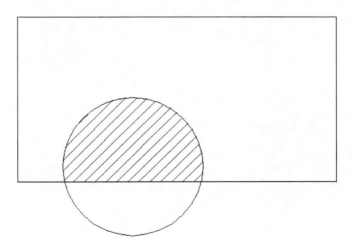

436

- **Move** the **Circle** to a slightly lower position. {The Hatch automatically updates as shown below.}

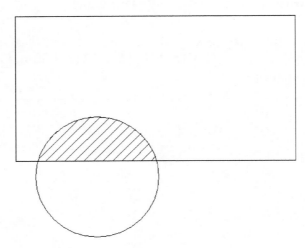

Note: The **Associative** option under **Options** on the **Hatch** tab allows for the **Hatch** to automatically update as Boundary Objects are moved or modified. This update will only take place only if the **Associative** Toggle is **On** at the time of **Hatching**. **Associative Hatching** modification is not always predictable: depending on the amount of boundary modifications, it may result in a solution that is unexpected such as in the one shown below.

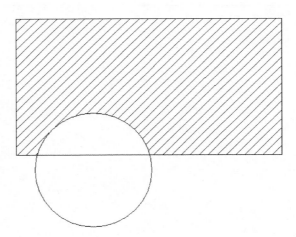

9. **Erase** the Objects and **Hatch** pattern.

10. Create the nested rectangular geometry similar to the one shown below.

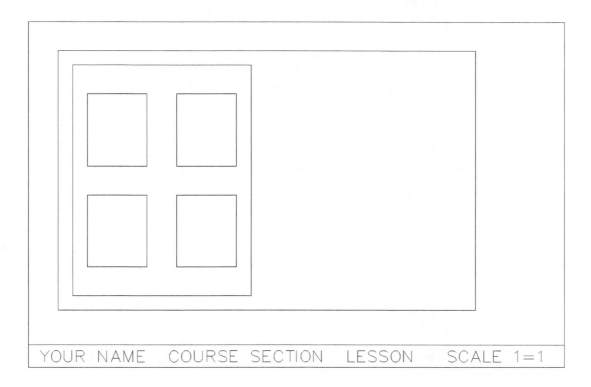

YOUR NAME   COURSE SECTION   LESSON   SCALE 1=1

11. Use **Advanced Hatching** by doing the following:

- Select the **Hatch** button from the **Draw** toolbar.

- In the **Islands** area Toggle **Normal** to *On* as shown below.

- Click on the **Add: Pick points** button and select a **Point** as shown below, then *[ENTER]*.

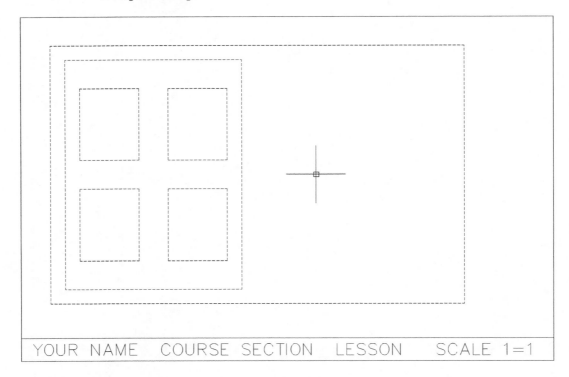

YOUR NAME   COURSE SECTION   LESSON   SCALE 1=1

- Select the **Preview** button. {A **Hatch** pattern with **Normal** setting appears.}

- Press the **Esc** key. {The **Hatch and Gradient** dialog box reappears.}

- In the **Islands** area Toggle **Outer** to *On*.

- Select the **Preview** button. {A **Hatch Pattern** with **Outer** setting appears.}

- Press the **Esc** key. {The **Hatch and Gradient** dialog box reappears.}

- In the **Islands** area Toggle **Ignore** to *On*.

- Select the **Preview** button.

- Press the **Esc** key. {The **Hatch and Gradient** dialog box reappears.}

- In the **Islands** area Toggle **Normal** to *On* again.

- Click **OK**.

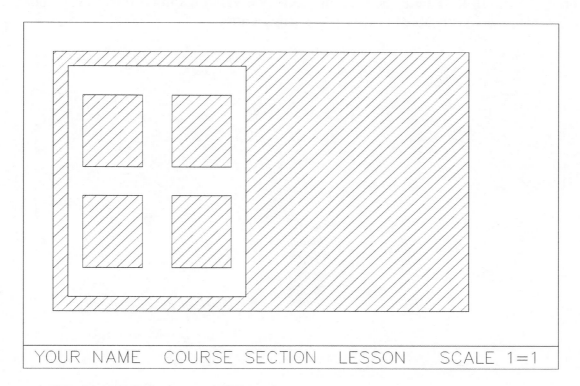

YOUR NAME   COURSE SECTION   LESSON   SCALE 1=1

12. **Edit Hatch** by doing the following:

- Load and Dock the **Modify II** Toolbar at the top of the Drawing Area.

- In the **Modify II** toolbar, select the **Edit Hatch** button.

- Select the **Hatch Pattern**. {The **Hatch Edit** dialog box will appear.}

440

Note: The **Hatch Edit** dialog box acts the same as the **Hatch and Gradient** dialog box, except that now you are able to **Edit** a pre-existing **Pattern**.

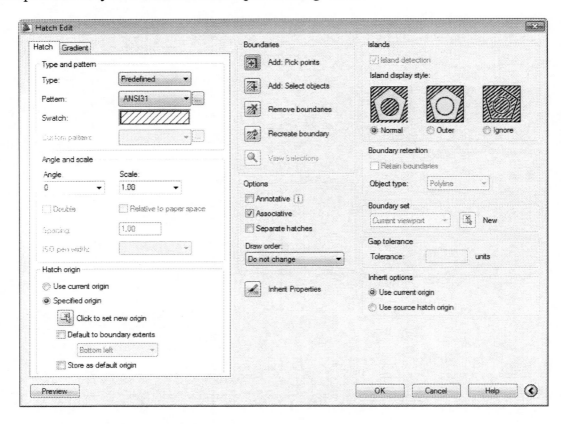

- Change the **Scale** to *0.50* then click **OK**.

- Double-click the pointer device on the **Hatch Pattern**. {The **Edit Hatch** window appears.}

- Set the **Angle** to *45* then click **OK**.

- Erase the Hatch Pattern only.

13. Use the **Tool Palettes Window** to apply a **Hatch Pattern** to an Object by doing the following:

- From the Menu Bar select **Tools, Palettes,** and then **Tool Palettes**. {The **Tool Palette** appears on the screen.}

- Select the **Hatches and Fills** tab of the **Tool Palettes** Window.

- In the **Imperial Hatches** area, select the **Steel** pattern as shown below.

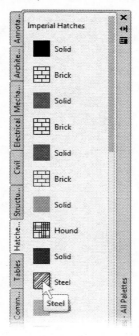

- Move the cursor onto the Drawing area as shown below. {The swatch will display the **Hatch Pattern** on the screen.}

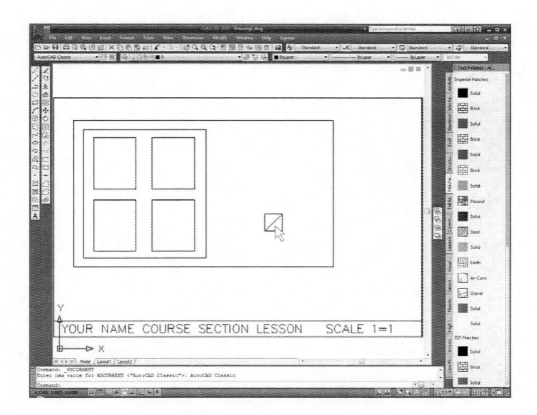

- Click to apply the **Hatch** to the area.

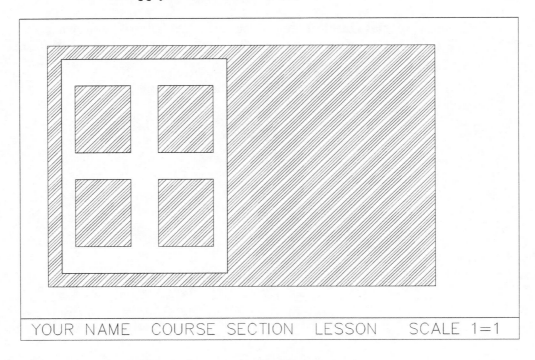

YOUR NAME   COURSE SECTION   LESSON   SCALE 1=1

- When finished, **Close** the **Tool Palettes** Palette.

- **Erase** the geometry and the **Hatch** from the screen.

14. **Trim** a **Hatch** by doing the following:

- Create a **Rectangle** at a user-specified Location, and **Hatch** as shown below. Exact size and **Hatch pattern** is user specified.

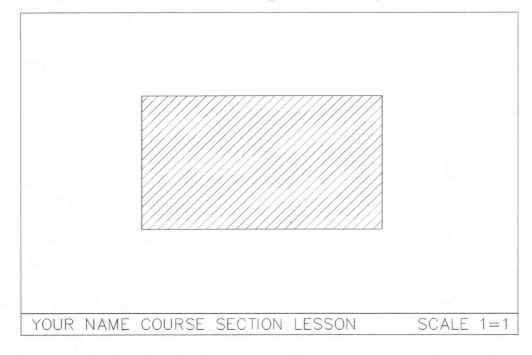

YOUR NAME COURSE SECTION LESSON   SCALE 1=1

- Draw a **Line** across the top right corner of the **Rectangle** as shown below.

- In the **Modify** toolbar, click on the **Trim** button.

- Select the **Line**, then *[ENTER]*.

- Select the **Hatch** that is above and to the right of the line, then *[ENTER]* {The **Hatch** is **Trimmed** as shown below.}

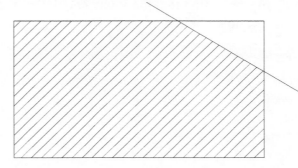

- When finished, **Erase** all Objects and **Hatching**, as well as the Template Border and **Text**.

Note: For this particular part to function properly, you will have to work outside of the Template border.

15. **Hatch** with a **Gap Tolerance** by doing the following:

- Draw a *3* x *2* **Rectangle** with the lower left corner located at *1,2*.

- Draw a **Line** over a small part of the top right corner with **Endpoints** located at *3.5,4.25* and *4.25,3.5*.

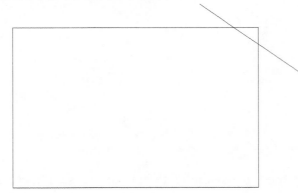

- Using the **Line** as your cutting edge, **Trim** the top right corner of the **Rectangle** and **Erase** the slanted **Line**. {The upper right corner of **Rectangle** contains a gap.}

444

Note: In general, attempting to **Hatch** shapes containing gaps may result in a **Valid Hatch Boundary Failure**.

- Select the **Hatch** button.

- Set the **Gap Tolerance** to **.5**, then use the **Add: Pick points** button to pick the area inside of the **Rectangle**.

Note: A Warning Box will appear stating that there is a gap within the allowed tolerance and hatching can adjust to it, as shown below.

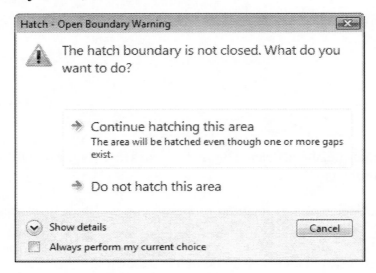

- Select the **Continue hatching this area option**, then *[ENTER]*.

- In the **Hatch and Gradient** dialog box select *OK*. {The **Rectangle** will **Hatch** within approximated borders as shown below.}

- When finished, **Close** the Drawing without saving changes.

1. Begin a **New** Drawing using your **My Template.**

2. Recreate a **Hatch boundary** by doing the following:

   - Create the geometry similar to that shown below. Exact size and location of shapes are user-specified.

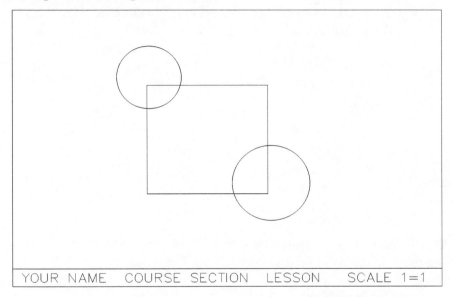

   YOUR NAME   COURSE SECTION   LESSON   SCALE 1=1

   - Use the **Add Pick Points** option to create a **Hatch** using the **BRICK** Pattern as shown below.

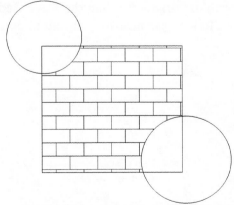

   - **Erase** the two **Circles** and the **Rectangle** while keeping the **Hatch Pattern**.

   - From the **Modify** Toolbar, select the **Edit Hatch** Tool and then select the **Brick** Hatch pattern from the screen.

   - As the **Hatch Edit** dialog box appears, in the **Boundaries** section, click on the **Recreate Boundary** button.

- Type **P** (for Polyline) and then *[ENTER]*

- Type **Y** (for Yes) and then *[ENTER]*. {The **Hatch Edit** dialog box appears again.}

- Click **OK** to finish the process. {A **Polyline** boundary inscribing the **Hatch** pattern is created as shown below.}

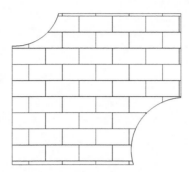

Note: Most of the time the Hatch pattern will not originate at the lower left hand corner of the Object. Use the following steps to solve this problem.

3. Change the **Hatch origin** by doing the following

- **Double-click** on the **Hatch**. {The **Hatch Edit** dialog box will appear}
- In the **Hatch origin** area, select the **Specified origin** option and then select the **Click to set new origin** button as shown below.

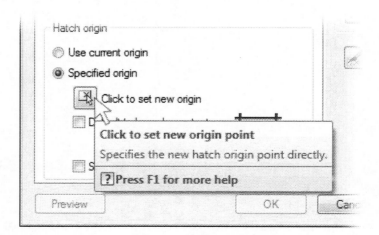

- Type **End** (for endpoint) and then *[ENTER]* and select the lower left hand corner of the Object. {The **Hatch Edit** dialog box will reappear.}

- Click **OK** to complete this process. {The Hatch pattern is now generated from the lower left hand corner of the Object as shown below}

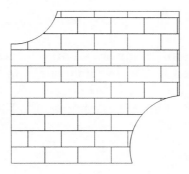

- Use the mouse to select the **Hatch** pattern and as **Grips** appear, then **right-click** and from the short cut menu, select **Properties**. {In the **Properties** Palette, the actual value for the **Hatch Area** is displayed as shown below.}

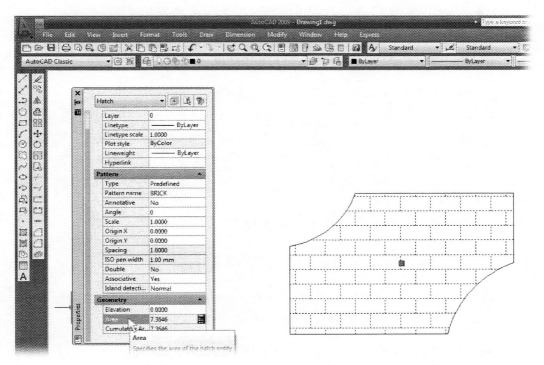

- Press the **Esc** key. {Hatch patter is unselected.}

- Closed the **Properties** Palette.

- Erase the geometry from the screen.

Area

1. Create a **Circle** with **R=*1.75*** at a user-specified location.

2. Create a **4-sided Polygon** having its **Center** located at the **Center** of the **1.75 Radius Circle, Inscribed in Circle** having a *1.5* unit **Radius**.

3. Use the **Polyline** Option of the **Fillet** command to **Fillet** the **Polygon** with **R=*0.50***

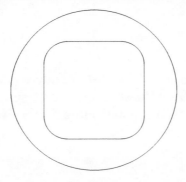

4. Calculate the **Area** by doing the following:

   - In the **Inquiry** toolbar, select the **Area** button.

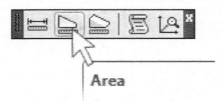

   - Type *A* (for **Add**) then *[ENTER]*.

   - Type *O* (for **Object**) then *[ENTER]*.

   - Select the **Circle**. {The **Area** and **Perimeter** of the **Circle** will appear in the Command Line as shown below.}

         Area = 9.62, Perimeter = 11.00
         Total Area = 9.62

   - *[ENTER]* to exit the **Add** mode.

   - Type *S* (for **Subtract**) then *[ENTER]*.

   - Type *O* (for **Object**) then *[ENTER]*.

- Select the **Polygon**. {The **Area** and **Perimeter** of the **Polygon** will appear in the Command Line, followed by the calculated area of the **Polygon** subtracted from the **Circle** as shown below.}

      Area = 4.29, Perimeter = 7.63
      Total Area = 5.34

- *[ENTER]* twice to exit the **Area** Command.

- When finished, **Erase** the screen.

Draw Order

1. Create three **New Layers** named *Red*, *Green* and *Blue* and apply the respective colors to each **Layer**. Keep **Layer 0 Current**.

2. Create a 3 x 2 **Rectangle** on the left side of the screen as shown below. Exact location is user-specified.

3. Create **Text** in the lower right corner of screen similar to that shown below. Exact size and location is user-specified.

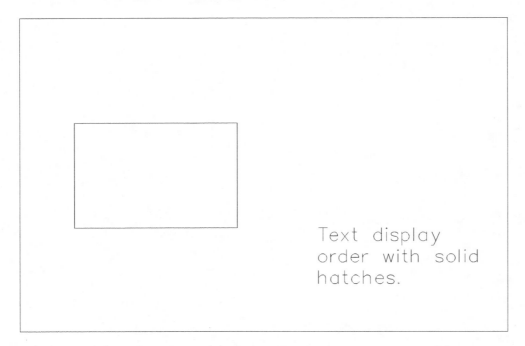

Text display
order with solid
hatches.

4. **Hatch** the **Rectangle** using the **Hatch Pattern Palette** by doing the following:

   - In the **Draw** toolbar, click on the **Hatch** button. {The **Hatch and Gradient** dialog box will appear.}

   - Click on the Pattern **Browse** button as shown below.

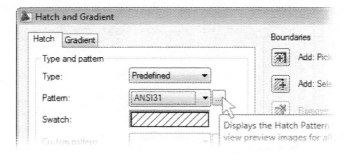

- As the **Hatch Pattern Palette** dialog box appears, click on the **Other Predefined** tab as shown below.

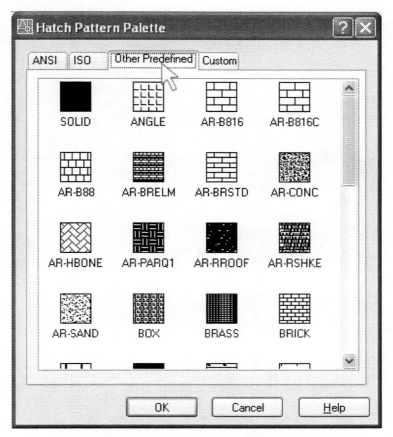

- Select the **Solid** Hatch, then click **OK**.

- Use the **Add:Select Objects** button to select the **Rectangle**, then *[ENTER]*.

- Click **OK**.

5. Copy the **Hatched Rectangle** (including the **Solid Hatch**) two times to the upper right, partly overlapping the entities as shown in the next step.

6. Place the original **Rectangle** and **Solid Hatch** to Layer **Red**, the first **Copy** to Layer **Green**, and the second **Copy** to Layer **Blue** as shown below. Refer to page 130 (item 6) if necessary.

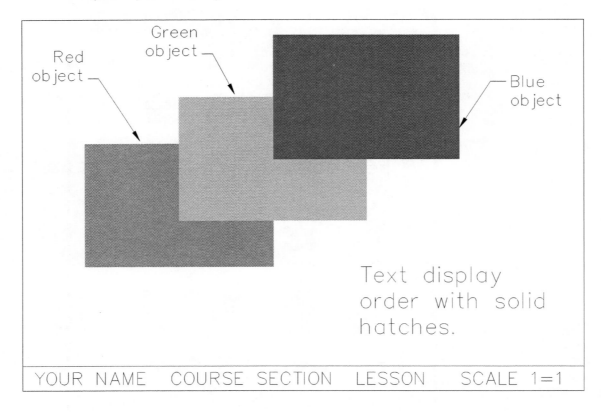

Red object

Green object

Blue object

Text display order with solid hatches.

YOUR NAME   COURSE SECTION   LESSON   SCALE 1=1

Note: The **Blue Rectangle** is sitting on top of the **Green Rectangle,** which in turn is sitting on top of the **Red Rectangle** because of the order in which the Objects were created. The first Object drawn is automatically placed on the bottom, while the last Object drawn is placed on top. AutoCAD allows you to change the **Draw Order**.

7. Set **Draw Order** by doing the following:

- Command: *Draworder* then *[ENTER]*.

- Use **Crossing** to only select the **Red Hatched Rectangle** then *[ENTER]*.

- When asked for **Object Ordering Option,** type *A* (for **Above Objects**) then *[ENTER]*.

- When asked to **Select Reference Objects**, use **Crossing** to select the other two **Hatched Rectangles (Green** and **Blue)** as **Reference Objects**, then *[ENTER]*. {The **Red Hatched Rectangle** moves to **Front.**}

- Use the technique given above to move the **Blue Hatched Rectangle** directly under the **Green**. This can be done by selecting the **Blue** Object first, using the **Under Objects** option, and selecting the **Green** Object as the **Reference Object**.

- Use the **Move** Command to relocate the **Text** to a location that overlaps the three **Hatched** Objects and **Regen** screen if necessary. {**Text** will be hidden behind the **Hatched** Objects.}

8. Bring **Text** to the front of shapes by doing the following:

- Command: ***Texttofront*** (one word) then ***[ENTER]***.

- Type ***T*** (for **Text**), then ***[ENTER]***.

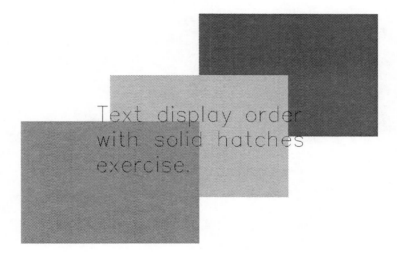

9. Close any Toolbars that were loaded for these tutorials.

10. **Exit** AutoCAD without saving.

Note: The above steps could also have been implemented by using the **Draw Order** toolbar.

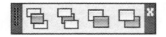

Aliases and Hot Keys

AREA...AA
EDIT HATCH...HE
LIST ....LI or LS
HATCHING..H
OBJECT PROPERTIES ....CTRL+1 or PR
SYSTEM VARIABLES ....SETVAR
SETVAR .... SET

Assignment 10

Objective:

1. To practice using the **Database** information.
2. To practice **Hatching**.

Instructions:

1. Launch AutoCAD and use your **MyTemplate** to begin a **New** Drawing.
2. **Save As** the Drawing file to your folder. Name it **"ASSIGN10_ _ _.dwg"** where the 3 blanks are your initials.
3. Create the Gasket geometry shown below using given **Circle** center point and **Radii**. Do not **Dimension** geometry.
4. Calculate Gasket **Surface Area** and place value within the Drawing using a 2 decimal place accuracy. The four small circles are drilled holes and need to be **Subtracted** along with the large inner circle.
5. Use **Database** information to calculate the lateral **Distance** between two Gasket holes. Use 2 decimal place accuracy to place the calculated **Distance** on Drawing.

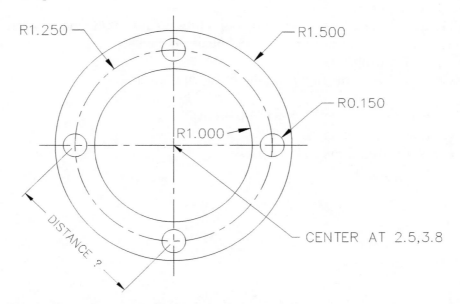

6. **Hatch** using **Brass Hatch Pattern** (under **Other Predefined** Hatches in the **Hatch Pattern Palette** dialog box) as shown in the final plot sample.

456

7. In the upper right portion of the **Drawing Area** to create the geometry as shown below. Do not **Dimension**. All Squares and the Rectangle are placed on a 0.1 **Grid**.

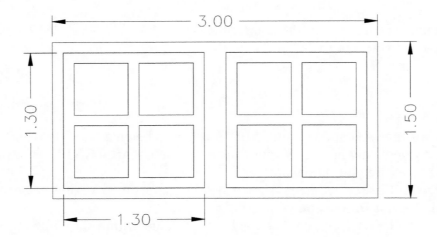

8. Vertically **Copy** the Shape to two new user-specified locations as shown on the following page.
9. Use the **Advanced Hatch** technique to **Hatch** each of the three geometries with a single selection for each as shown. For the **Hatch** Pattern, use the **ANSI31** with a **Hatch Scale** of *0.5*.
10. Use **Time** to check your **Total Editing Time** for this assignment before exiting. Approximate to the nearest minute and place on the Drawing.
11. **Save** your Drawing.
12. **Preview** and **Plot** Drawing using the following settings:

   - Paper size: Letter (8.50x11.00 **inches**)
   - Plot area: Limits
   - Plot offset: Centered
   - Plot scale: 1=1

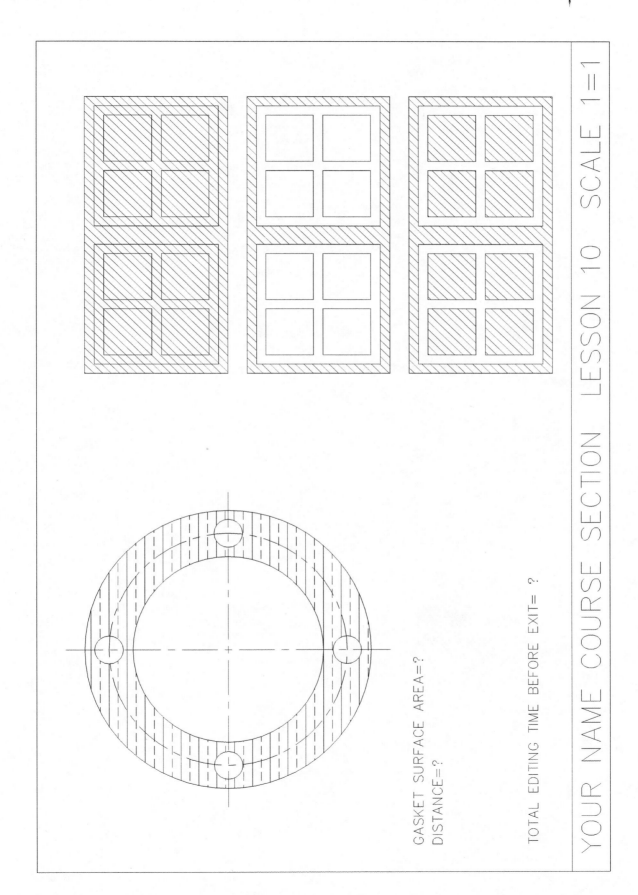

GASKET SURFACE AREA=?
DISTANCE=?

TOTAL EDITING TIME BEFORE EXIT= ?

YOUR NAME COURSE SECTION LESSON 10 SCALE 1=1

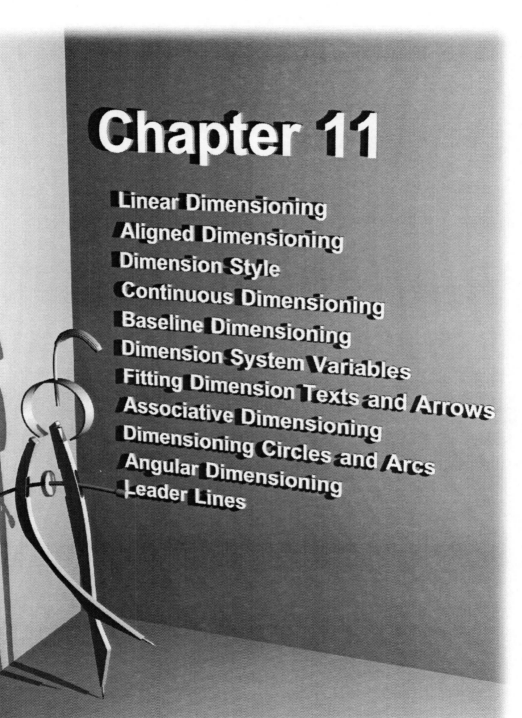

Chapter 11

Linear and Aligned Dimensioning

1. Launch AutoCAD and use your **Template** to begin a **New** Drawing.

2. From the **Status Line** make sure that **Snap**, **Grid**, **Ortho**, **Polar**, **OTrack, Ducs** and **Dyn** are set to *Off*. Set **OSnap** to *On*.

3. Use the **Line** Command to create the Object shown below.

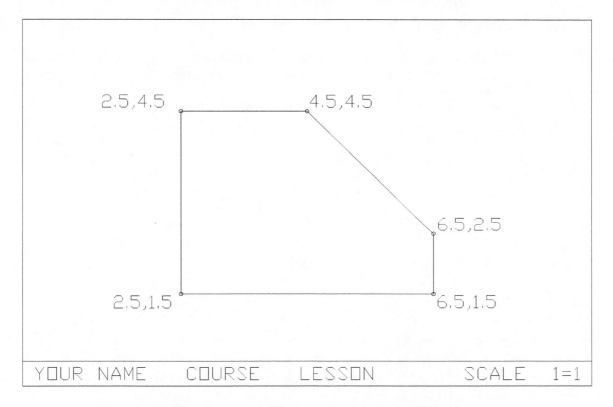

4. Activate the **Endpoint** option of running **Object Snap Modes**.

Note: When dimensioning lines, it is good practice to rely on **Object Snap** as opposed to the **Grid** and **Snap** settings. The use of **Object Snap** settings will allow you to dimension with precision.

5. **Linear Dimension** the Object by doing the following:

- Load and dock the **Dimension** toolbar at the top of the **Drawing Area**.

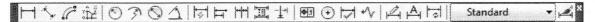

- In the **Dimension** toolbar, select the **Linear** button.

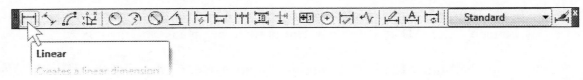

Linear
Creates a linear dimension

- **OSnap** onto the left **Endpoint** of **L1**.

- **OSnap** onto the right **Endpoint** of **L1**. {Dimensioning line will appear}.

- Click above Line **L1** by about **0.5**. {Line **L1** will be dimensioned as shown below. Your current font may be different than what is shown below.}

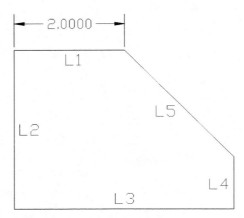

Note: In dimensioning Line **L1** above, it does not matter which endpoint is selected first. However, there are times when the order of endpoint selection does matter. Picking the **Endpoints** in the proper order comes into play when other tools are used such as **Continue or Baseline Dimension,** which we will cover later in this Chapter.

- From the **Dimension** toolbar, select the **Linear** button again.

- Pick the upper **Endpoint** of **L2**. (Be sure that you are picking up the endpoint of Line **L2** and not the endpoint of the dimensioning already completed for Line **L1**.)

- Pick the lower **Endpoint** of **L2**. {The Dimension line appears.}

- Click to the left of Line **L2** by about **0.5** units. {**L2** is dimensioned.}

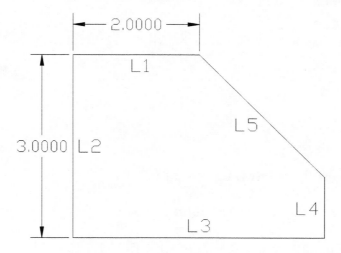

- Dimension the Lines **L3** and **L4** by using the **Linear** Tool.

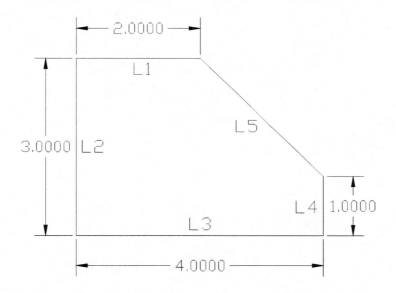

- Click on the **Linear** button in the **Dimension** toolbar again.

- Pick the upper left **Endpoint** of **L5**.

- Pick the lower right **Endpoint** of **L5**.

Note: The **Linear** tool forces the Dimension Line to appear and drag in either horizontal or vertical direction. When dimensioning lines that are positioned along an inclined face, you have the option to use the **Aligned** tool.

- Press the **Esc** key.

6. Dimension an inclined edge using the **Aligned** dimension tool by doing the following:

- In the **Dimension** toolbar, select the **Aligned** button.

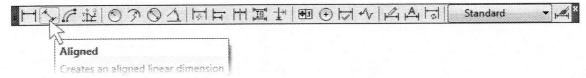

Aligned
Creates an aligned linear dimension

- **OSnap** to the upper left **Endpoint** of **L5**.

- **OSnap** to the lower right **Endpoint** of **L5**.

- Click the cursor by about **0.5** units away from **L5**.

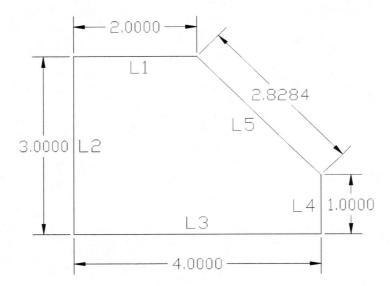

Note: In the above exercise you dimensioned more lines than needed. Note that by dimensioning lines L1, L2, L3 and L4, length of L5 becomes fixed and therefore L5 does not need to be dimensioned. Keep in mind that redundant (also known as over-defined) dimensioning is unnecessary.

- **Erase** the shape above including all of the associated dimensions.

Note: As you begin using your dimensioning tools, you will notice that a Layer named **Defpoints** is automatically created. This Layer is generated for internal use only. Do not set this Layer as current or place any Objects on this Layer.

- Use the **Line** Command to create the Object shown below.

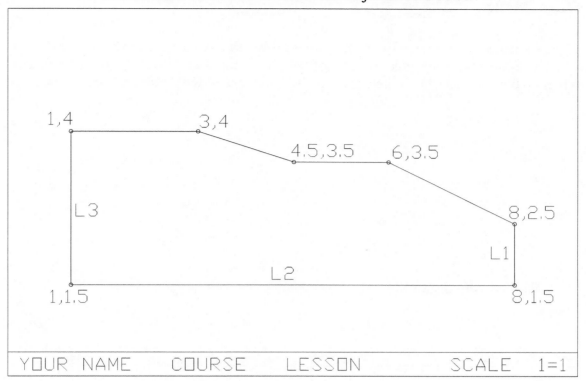

7. Use the **Linear** tool to dimension **L1**, **L2**, and **L3** as shown below.

Dimension Style

As discussed previously, most system variables have a default value. Next, you will change the default settings of some of the dimension variables using the **Dimension Style** tool, but first, let's learn the common terms associated with a dimensioned Object.

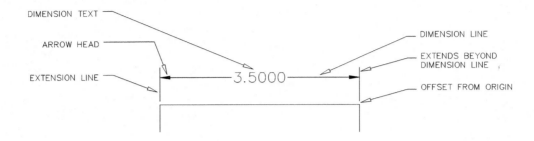

1. Modify **Dimension Style** settings by doing the following:

   • In the **Dimension** toolbar, select the **Dimension Style** button.

{The **Dimension Style Manager** dialog box will appear.}

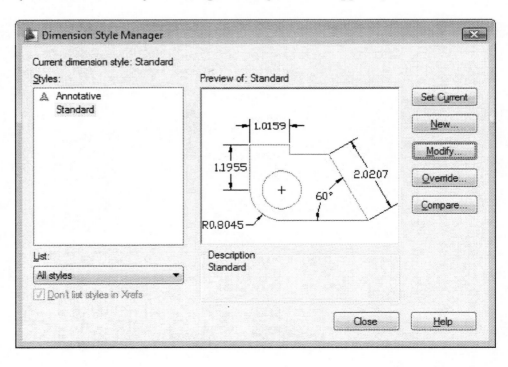

2. Select the **Modify** button. {The **Modify Dimension Style** dialog box will appear.}

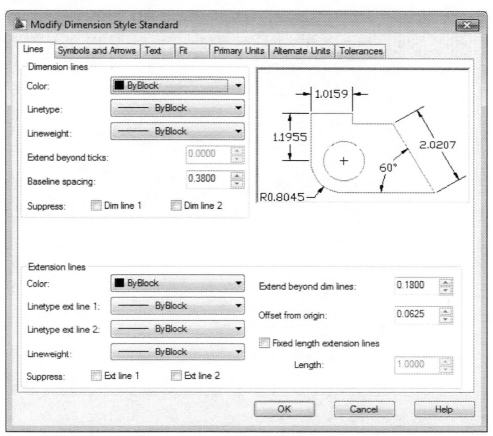

- On the **Lines** tab of the **Modify Dimension Style** dialog box, change **Baseline spacing** (under the **Dimension Lines** area) to **.3400**.

- Change **Extend beyond dim lines** (under the **Extension Lines** area) to **0.1400**.

- Change **Offset from origin** (also under the **Extension Lines** area) to **0.0900**.

- Select the **Symbols and Arrows** tab.

- Change **Arrow size** (under the **Arrowheads** area) to **0.1400**.

- Change the value (under the **Center Marks** area) to **0.1000**.

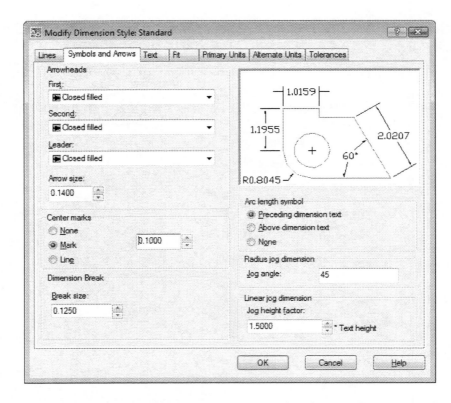

- Click on the **Text** tab of the **Modify Dimension Style** dialog box.

- In the **Text Appearance** area, change the **Text height** to **0.15**.

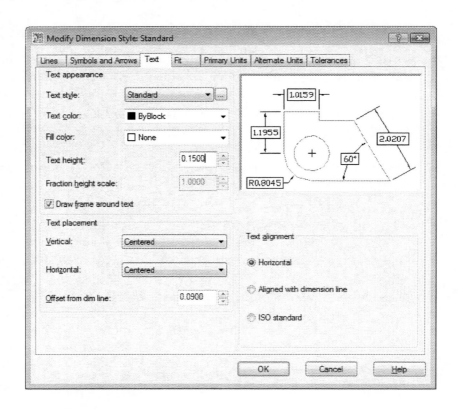

- Click on the **Primary Units** tab of the **Modify Dimension Style** dialog box.

- In the **Linear Dimensions Precision** drop-down menu, set the precision to 2 decimal places (**0.00**).

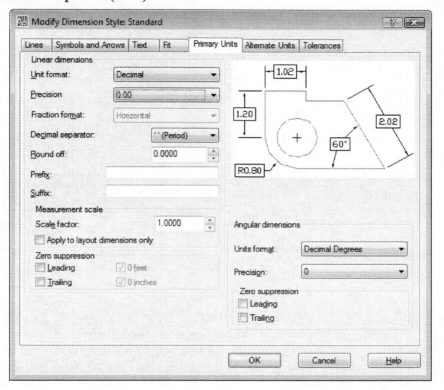

- Click **OK**.

- In the **Dimension Style Manager** dialog box click **Close**.

Note: In general, dimensions will automatically update as the Drawing **Dimension Style** values are changed. However, there may be times when you must force the update process.

3. **Update Dimensions** by doing the following:

- In the **Dimension** toolbar, select the **Dimension Update** button.

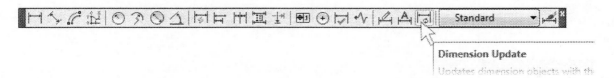

Dimension Update

Updates dimension objects with th

470

- Use the pickbox to select each of the **Dimensions** that are already drawn then *[ENTER]*.

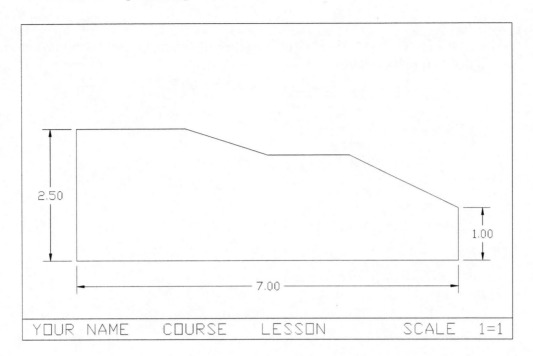

Note: In the previous set of exercises you modified the **Dimensioning** System Settings of the **Standard Style** (which is the default **Dimension Style** of AutoCAD). In a professional setting, it is generally good practice to keep the AutoCAD default settings intact. Therefore, it is best to create your own dimension style and then modify the settings. In the next chapter you will put the following **New Dimension Style** options to use.

4. Create a **New Dimension Style** by doing the following:

- Open the **Dimension Style Manager** dialog box by selecting the **Dimension Style** button.

- Click **New** in the **Dimension Style Manager** dialog box. {The **Create New Dimension Style** dialog box will appear as shown below.}

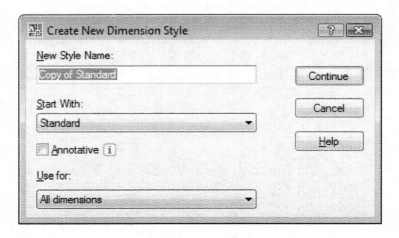

- **Name** the **New Style** as *My Dim Style*.

- Make sure that the **Annotative** property is set to **Off**.

- Click **Continue**. {The **New Dimension Style** dialog box will appear.}

Note: The **New Dimension Style** dialog box is the same as the **Modify Dimension Style** dialog box, only with a different name. It can be used in the same manner to **Modify** the **Dimension Settings**.

Also note that in this exercise, you are not using the **Annotative** property of your **Dimension Style**. In the next chapter, as you learn about **Layouts**, you will then be exposed to this Option and its purpose.

- Click **OK**.

- In the **Dimension Style Manager** dialog box select *My Dim Style* style and click **Set Current**.

- Click **Close**.

- When finished, continue to the next section without **Erasing** the screen.

Continuous and Baseline Dimensioning

1. Use the **Continuous Dimensions** by doing the following:

   - In the **Dimension** toolbar, click on the **Linear Dimension** button and horizontally dimension Line **L1** from left to right as shown below.

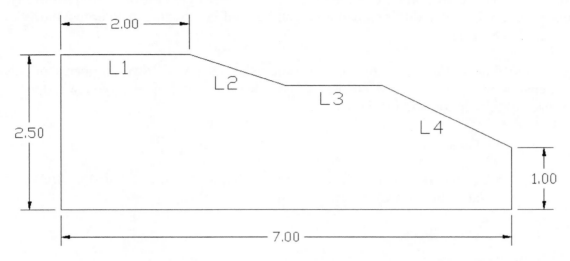

Note: In order to use the **Continue Dimension** tool, you must have a **Linear Dimension** already in the Drawing.

   - In the **Dimension** toolbar, select the **Continue Dimension** button.

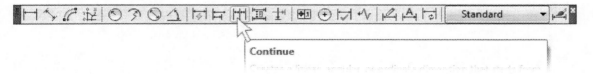

Note: When using the **Continue Dimension** tool, AutoCAD automatically uses the last dimensioning drawn to continue from. In this case, as long as you have not dimensioned other Objects since dimensioning **L1,** the left **Endpoint** of **L1** will be pre-selected.

- **OSnap** to the right **Endpoint** of **L2** as shown below.

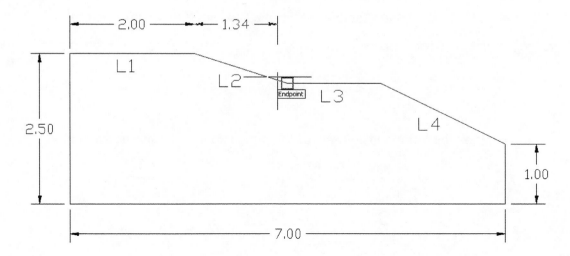

- **OSnap** to the right **Endpoint** of **L3** and again **L4** then *[ENTER]* twice to get out of the Command.

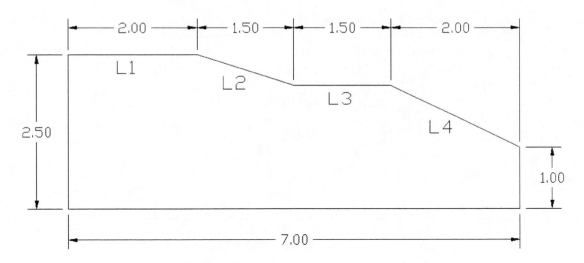

2. **Erase** the dimensioning associated with **L2, L3**, and **L4**.

Note: Just as in the case of **Continue Dimension** tool, the **Baseline Dimension** tool utilizes the last dimension drawn. However, because **L1** is not the last Object dimensioned, it is no longer in the selection buffer. Therefore as demonstrated on the next page, it will be necessary to select the **Dimension** again.

3. Apply **Baseline Dimensioning** to an Object by doing the following:

- In the **Dimension** toolbar, select the **Baseline Dimension** button.

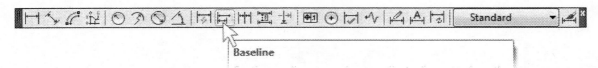

- Pick the left extension line of the dimension for **L1** as shown below.

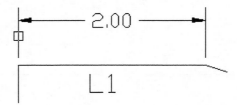

- **OSnap** to the right **Endpoint** of **L2** as shown below.

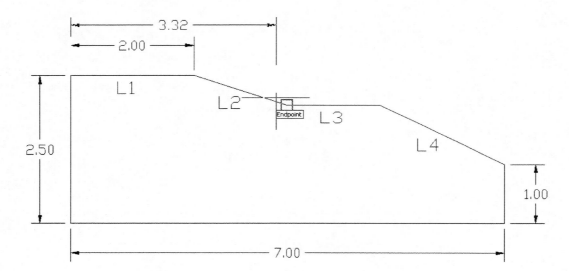

- Continue to **OSnap** to the right **Endpoint** of **L3** and **L4** then *[ENTER]* twice to get out of the Command.

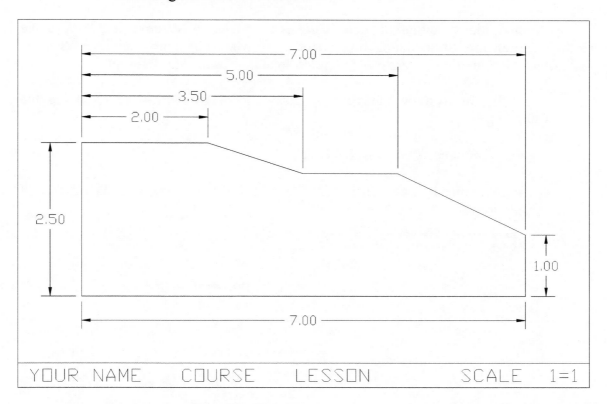

Note: When **Baseline Dimensioning** is used as in the case above, the **Dimension Spacing** is governed by the **Base Line Spacing** value set earlier in the exercise. However, this space could easily be modified directly from the Dimension toolbar.

- In the **Dimension** toolbar, select the **Dimension Space** tool.

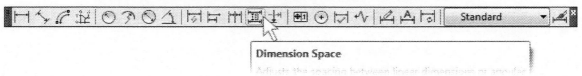

- Select the **original base dimension** line having the **2.00** unit **dimension**.

- Select the **dimension to space** by selecting the remaining **Dimension lines** having the values **3.50,5.00** and **7.00**, and then *[ENTER].*

- When prompted to **Enter value**, enter *0.25* and then *[ENTER].* { **Dimension Spacing** is set to **0.25**.}

- **U** (for **Undo**) and then *[ENTER].* { The **Base Dimension Lines** are set back to their original spacing.}

Dimension System Variables

When initially setting up your **Dimension Style,** it is convenient to use the **Modify Dimension Style** dialog box. However, when changing individual **System Variables**, it is sometimes more efficient to do so at the **Command Prompt**.

1. Get a list of **System Variables** associated with **Dimensioning** by doing the following:

   - Command: *Dim* then *[ENTER]*.

   - Command: *Status* then *[ENTER]*. {The **AutoCAD Text Window** will appear.}

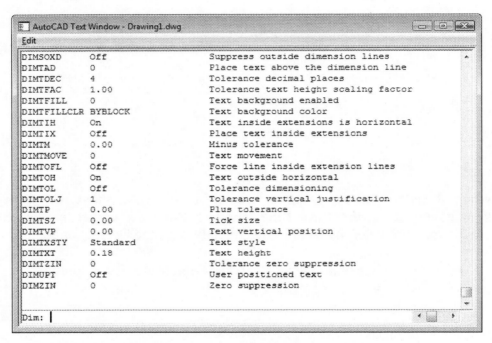

Note: When looking up the **Status** of **System Variables,** you are able to scroll through the **System Variables** using the scroll bar, and to the right of each **Variable** there is a brief explanation of the variable.

   - Press the **F2** key to close the **Text Window**.

2. Change a **System Variable** associated with **Dimensioning** by doing the following:

Note: It is important to first get a list of the **System Variables** associated with **Dimensioning** (as you did above) before attempting to change them. When you close the **Text Window** you will still be in the **Dim** Command at the prompt line. You may either change the **System Variables** from within this Command or you may **Esc** before beginning.

- Command: ***Dimdec*** then ***[ENTER]***. {This Command changes the number of decimal places.}

- Enter a new value of ***4.0*** then ***[ENTER]***.

Note: The dimensions on the screen may or may not automatically update as discussed when you changed **System Variables** using the **Modify Dimension Style** dialog box. You will "force update" after you have changed all the variables in this exercise.

- Command: ***Dimscale*** then ***[ENTER]***. {This Command changes the overall scale factor.}

- Enter a new value of ***.5*** and then ***[ENTER]***.

- Click on the **Dimension Update** button and use Pick box to select the four dimensions above the Object, then ***[ENTER]***. {All **Dimensions** having the **My Dim Style** are updated using the current system variables.}

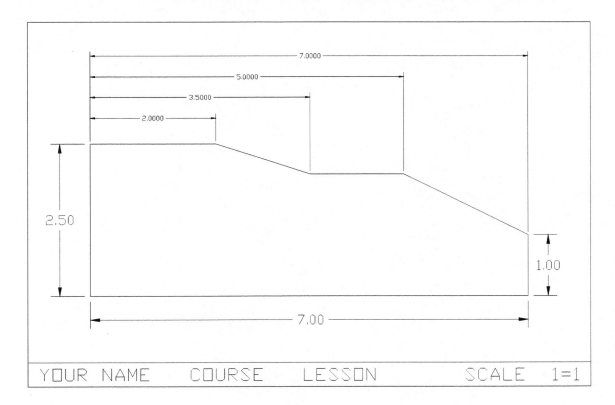

Note: Though normally you would want all dimensions in a Drawing to be consistent, in this example you will be able to compare the changes made against the previous settings by only updating some of the dimensions.

- Set **Dimscale** to *1* and **Dimdec** back to *2* places.

- **Update** all dimensions.

- When finished, **Erase** the shape and all Dimensioning from the screen.

Note: You did not fully dimension the above Object, but rather used it as an exercise to learn different **Dimensioning** techniques.

<u>Fitting Dimension Text and Arrows</u>

1. Set **Grid** and **Snap** to **On**.

2. Use the **Polygon** Command to create a 4- sided **inscribed** square. Exact location is your choice. When prompted for the **Radius**, move cursor *.75* units vertically up and click.

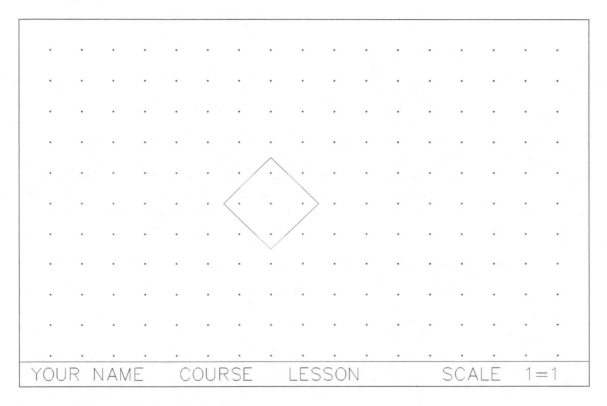

YOUR NAME   COURSE   LESSON   SCALE   1=1

3. Set **Grid** and **Snap** to *Off*.

4. Use the **Polyline** option of the **Chamfer** Command to truncate all four corners of the **Polygon**. Set **Chamfer Distance 1 and 2** to *0.20* {The Object shown below.}

480

5. Create **Linear Dimensions** in small areas by doing the following:

    -   Ensure **OSnap** running Mode is set to **Endpoint**.

    -   Use the **Linear Dimension** tool to dimension the left side of the Object by picking the upper **Endpoint** of the line, then the lower **Endpoint**, and finally drag about 0.5 units to the left of the Object then click.

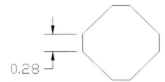

Note: Since there is not enough room between the extension lines, the Text and the arrows are automatically positioned to the outside and the Text is positioned on the side of the last point of entry. On the **Fit** tab of the **Modify Dimension Style** dialog box, there are options for the Text and arrows to go in different positions if either or both will not fit inside the extension lines. It is useful to know where these settings may be changed, but for the purposes of this exercise, you will leave the settings as default.

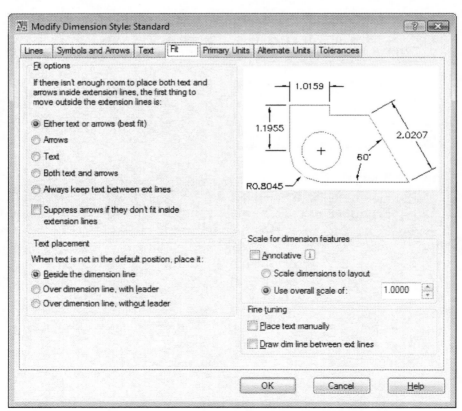

- **Linear Dimension** the bottom, right, and top **Chamfers** by picking the **Endpoints** in a counter-clockwise order.

Note: In each case, the **Dimension Text** falls on the side of the second extension line entry.

Associative Dimensioning

Next you will take advantage of **Associative Dimensioning**, in that if you **Move**, **Scale**, **Stretch**, or **Modify** an Object in any way, the **Dimensions Update** automatically.

1. Modify a dimensioned Object by doing the following:

   - Set **Ortho** and **Snap** to *On*.

   - From the **Modify** toolbar, select **Stretch**.

   - Use the **Crossing** option (by picking from right to left) to select the right half of the Object, including the **Dimension Lines** as shown below.

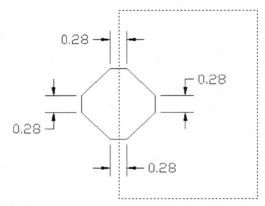

   - Press *[ENTER]*.

   - Stretch the Object horizontally to the right by **1.5** units as shown below. To properly stretch by this amount, for the second base point, move the mouse horizontally to the right and type *1.5* then *[ENTER]*. {Dimensions update as you stretch.}

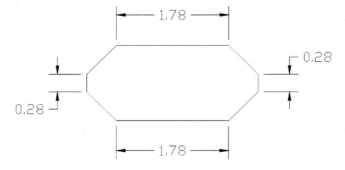

Note: Designs are constantly modified. However, as seen above, the Objects and their associated dimensioning usually do not have to be drawn from scratch again. As you **Scale**, **Stretch**, **Rotate** and further modify your design, the dimensioning will automatically update. Therefore, when modifying an Object that has already been dimensioned, the dimensions will automatically update.

- **Undo** the **Stretch** Command.

- Set **Snap** to *Off*.

- **Stretch** the Object vertically by **1.32** units. To properly stretch by this amount, for the second base point, move the mouse vertically up and type **1.32** then *[ENTER]*. {Object may move outside of the **Limits**.}

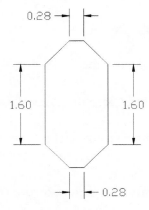

- Set **Ortho** to *off*.

2. Make use of **Associative Dimensioning** by doing the following:

- Select only the Object and **Move** it to about the center of the screen. {The Dimensions will automatically reposition with the Object.}

- **Scale** the Object with a user-specified **Base Point**, using a **Scale Factor** of **1.25** as shown below. {The Dimensions will scale along with the Object.}

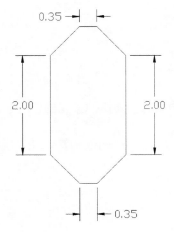

- Select just the Object one more time and **Rotate** it by *30* degrees from about the center as shown below. {The Dimensions should readjust to the rotation of the Object.}

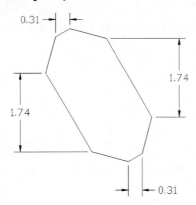

3. **Undo** both **Rotate** and **Scale** Commands.

4. **Disassociating Dimensions** from the Object by doing the following:

- Command: ***Dimdisassociate*** then *[ENTER]*.

- Select the two **Dimensions** to the left and bottom of the Object then *[ENTER]*. {The two **Dimension Lines** are now **Disassociated**.}

- Select and **Move** only the Object to the right. {The **Dimensioning** to the top and right of the Object will move with the Object, while the **Disassociated Dimensions** will remain in position.}

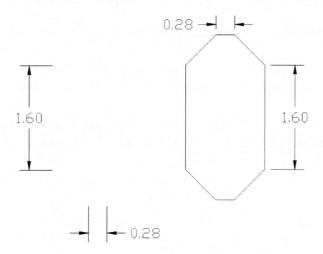

5. **Reassociate** the **Dimensioning** of the Object by doing the following:

- Command: ***Dimreassociate*** then *[ENTER]*.

- Use the pickbox to select the 2 **Disassociated Dimensions** starting with the **1.60 Dimension** Line, then *[ENTER]*. {**Markers** will appear indicating which point is to be **Reassociated** first as shown in the next step.}

- **OSnap** to the upper **Endpoint** of the left side of the Object as shown below.

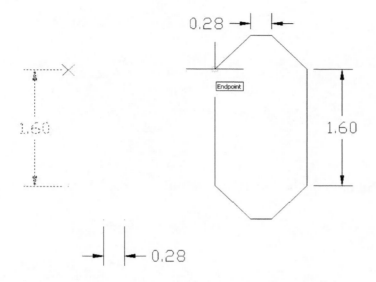

- **OSnap** to the lower **Endpoint** of the left side of the Object as shown below.

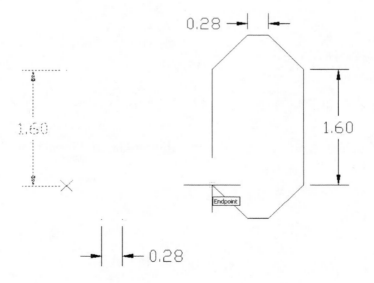

486

- **OSnap** to the bottom left **Endpoint** of the Object as shown below.

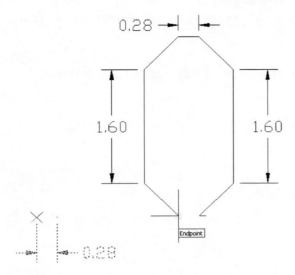

- **OSnap** to the bottom right **Endpoint** of the Object as shown below.

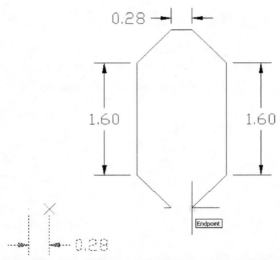

5. When finished, **Erase** the Object and all associated dimensions.

Dimensioning Circles and Arcs

1. Set **OSnap** to *Off*.

2. Create a **Circle** with **R=0.25** and center located at *2.0,4.5*.

3. Create a **Circle** with **R=0.75** and center located at *4.5,4.5*.

4. Using the **3 point** option, construct an **Arc** in the upper right corner of the Drawing area at a User Specified location.

5. **Copy** all three Objects to a lower position as shown below at a user-specified location.

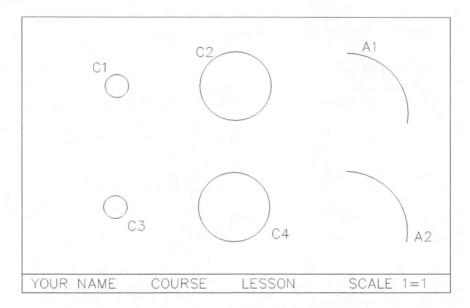

6. **Radius Dimension** Arcs and Circles by doing the following:

    *   In the **Dimension** toolbar, select the **Radius Dimension** button.

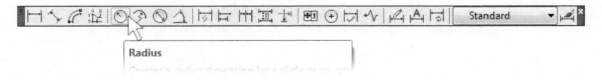

Pick Circle C1.

- Pick a user-specified point outside of Circle **C1** as shown by the cursor.

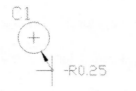

Note: The **Radius** tool places a leader on the outside and marks the center. The dimension notes places an **R** signifying the **Radius**. **Center Mark** size was one of the values you changed earlier in this Chapter under the **Modify Dimension Style** dialog box.

- Pick the **Radius** button again.

- Pick Circle **C2**.

- Pick a user-specified point outside of Circle **C2** as shown by the cursor.

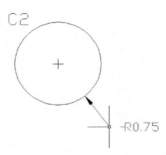

- Pick the **Radius** button again.

Note: Circles and Arcs can be dimensioned using the same dimensioning Commands.

- Pick Arc **A1**.

- Pick a user-specified point above Arc **A1** as shown by the cursor.

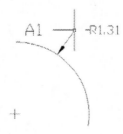

7. **Diameter Dimension** Arcs and Circles by doing the following:

- In the **Dimension** toolbar, select the **Diameter** button.

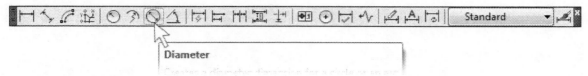

- Pick Circle **C3**.

- Pick a user-specified point outside of Circle **C3** as shown by the cursor.

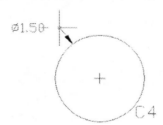

Note: When dimensioning the **Diameter** of a **Circle,** the **Dimension Text** carries a **Diameter** symbol Phi before the dimension as shown below.

- Click on the **Diameter** button again.

- Pick Circle **C4**.

- Pick a user-specified point outside of Circle **C1** as shown by the cursor.

- Click on the **Diameter** button again.

- Pick Arc **A2**.

490

- Pick a user-specified point above Arc **A2** as shown below.

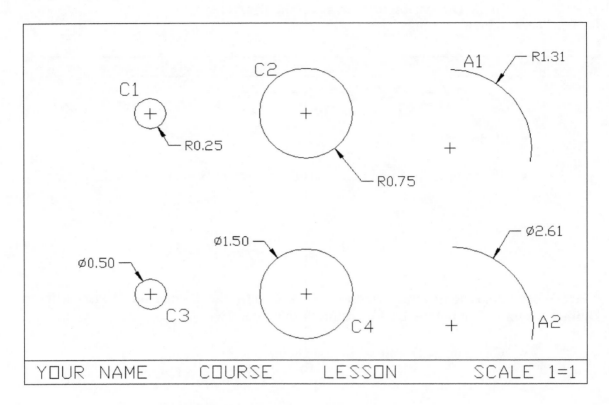

- **Erase** the geometry and Dimension from the screen.

8. Dimension an Arc's length by doing the following

- Create the **Arc** and the **Circle** at user-specified locations as shown below.

- From the Dimension Toolbar select the **Arc Length** tool

Arc Length

- Select the **Arc** and then move and click the cursor to a user-specified location to the outside of the **Arc** as shown below {arc's Length is dimensioned}

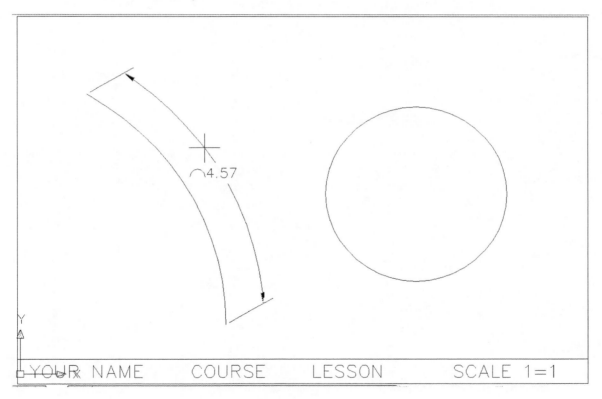

Note: You can use your knowledge of **Grips** to reposition/rearrange your dimensions. As an example, your Dimension text and the Dimension line could easily be repositioned using **Grips**.

492

9. Dimension an Arc or Circle with a **Jogged** Leader Line by doing the following:

- From the Dimension Toolbar select **Jogged**.

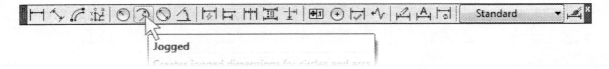

- Select the Circle.

- When asked to specify center override, pick a user-specified location as shown below by the position of the cursor.

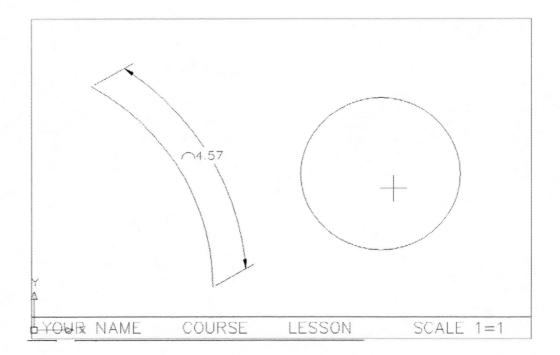

- For the Dimension Line location, pick a user-specified point as shown below by the cursor.

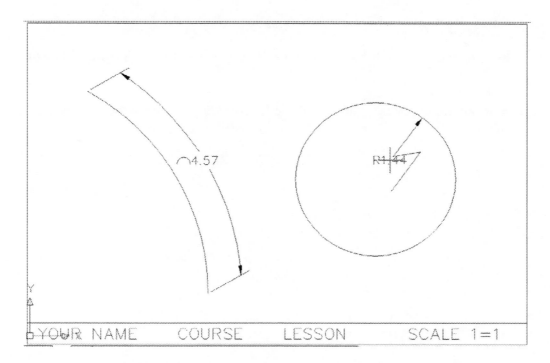

- To specify **Jog** location, select a user-specified point as shown below.

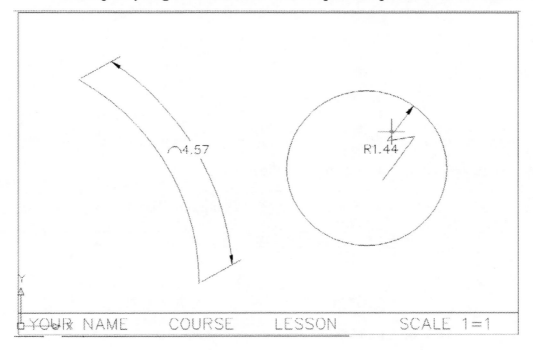

- **Erase** all geometry on the screen.

Angular Dimensions

1. Create a **Rectangle** with the two corners located at *2.0,1.5* and *7.0,4.5*.

2. **Chamfer** the lower left corner of the **Rectangle** with both **Chamfer Distances** of *2.0*.

3. **Chamfer** the upper right corner of the **Rectangle** with the same **Chamfer** setting as in item 2.

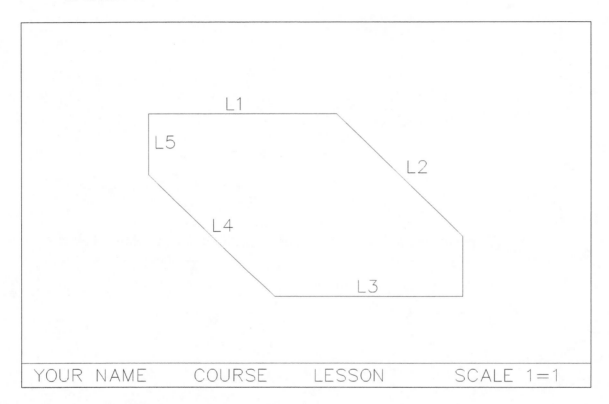

YOUR NAME   COURSE   LESSON   SCALE 1=1

4. **Angular Dimension** by doing the following:

   - In the **Dimension** toolbar, select the **Angular Dimension** button.

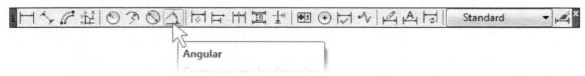

Angular

   - Pick Line **L1** and then **L2**.

- Drag the cursor to the position shown below and Pick. {The **Angular dimension** appears as shown.}

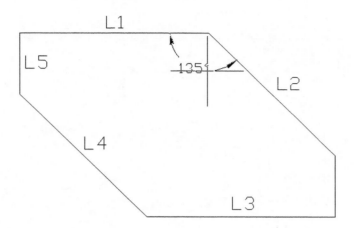

- Click on the **Angular Dimension** button again.

- Pick Line **L3** and then **L4**.

- Drag the cursor to the position shown below and Pick. {The **Angular Dimension** appears as shown.}

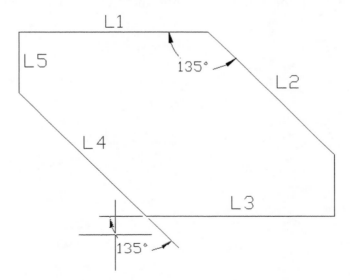

- *[ENTER]*. {This repeats the **Angular Dimension** Command.}

- Pick Line **L4** and then **L5**.

- Drag the cursor to the location shown and click. {The **Angular dimension** appears as shown.}

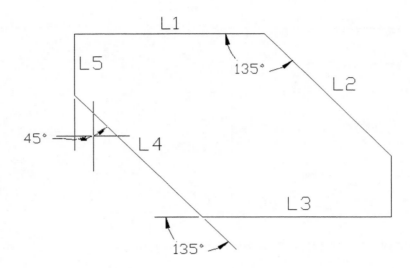

- Do not **Erase** the Object or its **Dimensioning** because you will be using it as a starting point in the next exercise.

Note: After any dimensioning is created, AutoCAD will create a **Layer** called **Defpoints**. This **Layer** is for internal use only; therefore, Objects should not be drawn on this **Layer**.

Multileader

1. Label an Object using **Leader Lines** by doing the following:

   - Load and Dock the **Multileader** Toolbar on the screen.

   - In the **Multileader** Toolbar, select the **Multileader** button as shown below.

   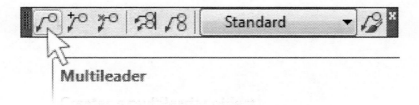

   - Click just above Line **L1** to define arrowhead location as shown below.

   - Click a second point as shown by cursor below. {The **Text Formatting** Dialog box appears.}

   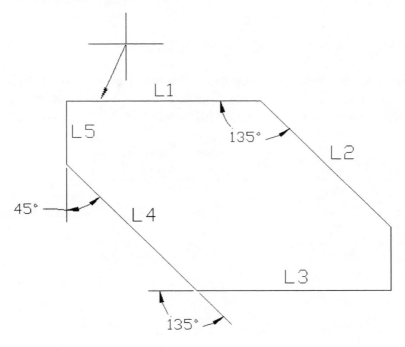

   - Type the Text: *ALUMINUM SURFACE*.

   - Select **OK**.

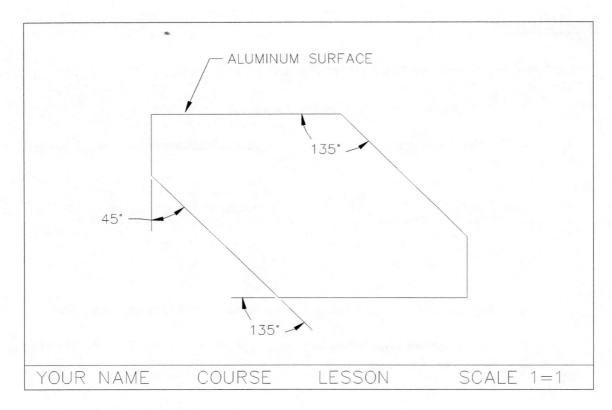

ALUMINUM SURFACE

135°

45°

135°

YOUR NAME   COURSE   LESSON   SCALE 1=1

2. **Exit** AutoCAD without saving.

Note: Just like the **Dimension** settings, when using the **Multileader**, you need to set the proper settings so that the **Leaders** appear at an appropriate size on the screen. Just like the Dimension Toolbar, you can **Modify** your **Multileader Style** as shown below.

Multileader

Creates and

Aliases

DIMALIGNED .... DAL

DIMANGULAR .... DAN

DIMBASELINE .... DBA

DIMDIAMETER .... DDI

DIMDISASSOCIATE .... DDA

DIMLINEAR .... DLI

DIMCONTINUE .... DCO

DIMSTYLE .... D

DIMRADIUS .... DRA

DIMREASSOCIATE... DRE

LEADER .... LEAD

QLEADER .... LE

Assignment 11

Objective:

1. To practice **Automatic Dimensioning**.

Instructions:

1. Launch AutoCAD and **Open** the Midterm Project.
2. **Save As** the Drawing file to your folder. Name it **"ASSIGN11_ _ _.dwg"** where the 3 blanks are your initials.
3. Modify the **Text** in the title box to read *Lesson 11* instead of *Mid-Proj* as shown below.

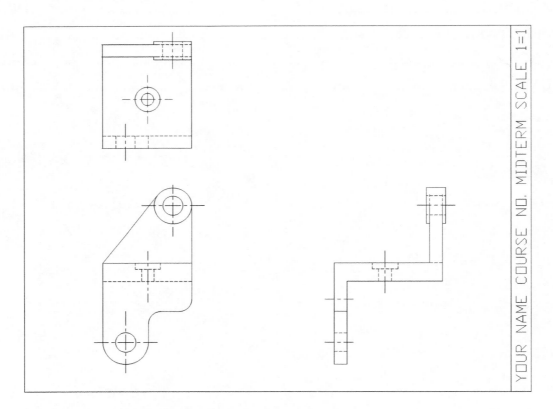

4. Modify the **Dimension Settings** given below:

- **Extend beyond dim lines**: *0.09*
- **Offset from origin**: *0.03*
- **Arrow size**: *0.075*
- **Text height**: *0.075*
- **Units format precision**: *0.000* (3 decimal places)

5. Dimension the Drawing as shown in the final plot sample.
6. **Save** your Drawing.
7. **Preview** and **Plot** Drawing using the following settings:

- Paper size: Letter (8.50x11.00 **inches**)
- Plot area: Limits
- Plot offset: Centered
- Plot scale: 1=1

8. When finished with assignment, close **Dimension** toolbar then **Exit** AutoCAD.

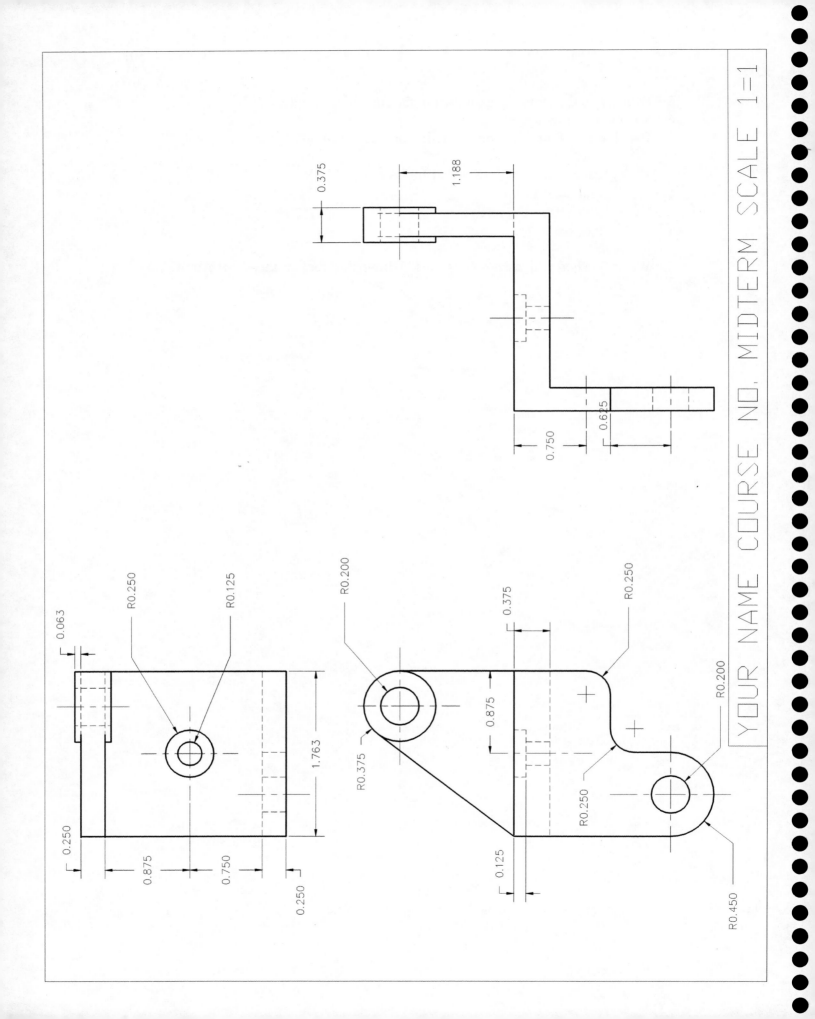

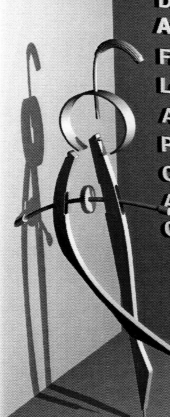

Chapter 12

Layouts

Viewports

Manipulate Geometry in Viewports

Dimension in Viewports

Annotative Dimensions

Freeze Layers in Viewports

Lock Viewports

Add Text to Layouts

Plotting

Create New Layout Tabs

ANSI Templates

Create a Template (Paper Space)

504

Layouts

1. Launch AutoCAD and use your **My Template** to begin a **New** drawing.

2. Set **Snap**, and **Grid** to *On*. Set **Ortho, Polar, OSnap, OTrack, Ducs,** and **Dyn** to *Off*. Make sure that your **Snap** value is set to *0.25*.

3. **Save As** the drawing as **Layouts and Plotting _ _ _.dwg** to your folder. For the three blanks use your initials.

4. Set your **Units** to **Decimal** with a **Precision** of 3 decimal places (*0.000*).

5. Create **Layers CEN, DIM,** and **HID** as shown below.

6. Assign **CENTER Line type** to **Layer CEN, HIDDEN Line type** to **Layer HID**, and keep **Layer DIM** as **Continuous**. Assign a user-specified **Color** to each **Layer**.

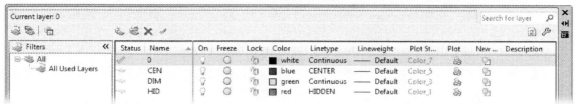

Note: Up to this point in the tutorials, you have been creating all Objects including the border and title block in the same **Space** as the actual geometry. This space is specifically referred to as **Model Space**. You have also been partly limited in your techniques for plotting. For instance, you have not been able to plot multiple views of the same Object using different scale factors on the same sheet. In addition, since your Objects/geometry and the title block are both in the same space, if you assign a Plot scale factor to your geometry, the title block will "unwillingly" scale as well. For these reasons and more, it would help to separate the two into two different spaces known as **Model Space** and **Paper Space**. Simply put, **Model Space** is where the actual geometry is constructed and the Title block resides in **Paper Space**.

7. Construct the Ring geometry by following these instructions.

   - Do not erase your current title block which currently resides in **Model Space**. This will be done later in the chapter.

   - Make sure **Layer 0** is the **Current Layer**.

   - Create Circle **C1** with center located at *4.5,3.0* and R=*1.75*.

   - Create Circle **C2** having the same center as **C1** and R=*1.5*.

506

- Create two center lines (currently drawn on **Layer 0**) through the Center of Circles extending **0.25** units beyond the circumference of Circle **C1** as shown below.

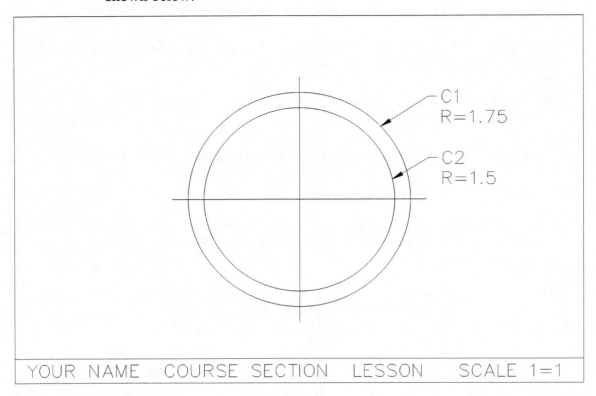

YOUR NAME   COURSE SECTION   LESSON   SCALE 1=1

- Use the **2P** option of the Circle Command to create Circle **C3** going through the 3 o'clock **quadrants** of Circles **C1** and **C2**. The **quadrants** are on **Snap**.

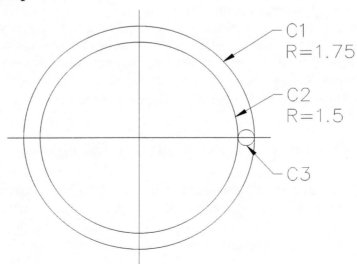

- Turn *Off* **Grid** and **Snap**.

- **Offset C1 Through** the **Center** of **C3** as shown below.

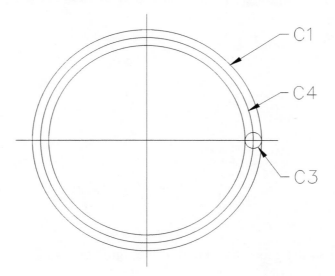

- Change the Layer Property of Circle **C4** and the two center lines to **Layer CEN** as shown below. Refer to page 122 if necessary. {The Objects take the property of **Layer CEN**.}

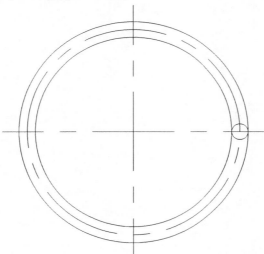

- **Freeze Layer CEN**. {Circle **C4** and the two center lines disappear.}

- **Zoom** in on Circle **C3**.

508

- **Offset C3** by *0.025* to the outside.

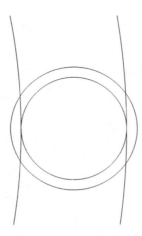

- **Trim** the geometry to that of the figure below.

Note: When you **Trim** Circles, they convert to Arcs. You can verify this by using the **List** Command.

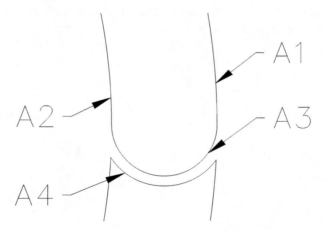

- **Offset** all four Arcs **A1**, **A2**, **A3**, and **A4** to the inside of the **Ring** by *0.025*. Then **Trim** as shown below.

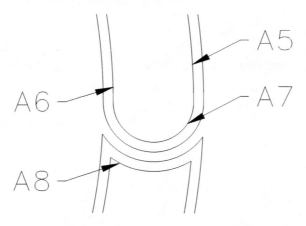

- Change the **Layer** propert of the new offset Arcs **A5-A8** to **Layer HID**. {The **Arcs** will take on the properties of **Layer HID**.}

- Set **LTscale** to *0.2*.

- **Freeze Layer HID**. {**Arcs A5**, **A6**, **A7**, and **A8** will disappear.}

- Create a Circle **C9** having the same Center as Arc **A3** with R=*0.075* as shown below.

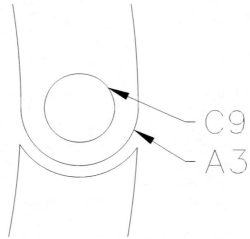

- **Zoom All**.

510

- **Polar Array** Circle **C9** about the geometric center of The Ring with the **Total number of Items** set to *12* as shown below.

- Thaw **Layer CEN** and **HID**.

Note: You are finished with the modeling phase of the Ring geometry as shown below.

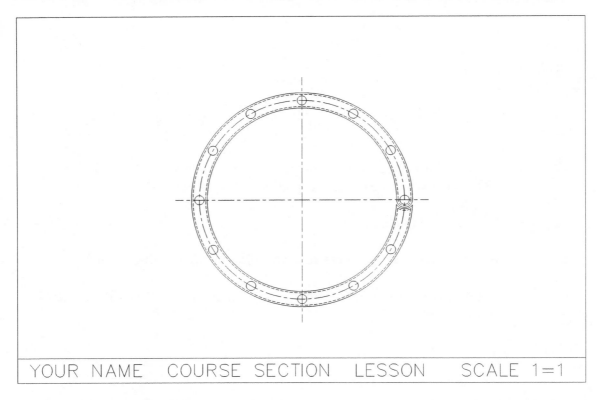

YOUR NAME   COURSE SECTION   LESSON   SCALE 1=1

8. **Erase** the title Block (including the rectangular border) leaving the Ring as the only geometry on screen.

Note: **Paper Space** is the space or area where the border and title Block are constructed so that they are kept separate from the actual geometry. **Paper Space** is also where the final layout of a Plot is arranged. To access **Paper Space**, you will be instructed to use the **Layout** Tabs located just above the **Command Prompt Area** as shown below.

In the event that your **Model** and **Layout** tabs shown below do not display on the screen, from the Menu Bar, you may select **Tools**, **Options**, **Display** tab, and in the **Layout elements** area, toggle the **Display Layout and Model Tabs** to *On*.

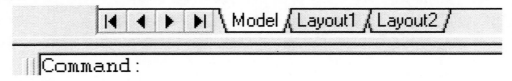

9. **Setup** a Drawing in **Paper Space** by doing the following:

- From the Menu Bar select **File**, then **Page Setup Manager...** {The **Page Setup Manager** dialog box will appear.}

- In the lower left corner of the **Page Setup Manager** dialog box, Toggle the **Display when creating a new layout** to **On** as shown below. Then click **Close**.

- Click on the **Layout1** tab. {The **Page Setup Manager** dialog box will appear.}

- Click **Modify**. {The **Page Setup** dialog box will appear.}

- In the **Printer/Plotter** area, set the **Name** to your **Plotter**. If you do not have a **Plotter**, leave it as **None**.

512

- Set **Paper size** to **Letter**.

- Check that **Plot Area** is set to **Layout** .

- In the **Plot scale** area, set **Scale** to **1:1**.

- Click **OK** to close the **Page Setup** dialog box, then **Close** to close the **Page Setup Manager** dialog box. {You will find yourself in **Paper Space**.}

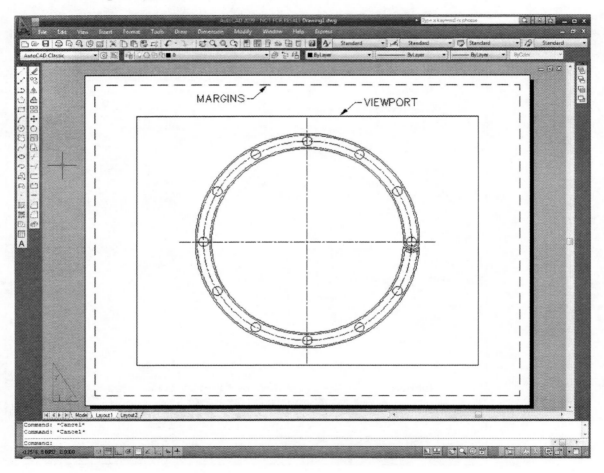

Note: The **Layout** displays a white area that represents your sheet of paper. The dashed rectangular border near the edge of the paper represents your plot margins. This border does not show up on the actual plot.

As you can see from the above image, AutoCAD automatically creates a single rectangular **Viewport** in your **Layout**. A **Viewport** is a window into **Model Space** so that you can view the geometry.

Viewports

1. Switch to **Model Space** while remaining in a **Layout** by doing the following:

   - Double click within the rectangular boundaries of the **Viewport**.

Note: While in a **Layout**, when you double click within a **Viewport,** you switch to **Model Space**. There are two clear indicators to let you know that you are in **Model Space.** The **Viewport rectangular** border will change to a heavy line and the triangular **Paper Space** icon will change back to the **Model Space** icon. The two icons are shown below.

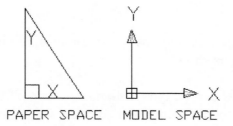

PAPER SPACE   MODEL SPACE

In general, due to space limitations, if and when necessary, it is best to modify the geometry from the **Model** tab as opposed to the **Layout** tab. You can also use the Max/Min Viewport button in the right side of the **Status Line** to toggle between **Paper Space** and **Model Space**.

2. **Erase** a **Viewports** by doing the following:

   - Double click outside of the **Viewport**. {**Layout** toggles back to **Paper Space**.}

   - Select the **Erase** Tool.

   - Use **Crossing** over the entire white area piece of paper from right to left. {Only the **Viewport** is selected as described in the Note below.}

   - *[ENTER]*. {The **Viewport** is **Erased**, and therefore your window into **Model Space** is removed.}

Note: When working in **Paper Space**, the Objects in **Model Space** are ignored and the only selectable Objects are **Viewports** or any other Objects that are created in **Paper Space**.

514

3. Load and dock the **Viewports** toolbar at the top of the **Drawing Area**.

4. Create and Modify **Viewports** by doing the following:

- In the **Viewports** toolbar, select the **Single Viewport** button.

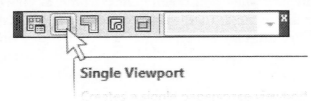

- Select a point near the lower left corner of the paper symbol but just inside the margins as shown below.

- For the other corner, type in **@5,5** and then **[ENTER]**. {A 5"x5" **Viewport** will appear and the Ring will automatically appear within the **Viewport** as shown below. Your Ring Zoom factor may be different as it will be addressed later}

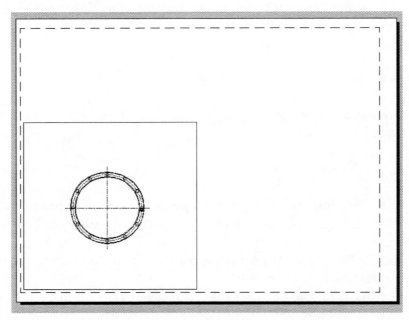

Note: Viewports are Objects in **Paper Space** and therefore can be generally edited like other Objects using the **Modify** Commands like **Copy, Move** and **Stretch**.

- Command: *Copy* and then **[ENTER]**.

- Select the edge of the **Viewport** then **[ENTER]**.

- Make sure **Ortho** is set to **On**.

- **Copy** the **Viewport** to the right so that the second **Viewport** also falls within the margins as shown below.

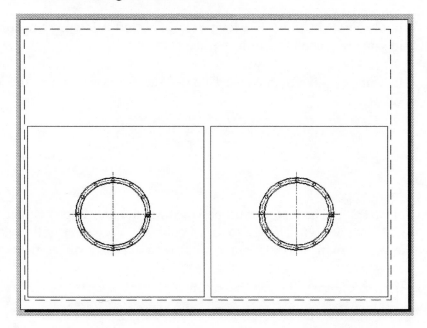

- **Move** both **Viewports** vertically up to about the center of the page as shown below.

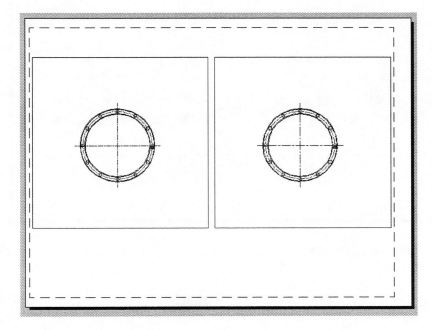

5. Set **Ortho** to *Off*.

<u>Manipulate Geometry in Viewports</u>

1. **Pan** and **Scale** the geometry within the **Viewports** by doing the following:

   - Double click in the left **Viewport.** {The left **Viewport** becomes **active** and you are placed in **Model Space**.}

   - Click on the **Viewport Scale Control** drop-down menu in the **Viewports** toolbar.

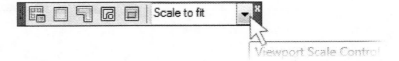

   - Select **1:1**. {The **Zoom** ratio between **Model** and **Paper Space** within the left **Viewport** will change to 1:1. Your left **Viewport** will look similar to the one shown below. Your right **Viewport** may differ than that shown below.}

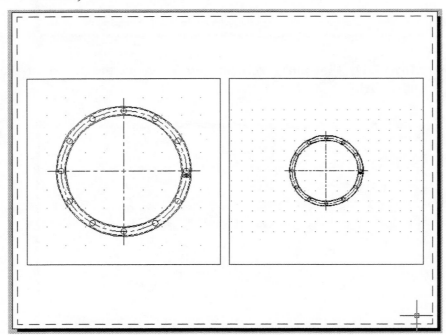

Note: As you will see later, you can also control **Viewport Scale** from the **Status Bar**.

Note: In the **Viewport** on the right, you will display a detail of the Ring by entering a different **Scale** Factor. Although the **Viewport Scale Control** drop-down menu has only certain preset scales, any scale ratio may be entered. Setting a non-preset scale can be done by highlighting the current scale value in the **Viewport Scale Control** and typing in a new scale ratio; however, here you will be using the **Mvsetup** Command.

- Click in the right **Viewport** to make the Viewport **active**.

- Use the **Pan** Command to pan the 3 o'clock quadrant area of the Ring to about the middle of the **Viewport**.

- Command: *Mvsetup*, then *[ENTER]*.

- Type *S* (for **Scale viewports**), and then *[ENTER]*.

- Select the **Viewport** on the right by its border, then *[ENTER]*.

- For the number of paper space units, type *10* and then *[ENTER]*.

- For the number of model Space units, type *1* and then *[ENTER]*. {The Object within the right **Viewport** will change to a scale ratio of 10:1, though the view may be panned differently than what is shown below.}

- Press *[ENTER]* to get out of the **Mvsetup** Command.

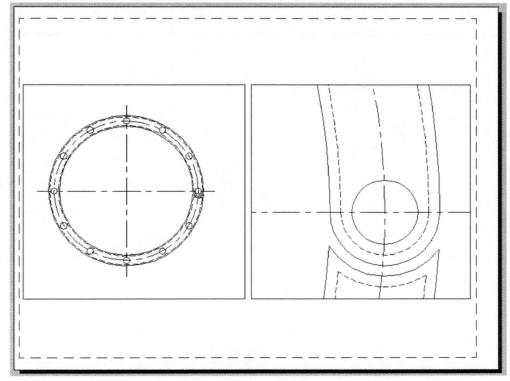

- Use the **Regen** Command to smooth out the Ring and update the **LTscale** value within the **Viewport**.

- **Pan** (do not **Zoom**) within the right **Viewport** so that the right quadrant of the Ring appears slightly to the left, approximately as shown below.

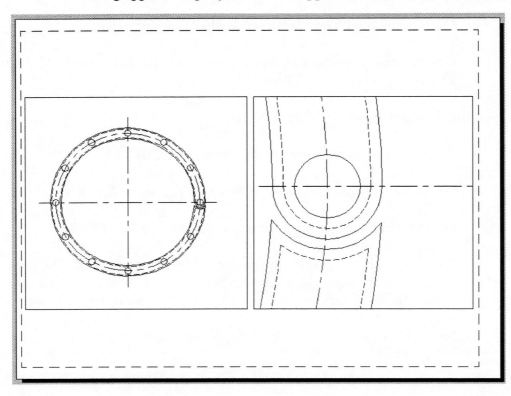

Dimension in Viewports

Dimensioning could be done by using the **Model** tab instead of through the **Layout**. However, this may cause you to dimension your geometry outside of the area shown in the **Viewport**. Here you will use a **Viewport** within the **Layout** to Dimension the Ring in **Model Space**.

1. Load and dock the **Dimension** toolbar.

2. Use the **Dimension Style Manager** dialog box to create a **New Style** with the following settings:

   - Name the New Style *Ring-Main* and make sure to Toggle the **Annotative** option to *On* and then select **Continue**.

   - On the **Symbols and Arrows** tab, change **Arrow Size** to *.14*, and **Center Mark for Circles Size** to *.10*.

   - On the **Text** tab, change **Text Height** to *.15*.

   - On the **Primary Units** tab, change **Decimal Precision** to three decimal places (*0.000*) and select **OK**.

   - In the list of Styles, select the **Ring-Main Style** and then select **Set Current** and then **Close**.

3. Make sure that **OSnap** is set to *Off.*

4. Click in the Left **Viewport**. {The Left **Viewport** is **Active**.}

5. Use the **Radius Dimension** tool to dimension the circles as shown on the next page within the left **Viewport**. In the event that you need to Zoom in/out while dimensioning, you will have to reset your **Viewport Scale** factor back to 1:1. Soon you will learn to **Lock** your **Viewports** so that unwanted Zooming and Panning does not occur accidentally.

520

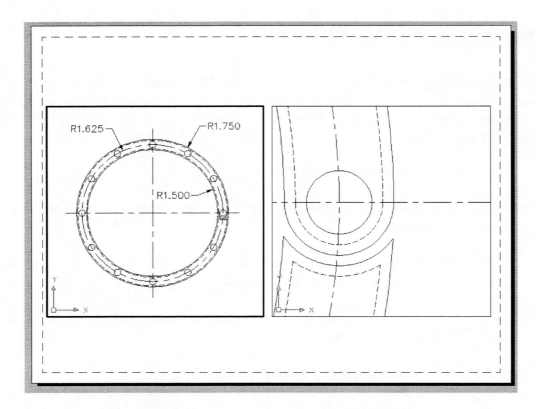

6. Click in the right **Viewport**. { Right **Viewport** is **active**.}

7. Use the **Radius Dimension** button in the **Dimension** toolbar to select the circle as shown below on the right.

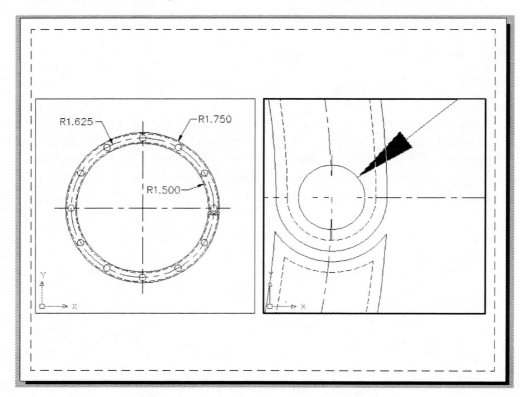

Note: As you can see, dimensioning a detail **Viewport** as shown below on the right, while using the **Dimension Style settings** of a standard **Viewport** can result in very large dimension objects. However, as long as your **Diminsion Style** is **Annotative**, this problem can be fixed by simply adjusting the **Annotation Viewport Scale** value directly from the Status Bar.

- Press the **Esc** key to cancel Dimensioning.

8. Set the **Annotation Viewport Scale** value by doing the following.

- Makes sure that your Right **Viewport** is still **active**.

- Regardless of the current **Scale Factor** settings, from the Status Bar, select the **Viewport Scale** button as shown below.

- As the Scale List appears, select a **Scale** ratio of **10:1** from the List.

- Dimension the small circle again using the **Radius Dimension** button on the **Dimension** toolbar. Your Drawing should look similar to the one shown below.

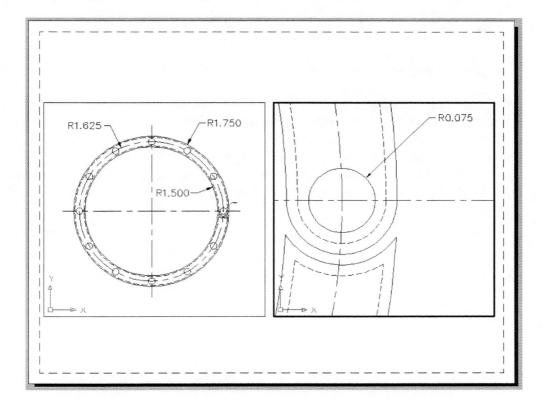

522

- Dimension the remaining four Arcs within the Right **Viewport** using the **Radius Dimension** button. Your Drawing should look similar to the one shown below. Keep in mind that based on your current visibility settings, the dimension objects of the right **Viewport** may (or may not display) in the left **Viewport**. This will be addressed later.

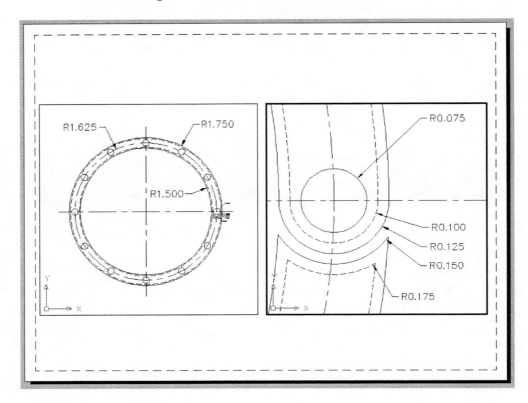

Caution: When you create a new **Dimension Style**, you have the option to assign a particular **Text Style** to your **Dimension Style**. This can be done from the **Text** Tab of the **New Dimension Style** dialog box. However, it is recommended that you use a **Text Style** having a default height of 0.0 (Ref. Page 280). In the event that your **Text Style** that is assigned to your **Dimension Style** has a non-zero default height value, your **Dimension Text** may appear abnormally larger than expected when dimensioning.

Freeze Layers in Viewports

In order to be able to separate the content of **Viewports**, AutoCAD allows you to **Freeze/Thaw** the **Layers** of each **Viewport** independently. This will allow you to display a set of objects in one **Viewport** and not necessarily in the other. For the sake of exercise and the clarity of the drawing, you will next freeze the **Hidden Layer** within the left **Viewport** only.

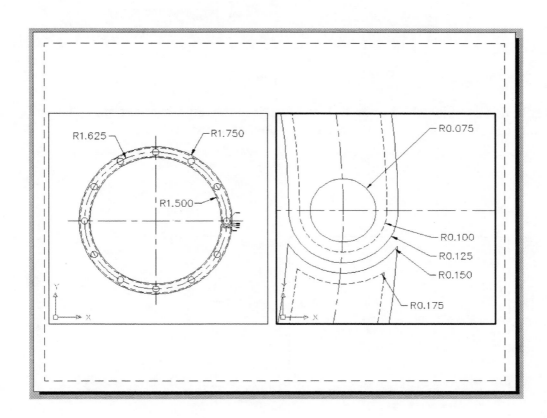

1. **Freeze Layers** within a **Viewport** by doing the following:

    - Click within the left **Viewport**. {Left **Viewport** becomes active.}

    - In the **Layers** toolbar, click on the **Layer Management** drop-down list as shown on the next page.

- Click on the **Freeze or thaw in current viewport** icon for the **Layer HID** as shown below.

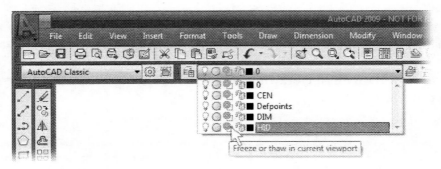

- Press *[ENTER]* to exit the drop-down.

Note: In this exercise, the **Layer HID** is **Frozen** in the left **Viewport** only. Therefore its contents can still be viewed in the right **Viewport** as shown below.

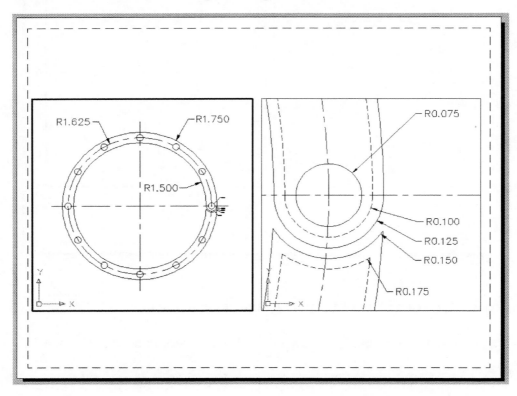

Note: Depending on you **Annotation Visibility** settings, your dimensioning of the Detailed **Viewport** above could currently display in both windows. Next you will use **Annotation Visibility** (as opposed to **Layer** control techniques) to hide certain dimensions.

Annotation Visibility

      Annotation Visibility makes it possible to make Annotation (in this case Dimensions) of a particular **Scale** factor to display within a Viewport. All other Annotations will remain invisible.

1. Toggle the **Annotation Visibility** within a **Viewport** by doing the following:

- In the **Status Bar** select the **Annotation Visibility** button to the **Off** position as shown below.

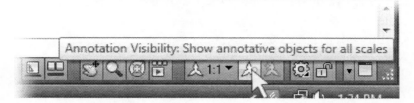

Note: The Dimensions of the right **Viewport** no longer display within the left **Viewport** as shown below.

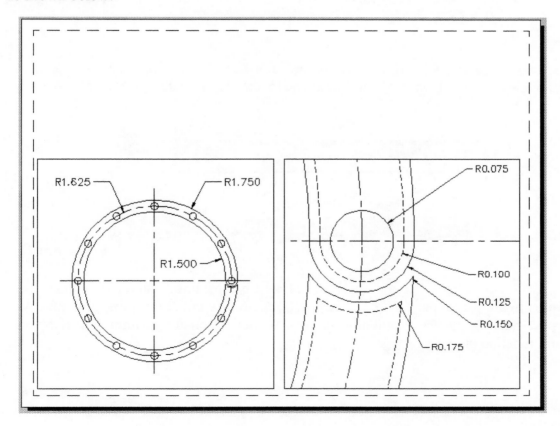

- **Thaw** the **HID Layer** within the left **Viewport** and then *[ENTER]*.

Lock Viewports

While in **Paper Space**, to ensure that the **Viewport Scale** is not changed accidentally, you can **Lock** the **Viewport**.

1. Check that both **Viewport Scale** ratios are correct. The left **Viewport** should have a scale of 1:1, while the right **Viewport** should have a scale of 10:1. If this is not the case, set the **Viewport Scale** again as you did on the previous page.

2. If necessary, **Pan** the Ring within each **Viewport** as shown before.

3. **Lock** the **Viewport Scale** by doing the following:

   - Command: *Mview* and then *[ENTER]*.

   - Type in *L* (for **Lock**) and then *[ENTER]*.

   - Toggle **Viewport View Locking** to *On* and *[ENTER]*.

   - Pick both **Viewports** either individually, or using **Crossing**, then *[ENTER]*.

Note: In AutoCAD 2009, so long as you are in a **Layout** Tab, you can also **Lock** an **Active Viewport** by selecting on the **Lock** icon located in the status bar as shown below.

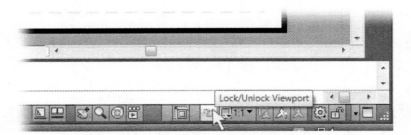

When a **Viewport** is **Locked**, you will not be able to **Pan, Zoom,** or change the **Viewport Scale** within the **Locked Viewport(s)**. Any attempt at **Panning, Zooming**, or **Viewport Scaling** will be essentially ignored. Other Commands within **Model Space** will still function properly.

Add Text to Layouts

1. Add **Text** to a **Layout** by doing the following:

    - Make sure that you are in **Layout1** and that you are in **Paper Space**.

    - Make sure that the **Layer 0** is the **Current** Layer.

    - Use the **Text** Command to place the **0.2"** Text beneath the **Viewports** as shown below.

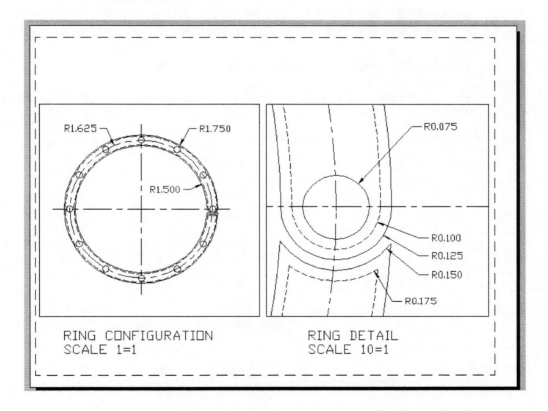

Note: Objects created within **Paper Space** are plotted at a scale of 1:1. As mentioned before, the **Viewports** are Objects in **Paper Space**, whereas the geometry that is displayed through the **Viewports** resides in **Model Space**.

2. **Save** your Drawing.

Plotting

1. **Plot** from a **Layout** by doing the following:

   - From the Menu Bar, select **File** then **Plot**. {The **Plot** dialog box will appear.}

   - Make sure that the settings are as follows:

       Paper Size: **Letter**
       Plot Area: **Layout**
       Scale: **1:1**

   - Click on **Preview**. {No changes should be needed.}

   - Right-click and select **Plot** (or **Exit** and **Cancel** if you decide not to **Plot**).

2. **Close** the Drawing without **Saving** changes.

<u>Create and Delete Layouts</u>

1. Begin a New Drawing using your **My Template**.

2. Load and dock the **Layouts** toolbar.

3. Create a **New Layout** by doing the following:

    •   In the **Layouts** toolbar, click on the **New Layout** button.

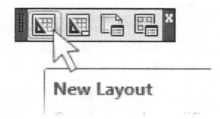

    •   When asked to **Enter new Layout name**, type *My Layout* and then *[ENTER]*. {The new layout tab will appear after the default **Layout** tabs.}

    •   Click on the **My Layout** tab. {The **Page Setup** dialog box will appear.}

    •   In the **Page Setup** area, as **My Layout** is highlighted, select **Close**. {A new **Layout** is created.}

4. **Delete** a **Layout** by doing the following.

    •   Right-click on the **Layout1** tab and from the list, select **Delete** and then select **OK**.

    •   Right-click on the **Layout2** tab and from the list, select **Delete** and then select **OK**.

Note: You can also **Rename** a **Layout** by right-clicking on that **Layout** Tab and selecting **Rename** from the List.

ANSI Templates

1. Create a **Layout** using an existing **Template** by doing the following:

    - In the **Layouts** Toolbar, select the **Layout from Template** button. {The **Select Template from File** dialog box will appear as shown in the next step.}

    - As the **Select Template From File** dialog box appears, if necessary, select the **Views** button and then **List**. {A list of available Templates appear.}

    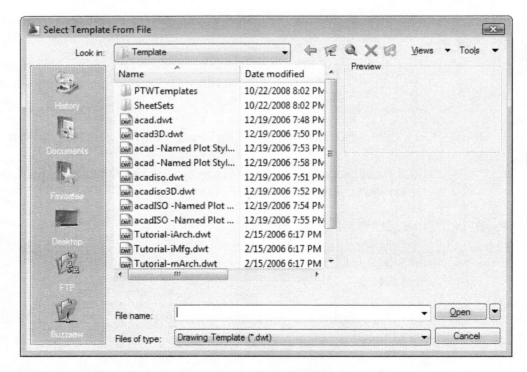

Note: From the list of **Templates** above, a suitable template can be selected to be used in **Paper Space**. However, you will next create your own customized **Paper Space** Template.

    - Select **Cancel**.

    - **Close** the Drawing without **Saving** changes.

Create a Template (Paper Space)

In Chapter 3, you created the **My Template.dwt** template file. Here you will again create a Template. However, this time it will be created in **Paper Space.** You will make use of this Template in your assignment 12 as well as the Final Project(s).

1. Create a Drawing Template in **Paper Space** by doing the following:

    • From the Menu Bar, select **File, New,** and then use the **acad.dwt** Template to begin a blank Drawing.

    • Set your **Units** to **Decimal** with **Precision** set to two-decimal-place accuracy (**0.00**).

    • Click on the **Layout1** Tab,

    • As the **Page Setup Manager** dialog box appears, select the **Modify** button. Make sure that **Paper size** is set to **Letter**, **Plot area** to **Layout,** and **Plot Scale** to **1:1**. Select **OK** to close the **Page Setup-Layout1** dialog box and finally select **Close** to close the **Page Setup Manager** dialog box.

    • Notice that the image of an A size (letter size) paper is displayed on the screen and you are placed in **Paper Space** as indicated by the **Paper Space** right triangle icon as shown below.

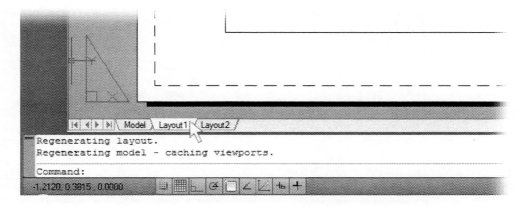

    • **Erase** the default **Viewport** shown in the form of a rectangular object. Soon a new **Viewport** will be created that is more suitable to your needs.

- Create the title page having the given dimensions shown below. A good approach would be to use the **Rectangle** tool to create a 10 x 7.5 rectangle with the first corner located at coordinates **0.2,0.2** and the other corner located at coordinates **10.2,7.7**. Then use the **Explode** tool to explode the rectangle and **Offset** the lower edge upwards by **0.40** units as shown below.

- Make sure that the entire geometry falls within the rectangular margins as shown by the dashed line type. **Move** the geometry as necessary.

- Use the **Text** Command to place your name, course section, lesson number, and scale in the title block as shown below. Start text at a user-specified location with a height of 0.2 units while making sure it falls within the title block similar to that shown below. Font is user-specified.

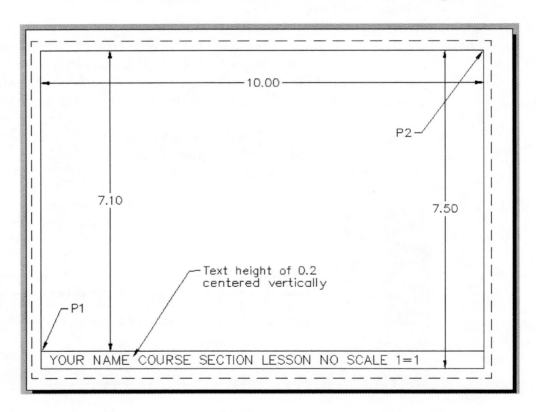

- Use the **Viewports** Toolbar and the **Endpoint** option to create a **Single Viewport** with corners located at **P1** and **P2** of the diagram of the previous page.

- To switch to **Model Space** of the **Layout**, double-click within the **Viewport** area. {The **Viewport** boundary becomes bold as shown below.}

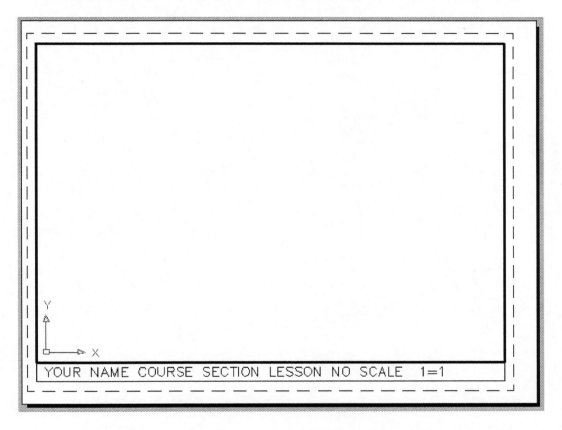

```
YOUR NAME COURSE SECTION LESSON NO SCALE  1=1
```

- Switch back to **Paper Space** by double-clicking outside of the **Viewport**.

- **Save As** the file using a **dwt** file type. For the name, type *My Paper Space Template A size* and **Save in** to your folder.

Note: Make sure to force the **.dwt** file type (as opposed to the default **.dwg**) as this Template will be used in your assignment as well as the final project(s).

Also note that a Template file is generally not to be opened directly unless it is to be modified. In Assignment 12, you will get exact instruction on how to insert a Paper Space Template into a Layout of an existing drawing.

- **Exit** AutoCAD.

534

<u>Aliases</u>

MVIEW..MV
VIEWPORTS.. VPORTS

Assignment 12

Objective:

1. To practice using **Layouts,** working with **Paper Space** and **Viewports.**

Instructions:

1. Launch AutoCAD and **open ASSIGN08_ _ _.dwg**. {The Guitar Drawing appears on the screen.}

2. **Erase** the 48 by 32 rectangular border and title information so that only the guitar geometry remains on the screen.

3. **Save As** the Drawing file to your folder. Name it **"ASSIGN12_ _ _.dwg"** where the 3 blanks are your initials.

4. Right-click on **Layout1** tab and from the shortcut menu, select the **From Template…** option and locate your **My Paper Space Template A size.dwt to insert** into the Drawing.

5. As a new **Layout** Tab is created, **Rename** it as **Guitar Project**. You can do this by right-clicking on the just created **Layout** Tab and then selecting **Rename**.

6. Right-click on the **Layout1** Tab and select the **Delete** option to delete **Layout1**. Similarly, **Delete** the **Layout2** Tab.

7. Select the **Guitar Project** tab. In the event that the **Page Setup Manager** appears, **Toggle** *Off* the **Display when creating a new layout** and then select **Close**.

8. While in **the Guitar Project** Layout, make sure to be in **Model Space** and then **Zoom All** to view the entire guitar geometry.

9. Switch to **Paper Space** and then **Erase** the **Single Viewport**. {Viewport is **Erased** and the guitar geometry disappears momentarily.}

10. From the **Viewports Toolbar**, select the **Single Viewport** Tool and use the information given below to create the 3 **Single Viewports** shown on the next page.

    *   The lower left **Viewport** is located at *0.4,1.0* and the other corner is located at *5.7,3.8* .

- The **Viewport** located in the upper left corner of the **Layout,** is a **Copy** of the first **Viewport** with its lower left corner located at coordinates *0.4,4.1* .

- The larger **Viewport** located on the right side of the **Layout** has its lower left corner located at coordinates *6.0,1.0* the upper right corner of *10.1,6.9*

11. **Assign Scale** to the **Viewports** using the following information:

- Lower left **Viewport** has a scale of *1:8*.
- Upper left **Viewport** has a scale of *1:2*.
- Right **Viewport** has a scale of *1:1*.
- In each **Viewport**, **Pan** as necessary to closely match the **Layout** shown below. While **Panning**, do not **Zoom** as it will change the **Viewport Scales** factors.
- Lock all 3 **Viewports**.

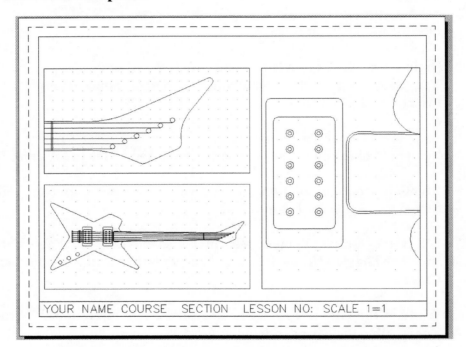

YOUR NAME COURSE   SECTION   LESSON NO: SCALE 1=1

12. Switch to Paper Space and then use **Text** to label each **Viewport** and add your information as shown on the final plot sample.
13. **Save** the Drawing again before **Plotting**.
14. **Preview** and **Plot** from the **Guitar Project** tab using these settings:

- Paper size: Letter (8.50x11.00 **inches**)
- Plot area: Layout
- Plot scale: 1=1

11. Make sure to close the **Layouts**, **Viewports** and **Dimension** Toolbars before exiting AutoCAD.

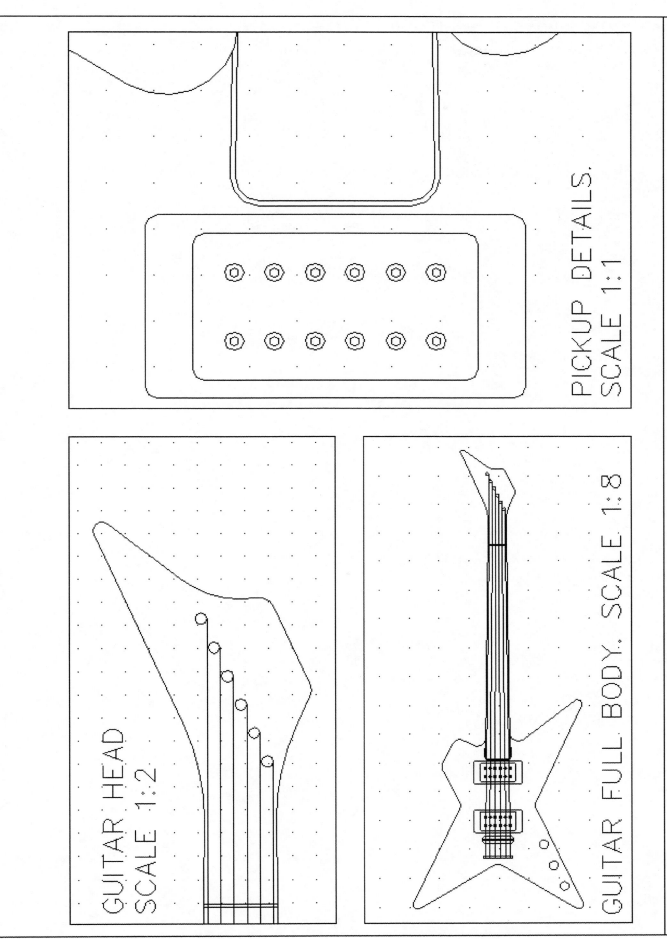

PICKUP DETAILS.
SCALE 1:1

GUITAR HEAD
SCALE 1:2

GUITAR FULL BODY. SCALE 1:8

YOUR NAME COURSE SECTION LESSON NO: SCALE: LAYOUT

Final Project - Mechanical

Objective:

1. To practice using all tools/Commands from Chapters 1-12.

Instructions:

1. Create the 3-view orthographic projection using the following instructions and information:

   - Launch AutoCAD.
   - Set **Units** to **Decimal** with **Precision** set to **0.000** (3 decimal places).
   - Set **Limits** to Lower Left **0,0** and Upper Right **18,12** .
   - **Zoom All**.
   - Use the given Dimensions to set **Snap** and **Grid** to appropriate values while making sure that **aDaptive Grid** option is set to **No**.
   - Create **Layers CEN**, **HID**, and **DIM**. Assign appropriate **Linetypes** to **CEN** and **HID** Layers.
   - **Save As** the 3-view orthographic Drawing File to your folder as *Final Mech Ortho_ _ _.dwg* where the 3 spaces are your initials.
   - The 3-Dimensional images shown below are strictly for better visualizing the Object and are not to be constructed.

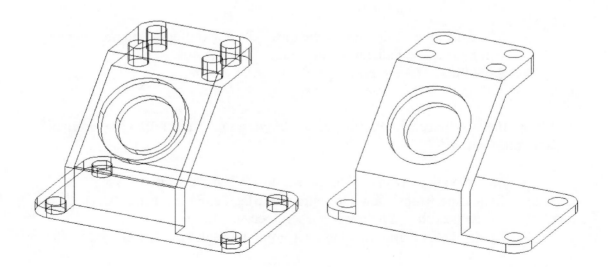

- For a review of Orthographic Projections, Section, and Auxiliary views, refer back to Chapter 3.

- Create the 3-view orthographic projection as shown below. Dimensions are given on the Final Plot Sample. Draw the Continuous, Hidden, and Center lines but avoid the dimensioning at this point.

- When creating the ellipses that are composed of two line types, do not use the **Break** Command; rather, use the **Trim** Command and the Arc Option of the **Ellipse** Command to recreate the Hidden Line portions.

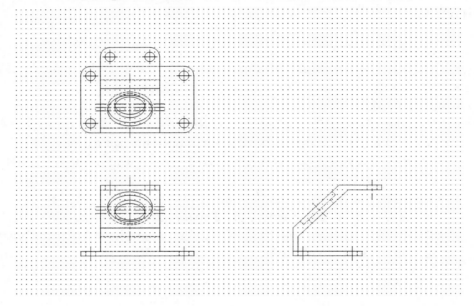

- Make a **Block** of the right view of the 3-view orthographic projection as it will be inserted in the next Drawing.
- Save **Final Mech Ortho_ _ _.dwg** and **Close** file.

2. Create the Auxiliary and Section view Drawing using the following instructions and information:

- Start a **New** Drawing using the **acad.dwt** Template File.
- **Insert** the Right View Orthographic Block from the **Final Mech Ortho_ _ _.dwg** as shown below at a User Specified location.
- Create the Construction line **CL1** going through Point **P1** and **P2** as shown below.
- **Offset CL1** by a user-specified distance to create **CL2** as shown.
- Create **Construction Line CL3** such that it goes through **P1** and is **Perpendicular** to **CL2**.

- **Offset CL3** to create the other needed **Construction Lines** going through

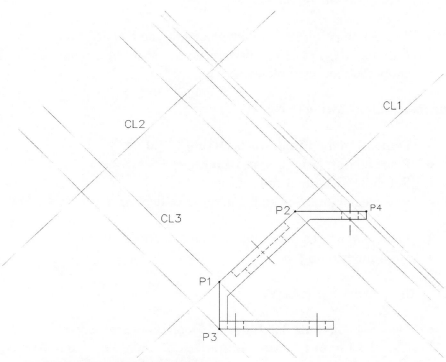

P2, **P3**, and **P4** as shown below.

- Create additional lines using **Offset** as necessary to define the boundaries of the Auxiliary view.
- Keep in mind that the 0.20" Radius holes (six places) appear as ellipses in the Auxiliary.
- Do not draw the hidden and center lines of the Auxiliary view.

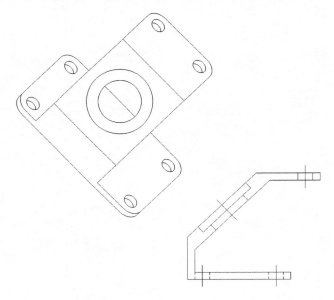

- Save Drawing as **Final Section and Auxiliary _ _ _.dwg**

3. Hatch the Section view (Chapter 10):

   - The Hatch pattern should be placed on the Hatch Layer.
   - Use the **ANSI31** Hatch pattern with a scale of 0.6 and an angler of 30 to show the sectioned plane.

4. Dimension the Drawing (Chapter 11):

   - Dimension the **Final Mech Ortho_ _ _.dwg**:
   - Place all dimensioning on **Dim** Layer.
   - Set Suitable Dimension settings.
   - Pay special attention to the number of decimals displayed.

   - Dimensioning of the Final Section and Auxiliary _ _ _.dwg
   - No dimensioning required.

5. Set up the Layout tabs (Chapter 12):

   - Open the **Layouts Toolbar** and Dock on the screen area.
   - Use the **Layout from Template** tool and select your **My Paper Space Template A size.dwt** to create a **Layout** for both Drawings.
   - Use **Model Space** in each Drawing to set the **Viewport Scale** factor to **1:2**

6. **Use the Plot setup window** to **Plot** both Drawings using these settings:

   - Paper size: Letter (8.50x11.00 **inches**)
   - Plot area: Layout
   - Plot scale: 1=1

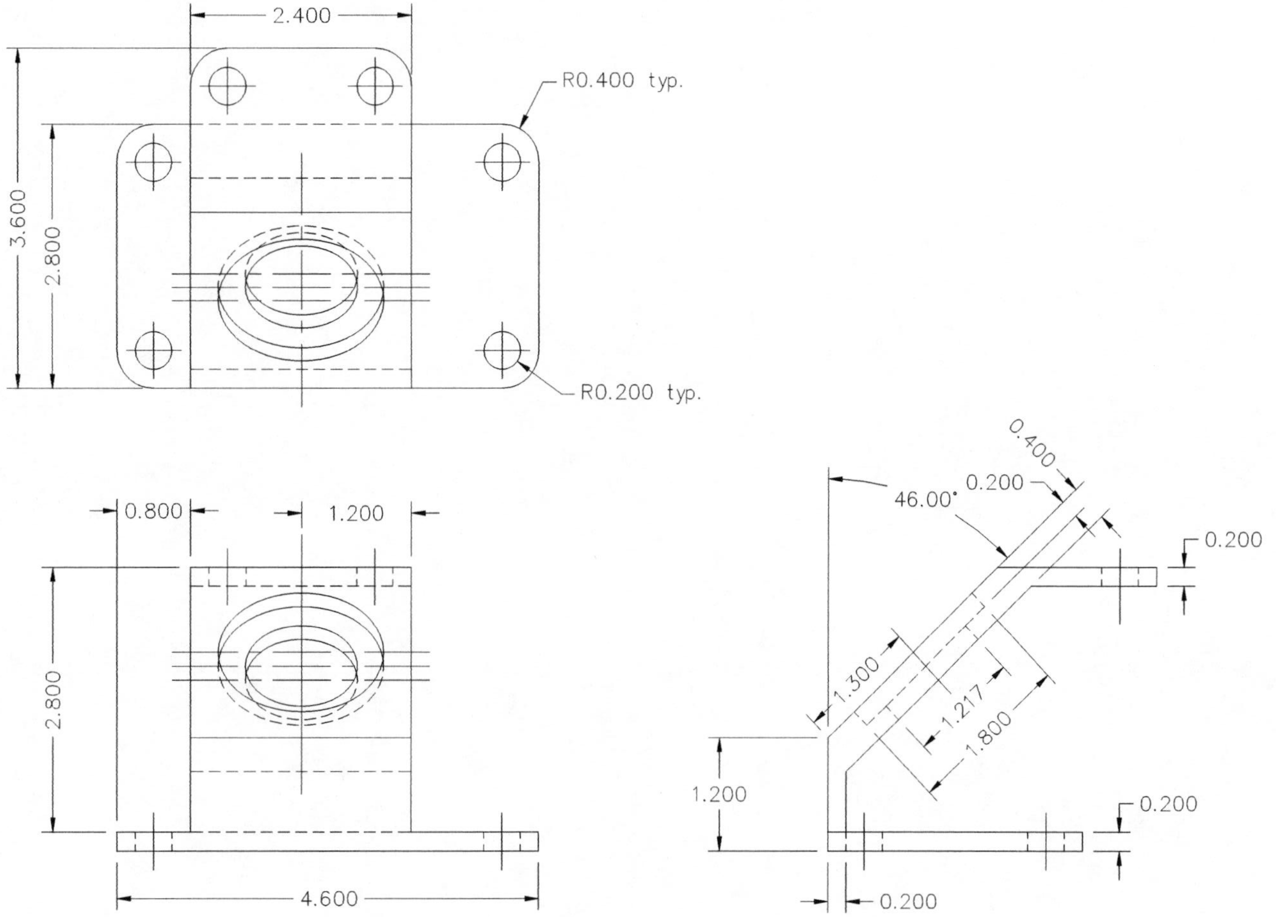

YOUR NAME COURSE SECTION FINAL MECH ORTHO SCALE 1=2

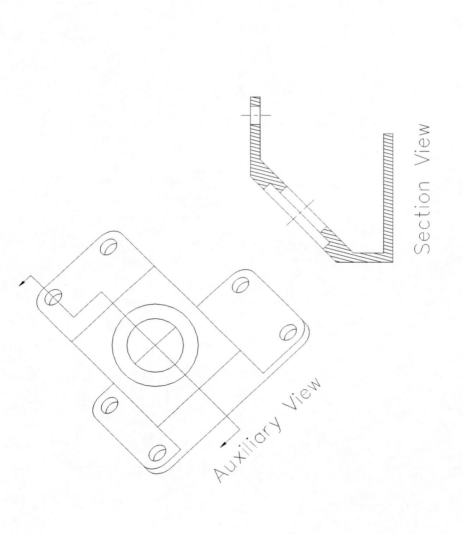

Auxiliary View

Section View

Final Project - Architectural

Objective:

1. To practice using all tools/Commands from Chapters 1-12.

Instructions:

1. Create the Plan and Elevation Drawing using the following instructions and information:
   - Launch AutoCAD.
   - Set **Units** to **Architectural** with **Precision** of ½".
   - Set **Limits** to *0,0* and *120', 90'* and *Zoom All.*
   - **Save As** Drawing to your folder as ***Arch Proj Plan and Elevation_ _ _.dwg*** where the 3 blanks are your initials.
   - Set **Snap** and **Grid** to suitable values with **Adaptive Grid** set to *Off*.
   - Create **Layers HATCH** and **DIM**.
   - Use the Dimensions given in the final plots to model all geometry.
   - When entering data using keyboard entry, pay special attention to the inch (") and the foot (') symbols. When using Architectural units, make sure to enter your units symbol. If not, system will interpret as inches.
   - Create the Plan and Elevation both within the same Drawing as shown below knowing that:

Front door is *36"* wide. Interior room doors are *30"* wide.
Hall closet, bedroom closet, and bathroom doors are *24"*wide. Kitchen closet doors are *16"* wide.
Walls are *4"* thick and unless dimensioned, door jams are *4"* from the walls as shown here.
Kitchen Counter is *24"* wide.

   - Keep the Plan and Elevation vertically aligned making it easy to use projections lines for more efficient modeling. Star point is user-specified.

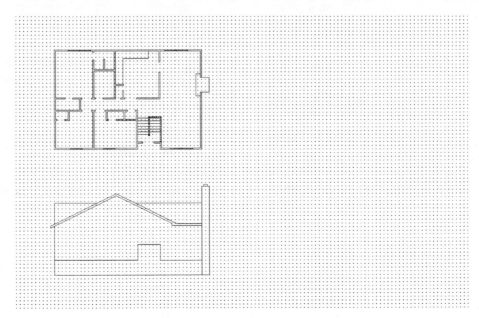

- When finished with the above geometry, **Save** the Drawing and **Close** the file. You will come back to it later.

2. Create the Symbols Drawing using the following information and instructions:

   - Launch AutoCAD.
   - **Units** are **Architectural** with **Precision** of ½".
   - Set **Limits** to *36' x 24'.*
   - Set **Snap** and **Grid** to suitable values. Set the **aDaptive Grid** option to **No.**
   - **Save As** Drawing to your folder as *Arch Symbols_ _ _.dwg* where the 3 blanks are your initials.
   - Construct all 14 symbols and position them similar to that below. The size and dimensions are given in the final plot.

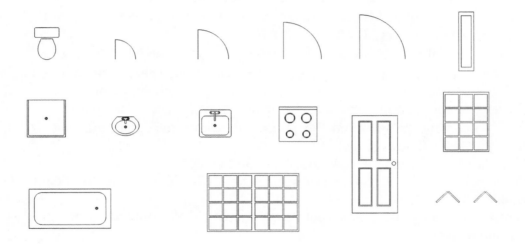

   - Do not **Dimension** or label the Symbols at this stage.

3. Make **Blocks** (Chapter 9) using the following information and instructions:

   - Make **Blocks** from all 14 Symbols with suitable insertion points. These symbols will later be inserted in the *Arch Proj Plan and Elevation_ _ _.dwg* file. It is your decision to either use the **Design Center** or the **Wblocking** technique to make these insertions take place.
   - Before closing this Drawing, test all 14 blocks by making sure they insert properly and as expected.
   - Save the *Arch Symbols_ _ _.dwg* one last time and close file.

4. Open *Arch Proj Plan and Elevation_ _ _.dwg* and insert all symbols in their given positions.

5. Hatch the Plan and Elevation (Chapter 10) using the following information and instructions:

- All Hatch patterns should be placed on the **HATCH Layer**.
- Front Elevation uses the following information:
  - Chimney uses the **AR-BRSTD** pattern with a scale factor of *1.0*
  - Roof shingles use the **AR-RSHKE** pattern with a scale factor of *1.0* .
  - Aluminum Siding uses the **User Defined** pattern with a spacing of *4"*.
- Plan View uses the following information:
  - Fire Place has a **User-Defined** Hatch pattern with a spacing of *4"*

6. Dimension the Drawings (Chapter 11) using the following information and instructions:

- Dimensioning the **Arch Proj Plan and Elevation_ _ _.dwg**:
  - Place all dimensioning on **DIM** Layer.
  - Set suitable dimension settings for the **Arch Proj Plan and Elevation_ _ _.dwg** keeping the large size of Objects in mind.
  - Just like the **Dimensions**, select suitable **Multileader** settings for the **Leaders** used in the Elevation portion of the Drawing.
- Do not dimension the *Arch symbols_ _ _.dwg* file.

7. Set up the Layout tabs (Chapter 12) using the following information and instructions:

- Open the **Layout** and **Viewports** toolbars and Dock on the screen area.
- Use the **Layout From Template** tool and select your **My Paper Space Template A size.dwt** to create two new Layout tabs.
- Right-click on the two new **Layout** tabs and **Rename** them as **Plan** and **Elevation** as shown below.

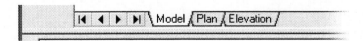

- For each of the two Layouts (**Plan** and **Elevation**) enter **Model Space**. Pan as necessary and assign the **3/16"=1'** scale factor to both layouts.

8. You are to **Plot** three Layouts. Two are from the *Arch Proj Plan and Elevation_ _ _.dwg* (**Plan** and **Elevation** Layouts) and the other from the *Arch symbols_ _ _.dwg* using the following information:

- Paper size: Letter (**inches**)
- Scale: 1:1
- Plot area: Layout

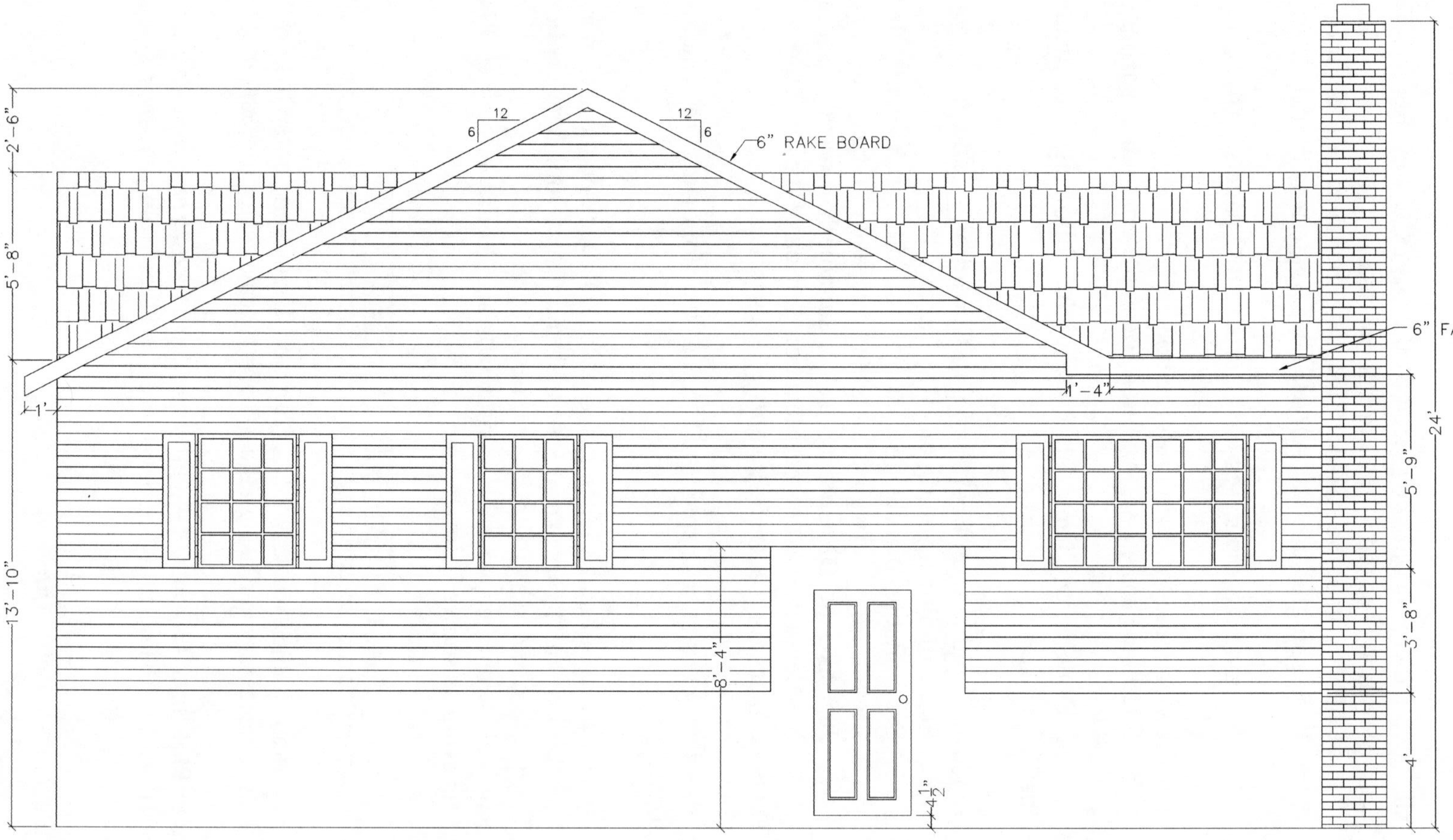

6" FASCIA BOARD

24'

6'-9"

5'-9"

3'-8"

4'

1'-4"

6" RAKE BOARD

6
12

6
12

4 1/2"

8'-4"

2'-6"

5'-8"

1'-4"

13'-10"

YOUR NAME COURSE FNL PROJ: ELEVATION SCALE 3/16" = 1'

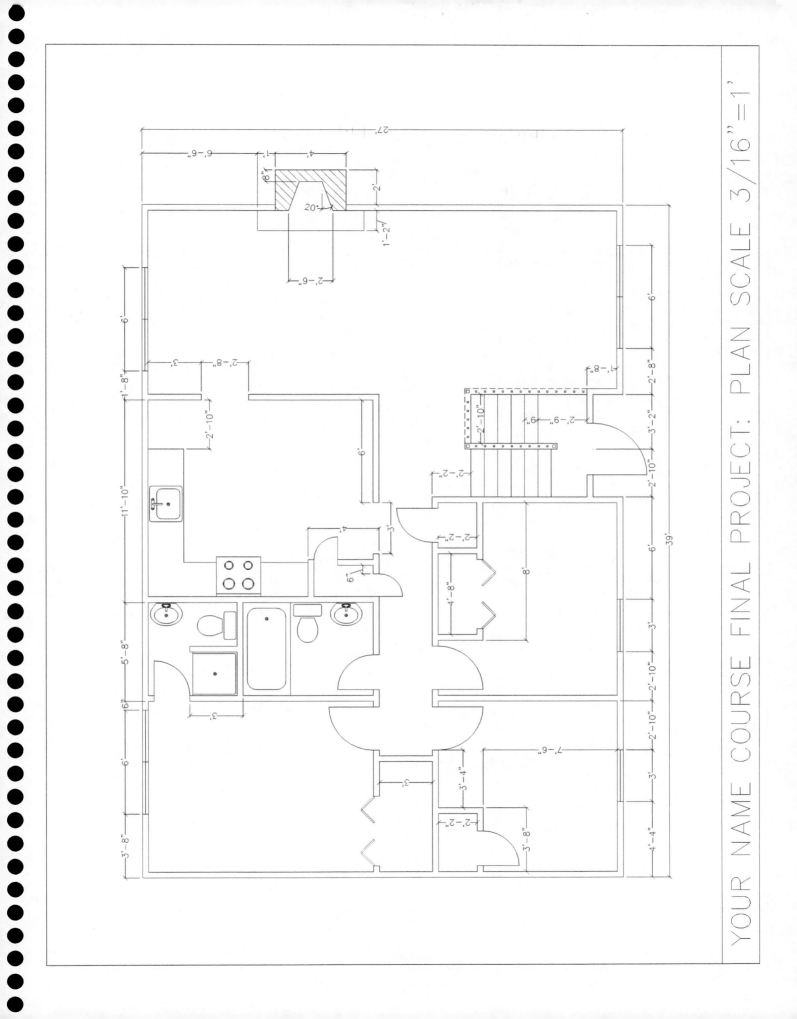

YOUR NAME COURSE FINAL PROJECT: PLAN SCALE 3/16"=1'

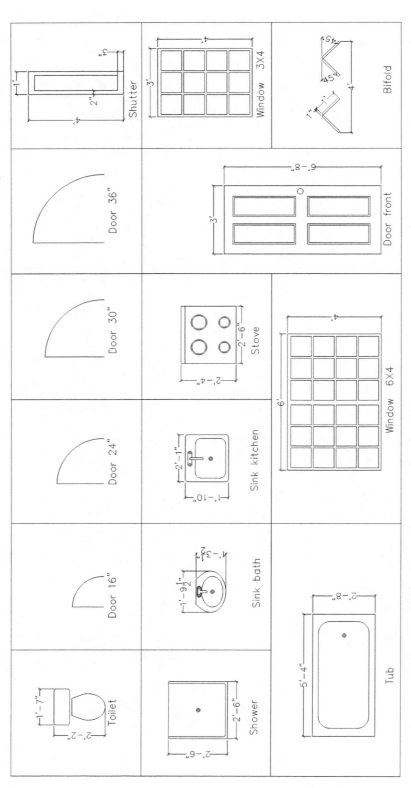

Some dimensions such as the window panes, stove burners and faucets are User Specified.

YOUR NAME COURSE FINAL PROJECT: PLAN SCALE 1/4" =1'

Congratulations. You have just finished twelve chapters containing many valuable AutoCAD Commands and techniques. You should feel confident in your knowledge of the essentials. Keep in mind that retaining the knowledge through practice makes for an efficient CAD operator.

Please note that the **Introduction to AutoCAD 2009, The Academic Solution** textbook is the first book of a three-part series authored by **VESD, Inc**. If you found the book to be informative and easy to follow, you are encouraged to download the first four chapters of the books **Advanced AutoCAD 2009, The Academic Solution** and **3D Design Using AutoCAD 2009, The Academic Solution**. To do so, log onto **www.vesdesign.com** and select the **Downloads** tab to select the book of your choice. The **Academic Solution Textbook Series for AutoCAD** is designed to furnish you with the required edge needed to succeed in the Computer-Aided-Drafting and Design industry today. Also consult with your instructor on "The Road Ahead".

Appendix A: Aliases

ALIGN	AL
APPARENT INTERSECTION	APPINT
ARC	A
AREA	AA
ARRAY	AR
BLIP MODE	BLIPMODE
BLOCK	B
BREAK AT POINT	BR
CENTER	CEN
CHAMFER	CHA
CIRCLE	C
CONSTRUCTION LINE	XLINE or XL
COPY	CO
CROSSHAIR SIZE	CURSORSIZE
DIMALIGNED	DAL
DIMANGULAR	DAN
DIMBASELINE	DBA
DIMCONTINUE	DCO
DIMDIAMETER	DDI
DIMDISASSOCIATE	DDA
DIMLINEAR	DLI
DIMRADIUS	DRA
DIMREASSOCIATE	DRE
DIMSTYLE	D
DIVIDE	DIV
DYNAMIC TEXT	DTEXT or DT
EDIT HATCH	HE
EDIT TEXT	DDEDIT or ED
ELLIPSE	EL
ENDPOINT	END

554

Appendix B: Hot Keys and Function Keys

CTRL+A .... SELECTS ALL OBJECTS

CTRL+B .... TOGGLES SNAP MODE

CTRL+C .... COPIES TO CLIPBOARD

CTRL+SHIFT+C .... COPY WITH BASEPOINT

CTRL+D ....SWITCHES COORDINATE DISPLAY

CTRL+E .... CYCLES THROUGH ISOPLANES

CTRL+F ....TOGGLES GRID DISPLAY

CTRL+G ....TOGGLES GRID DISPLAY

CTRL+H ....TOGGLES PICK STYLE

CTRL+K ....HYPERLINKS DIALOG BOX

CTRL+L ....TOGGLES ORTHO MODE

CTRL+N .... STARTS NEW DRAWING

CTRL+O .... OPENS DRAWING FILE

CTRL+P ....PLOTS DRAWING

CTRL+Q .... QUITS AutoCAD

CTRL+R ....CYCLES THROUGH VIEWPORTS

CTRL+S ....SAVES DRAWING

CTRL+SHIFT+S .... SAVE DRAWING AS DIALOG BOX

CTRL+T.. TOGGLES TABLET MODE

CTRL+U ....TOGGLES POLAR TRACKING

CTRL+V ....PASTES FROM CLIPBOARD

CTRL+SHIFT+V ....PASTE WITH INSERTION POINT

CTRL+X .... CUTS TO CLIPBOARD

CTRL+Y .... REDOES LAST UNDO

CTRL+Z.. UNDOES LAST COMMAND

CTRL+0 ....TOGGLES CLEAN SCREEN MODE

CTRL+1 .... TOGGLES PROPERTIES WINDOW

CTRL+2 ....TOGGLES DESIGN CENTER WINDOW

CTRL+3 ....TOGGLES TOOL PALETTES WINDOW

CTRL+6 ....TOGGLES DBCONNECT MANAGER

F1 ....DISPLAY ONLINE HELP

F2 .... TOGGLES TEXT AND GRAPHICS WINDOWS

F3 .... TOGGLES OBJECT SNAP

F4 .... TOGGLES TABLET MODE

F5 .... CYCLES THROUGH ISOPLANES

F6 ....DYNAMIC UCS

F7 ....TOGGLES GRID DISPLAY

F8 ....TOGGLES ORTHO MODE

F9 .... TOGGLES SNAP MODE

F10 ....TOGGLES POLAR TRACKING

F11 ....TOGGLES OBJECT SNAP TRACKING

CTRL+F4... CLOSES DRAWING

CTRL+F6.. SWITCHES TO NEXT DRAWING

ALT+F8 .... RUNS VBA

ALT+F11 ....OPENS VBA IDE

Other Keys

Esc...CANCELS COMMANDS AND GRIPS

DELETE .... DELETES SELECTED OBJECTS

ENTER...EXECUTES AND REPEATS COMMANDS

SHIFT+RIGHT-CLICK...OBJECT SNAP SHORTCUT MENU

A

B

C

560

D

E

562

I

J

L

M

N

O

P

564

U

V

566

W

Z